umbundu

ubnuda

umbundu

folk tales from angola

collected and translated by Merlin Ennis

comparative analysis by Albert B. Lord

beacon press   boston

To *the* *memory* of
ELISABETH RUTH LOGAN
my *wife*

preface

These stories from the Umbundu, language and culture of the Ovimbundu, were collected in Angola, Portuguese West Africa, between the years of 1904 and 1944—the period of my missionary service in Angola for the American Board (Congregational). I wish to give full credit to Ricardo Chindemba Muelehombo, a native teacher in a village school, who transcribed a major portion of these folk tales in a beautiful and clear Umbundu. I translated these stories from the Umbundu into English after returning from Angola to the United States. With but one exception, all the stories have been translated from scripts written in Umbundu by Africans. This collection is but a sample from the great reservoir of yet uncollected and untranslated stories in the Umbundu.

I have sought, in translating these stories, to keep the English version as close to the African meanings as possible. I have avoided the use of slang and dialect, but I have also avoided excessively literal translation. I have chosen the English words, phrases and idioms which communicate the approximate African meanings in the simplest and most direct way. The rhythms of the original Umbundu have been reproduced in English, so far as possible, in the case of the songs, but not in the case of the narrative prose. The tunes of these songs are traditional, familiar to most African people, and the storyteller's audience usually joins in the singing of the verses.

It is my hope that the reader will feel both sympathy and affinity for the African people after reading these stories and appreciating their very human qualities. Despite differences in color, language, culture, social life and religious beliefs, people everywhere share a common humanity—be they young or old, male or female, African, Asian, European or American. We should be able to recognize and better understand much of our own culture, society and human nature in these stories.

MERLIN ENNIS

contents

folk tales of community life

a comparative analysis

by
Albert B. Lord

The structural characteristic that strikes one immediately and constantly in reading this splendid collection of Ovimbundu tales is repetition. It pervades almost all of the stories; it takes a number of forms. As a phenomenon in oral literature, in products of verbal art, repetition always, it seems likely, had something of the magical about it. This would account for the respect and even affection with which it is treated by those who tell stories in either prose or verse, and it would explain its persistence and preservation. Repetition of sounds and words is a peculiar feature of incantations and charms; it enhances the effectiveness of the magical spell. It is one of the most basic and ancient techniques of the magic art. Repetition of incidents and repeated patterns of incidents are, moreover, charactertistic compositional devices of oral style. The storyteller, in prose as well as in verse, needs a repertory not only of common phrases but also of frequently recurring incidents and groups of incidents in order to rebuild any tale in its retelling or even to remember it as he listens to it for the first time. Such common incidents and patterns are a mark of oral literature.

In the present essay I should like to examine some of the varieties of repetition in the Ovimbundu tales in order to better understand their structure and their meaning. I also wish to illustrate by this amazing narrative material a more general theory of composition and transmission of oral narrative, applicable not only to these tales but also to all truly oral traditional stories.

Just as in magic an act and/or an incantation is performed a number of times until some result is obtained, so in a number of our stories the same thing occurs over and over again in a series of repetitions until something happens to interrupt. In some cases also there is not merely action but a song as well that is repeated. Sometimes the same thing happens several times to the same persons or characters in the story; sometimes the personnel changes in whole or in part but the action is repeated. In the tale "A Childless Woman," for example, the baby changes into a little old woman during the absence of the woman who had found it, abuses the stepson who had been left to care for it, and dances and sings a song. This incident happens twice, and the narrator adds that it happened many times before it was stopped. The characters here are the same in all the repetitions, as in the significant song that tells the truth about the baby, namely, that it does not belong to the woman but was found by her. Another example of a tale in which the repeated incidents happen to the same characters is in "A Junior Wife's Jealousy." The junior wife sends her stepdaughter with mush to the clubhouse and when the child returns she shows her her mother's head. The child screams, her father comes, but her stepmother gives some other reason for the child's scream. This happens, and is recounted twice, with slight variations, and again the narrator indicates that it then happened many times before the conclusion. A third and final instructive example comes from a tale with a somewhat similar pattern to the two just given, "The Burial of Ching-uli." In it a caravan stops by the tomb in which Ching-uli has been buried alive. The men hear her song, which, like the one above in "A Childless Woman" betrays the crime to him who understands, but they are only bewildered and pass on. The narrator in this case does not repeat the incident in full, as was true in the other instances, but gives a short one-sentence summary: "After these men had left, another caravan came along, and the men of this caravan acted the same as the men of the first caravan." In the third repetition, Ching-uli's father is in the caravan, and the crime is discovered.

It will be noted that in these examples the repetition does not form a long series in the narration, although it might well have done so, but that the narrator after one or perhaps two repetitions simply states that the incident happened many times.

Other series of repeated incidents change not the action but the characters, in part, at least, from repetition to repetition. In the tale "Naming Foods in a Time of Famine," for instance, there is a food named *olungundonde* that can be eaten only by those who pronounce its name. It is possessed by a people whose animal neighbors are suffering from famine. The animals send a series of individuals, from Hare to Lion, to get some of the food from their friends, but they always forget the name before they return. Tortoise finally saves the day. The incident of sending and returning is repeated with slight variations for each animal, namely, for Hare, Duyker, Roan Antelope, Leopard, and Lion. It is to be noted, of course, that the series of animals is really a progression from small to large, from least to most important or dignified. Another similar series can be found in the story "Tortoise and an Old Woman Hunt Animals." In it Tortoise tells "a little old woman" that he is a hunter and joins forces with her to hunt. He is to drive the animals to her house and she is to kill them. He entices them inside with offers of their favorite food, and then he tells them to pick him up and throw him outside when they hear a scraping sound. As they throw him out they are to say "I am throwing out a bone," and a short time after that they are to come out themselves. As they emerge the old woman cuts off their heads with her hoe. This, of course, is exactly what happens to one animal after another—Duyker, Bushbuck, Wart Hog, Roan Antelope, Waterbuck, Gnu, Eland, Elephant. The same incident, varying only the name of the animal and the type of food, is repeated over and over again, like a chant to trap animals! Here again the series is a progression, this time in the size of the animals involved.

Repetitions in the tales can involve more than a single incident. This is especially true when the repetition takes the form of the cumulative story; that is to say, when one of the characters in the story repeats to another character, or to a series of other characters, what has happened in the story up to that point, adding new material with each retelling. A perfect example of this is the second story in the book, "Mupuiyakalangi."

This tale tells a straightforward and amusing story of a man who goes with his wife to visit her family and after a series of misadventures finds himself stuck halfway in and halfway out of the "wrong" end of an elephant. To the hunter and his friends who eventually free him from this predicament, he recounts in full the tale thus far, in explanation of his peculiar position. Soon after this he has another encounter, this time with a king who is surprised at his emaciated and pale condition, and Mupuiyakalangi has to tell him the whole story again in full, adding, of course, the incident with the hunter and his friends who saved him from the elephant, and even including the repetition of previous events. The man has one more adventure before he reaches home, and this provides audience and excuse for further repetition; and, of course, when Mupuiyakalangi is finally in the bosom of his family again he must repeat for the last time the whole story once more. Such a story deserves the name "cumulative" which is usually applied to this type of "formula" tale.* The whole point of such a tale is the full, detailed, almost word-for-word repetition of an ever growing story.

In analyzing oral literature we term repeated incidents and descriptions *themes*. They are the narrative building blocks of any story in tradition. The repetitions with which we have so far been concerned in themselves constitute traditional themes. We have seen, for example, the *theme* of the repeated unchanged incident (in "A Childless Woman," "A Junior Wife's Jealousy," and "The Burial of Chinguli"), the *theme* of the repeated incident with a progression in the size or dignity of the characters (in "Naming Foods in a Time of Famine," and in "Tortoise and an Old Woman Hunt Animals"), and the *theme* of the repeated retelling of the events of the story with increments—the cumulative tale type—in "Mupuiyakalangi." These themes of repetition are themselves demonstrably repeated. We have observed also that in the repeated incidents in the themes of repetition there are usually slight variations. The incident is rarely repeated exactly word for word. Sometimes the variation is very slight; sometimes it is more noticeable.

In addition to the theme of repetition itself there are many other repeated themes in the tales; incidents, or groups of incidents are found in more than one tale. Such, for example, is what we find in the three stories the central episode of which is the seclusion of a woman in a stronghold, which is besieged, and eventually penetrated by an ogre or wild beast. This conglomerate of themes is to be found in "The Maiden and the Lion," "A Hunter Takes His Beautiful Wife Away from the Village," and "A Maiden Alone in the Wild." Vaguely related here also is "The Recluse." "The Maiden and the Lion" and "A Maiden Alone in the Wild" are especially related in the beginning, because they present a maiden who protects herself in a

---

* (For further information on these terms see Stith Thompson, *The Folktale*, New York, 1946, pp. 230 ff.).

stockade, in the first instance because she would not marry and the inhabitants of the town would not take her with them when they moved away, and in the second because the region was terrorized by an ogre or lion and the population was fleeing. In fact these opening themes are multiforms of a single idea, namely, everyone leaves and the maiden remains alone; she protects herself by a stockade. The opening theme of "A Hunter Takes His Beautiful Wife Away from the Village" is different, not only because the woman is not a maiden but a wife, but also because she lives in the stockade not alone but with her husband, the hunter. Nonetheless, in the remaining parts of the tale this story is closer to that of "A Maiden Alone in the Wild" than is "The Maiden and the Lion." The central section of these tales deals with the manner in which the ogre or lion penetrates the stockade. In "The Maiden and the Lion" there is an almost ritual breaking through of one stockade after another, with a repetition of the same words by the lion and of the same song by Chitunda. The maiden is here surrounded by five stockades. On the other hand, in the other two tales under consideration, recognition of the voice of husband or ogre plays a decisive role, as the ogre tries to persuade the woman to open the gate. In both cases the ogre or lion disguises his voice in order to deceive the woman, in one case imitating the voice of the husband and in the other imitating the voice of a girl whom the maiden wishes to let in for company. It is also to be noted that in these two tales the lion or ogre kills the woman, whereas in "The Maiden and the Lion" Chitunda marries the lion and they have children, five of whom are human and one of whom is a lion. In time Chitunda and her five human children fly away on vines back to her family where they are well received.

In the previous section we saw three tales which were clearly related to one another yet also just as clearly not versions of the same story. As another example we might take "Tortoise Wins a Wife," "The Perserverance of Tortoise," and "Nduva" (unpublished, Folio IX, No. 1, Tale 10). All three of these tell of the winning of a bride by Tortoise, and of his death. The first two tales vary considerably. In one the competition for the girl is in discovering her secret name; in the other it consists in climbing a pole to obtain the feather of the okangungu in spite of the distraction caused by the singing and dancing of an old crone. An added test is placed also in the first tale, where Tortoise,

after he has named the girl's secret name, must provide a live
duyker and the fat of a python for the wedding feast. The two
are closest in their accounts of Tortoise's death by drowning
in a pot of beer in one case and of gruel in the other. In both
stories he topples into the pot from a stack of stools that he has
built in order to reach the beer or a dish of bean butter. This
death from a fall after a climb is especially effective by its irony
in the case of the variant in which Tortoise wins his bride by
climbing the pole to fetch the feather, and I suspect that this ending "belongs" with this version of the tale. It makes less sense
in the story with the naming. In this way the study of one version may assist in understanding more fully what is puzzling in
another. The unpublished story "Nduva" is a true variant of
"The Perseverance of Tortoise" although it is longer and fuller
and has some minor differences. In it Nduva is the name of a
girl whose family placed her among the small branches in the top
of a very tall tree and then announced that she would marry the
man who could climb up and fetch her from the tree singing a
given song. The animals try one after another beginning with
Lion, who was unsuccessful, and then Rhinoceros, Leopard, and
Roan Antelope. There is thus a series of incidents repeated for
each animal. Finally Tortoise comes along and wants to try in
spite of the fact that the others mock him. He, of course, gets
the girl and they are married and have fine children. Not only is
the climbing of the pole elaborated in greater detail in this
variant, or more properly, lengthened by repetition, but so also
is the section on the death of Tortoise. After Tortoise has fallen
into the gruel from the stack of stools he had made in order
to reach some cowpeas, the tale is expanded by the search that
his wife undertakes to find him, and to it is added her lament on
his death. This longer variant, in spite of its fullness, omits an
interesting and striking part of the theme to win the bride by
climbing the pole. This is the element of the singing and dancing of the old crone who tries to distract the climbers by her
comedy. Whence comes this element?
(unpublished, Folio IX, N...
    Is she not related at least to two other figures which we see
in these tales? Functionally, is she not like the undolo bird in
"Tortoise Hunts the Undolo Bird," who frightens all those who
try to cut down the tree (here is the tree, again) in which it
has its nest and eggs? Indeed, there seem to be a number of
multiforms of a theme of distraction, a theme, one might add,

that reproduces one of the protective devices of many animals. The parent bird or animal frequently distracts a potential enemy from its young, and this theme is common in these tales and takes many forms. Let us review here briefly the instances of the theme of distraction as we have seen it in the tales here presented.

The theme of distraction is found especially, it would seem, in those tales in which a series of people (or more frequently and perhaps, significantly, animals) attempt to do something but are distracted therefrom; only the hero steps in finally and does not yield to the distraction. We have seen two cases of it in "The Perseverance of Tortoise" and "Tortoise Hunts the Undolo Bird." This general pattern is typical of the Tortoise Saga. One finds it in "A Community Cornfield Over an Abandoned Village," in "Naming Foods in a Time of Famine," in the unpublished "Omutia Kuvingi" (Folio IX, No. 1, Tale 5); and in the unpublished "Elephant Swallows a Gourd" (Folio IX, No. 1, Tale 13). Looking at these, we note that there are two kinds of distraction offered: one is taking the attention by something interesting, amusing, or fascinating, and the other is by frightening with a false sound. Our two first examples illustrate these two types. In "The Perseverance of Tortoise" the distraction offered by the old woman is amusing and fascinating, but not frightening; in "Tortoise Hunts the Undolo Bird" the distraction is from the whirring sound and the flashing white belly of the bird, sounding and looking like thunder and lightning.

In "Naming Foods in a Time of Famine" the distraction is of the pleasant variety; a beautiful, small animal, gleaming bright and dancing, and thus fascinating all the animal messengers so that they forgot the name of the food. Similarly the distraction in "Elephant Swallows a Gourd" is the drumming and singing of Toad which makes the animals dance. The story is as follows: At a meeting of the animals, they cooked some gourds and Lion challenged anyone to swallow a small gourd whole. Elephant undertook it, and the hot gourd stuck in his throat. One after another the animals went to the stream for water to cool the gourd in Elephant's throat, but Toad was at the stream delaying them by singing and playing the drum. The song is a long one and it is repeated for each animal, using the animal's name. The animals on hearing the drum and song stop and dance and fetch no water. We have a familiar series of animals; Duyker, Waterbuck, Reedbuck, Leopard, and all the other animals until finally Tortoise alone is left. The others are dancing, entranced by Toad's music. Tortoise, of course, pays no heed to the drum and song and fetches the water for Elephant. He is too late, however, because Elephant's throat is so badly burned that he dies.

In "A Community Cornfield Over an Abandoned Village" the distraction is of the frightening variety, the deceptively frightening. Here Corn Borer in a solemn voice pretends to be Earthshaker, who stabs the elephant, skins the hide from the roan antelope, and so on. The voice frightens away the animals one after another until Tortoise, in spite of the objections of everybody, fearlessly uncovers the imposter, Corn Borer. Similarly in the unpublished "Omutia Kuvingi" the distraction is frightening by its sound, and once again we find the figure of the little old woman. It is she who owns the field where food can be found in a time of famine. She has one great tooth which is thick and long, and when she is angry her scolding sounds like thunder. It is this distracting false thunder that makes the animals, one after another, look into the hamper in which they are carrying the food, thus breaking the tabu against watching the food; the food returns to the field. Only Tortoise, of course, is successful in fetching the food, paying no attention to the little old woman's thundering.

In the three cases of frightening distraction which we have seen it is sound that frightens in all instances; the solemn voice of Corn Borer with its threats; the thunder-like scolding of the little old woman with the thick long tooth; the thundering whir and the flashing of the Undolo Bird. In essence the element seems to be thunder. The constant element in the instances of pleasant distraction is less that of sound than of action, namely, *dance*, although song and drum may also be associated with the dance, as is only natural. Thus we find the small gleaming animal with its dance; the little old woman with her song and dance; and Toad with the drum and song that make the animals dance. These are then multiforms of a single idea, either "thunder," or "dance," as distractions.

There are some stories, or parts of stories, that, in spite of difference of subject matter, are clearly the same as far as framework or structure is concerned. For example, both "Crane's Eggs and Olondongo" and "The Woman Who Insulted a Pebble" have, in part at least, the frame of a barrier set up (in one case a bridge, in the other a mountain) which allows the innocent to pass but brings destruction on the guilty. Thus the Cranes discover which girl took the eggs and kill her, and the mountain swallows the woman who insulted the pebble. Structurally these stories are alike, and by placing the two side by side we can see one of the useful frames in the composition of these tales.

A related phenomenon is found in "A Girl Believes That Her Brother-in-Law Laughs at Her" and "A Ghost Interrupts the Making of a New Field." These stories are tied together by two striking themes: one, the acquiring of a knowledge of the language of creatures, which, however, brings death to the possessor if he tells anyone of it, and two, the theme of hair braiding, laughing at words of ants, suicide threat, recounting of why one laughs, and the subsequent death. The initial circumstances differ greatly, but the main matter of the two stories is the same.

The latter of these two stories, as a matter of fact, belong with a larger category of tales, that of journeys to the world of the dead. Even the first of the stories, "A Girl Believes That Her Brother-in-Law Laughs at Her," is closely related by implication to this theme of journey to the world of the dead. Compare these stories with "A Ghost Interrupts the Making of a New Field," and "A Bee Hunter and His Wife." In both, despite great differences, a man enters into the world of the dead while pursuing something—in one case two ghosts, in the other case a herd of wart hogs—through a burrow in the ground. In both cases the man receives knowledge and the admonition not to divulge it, on pain of death.

Another story of a journey to another world, in this instance not to the land of the dead, is "Goodhearted Ngeve, Kindhearted Chilombo." This tale is much more elaborate than the others just mentioned, but it too places the other world in the ground. (The man reaches the other world on the back of a termite!) In the other instances the hero of the tale receives knowledge in the other world, but in this story the man has been seeking his wife, whom he finds in the lower world, but when he finally wins her release, it is with tabus. As in the other stories, the protagonist breaks the tabus upon his return to the world of reality. He does not die, but his wife becomes a revenant, and he flees back to his own people.

It is a comfort to the student of epic poetry and of myth to find among the Ovimbundu these tales of journeys to the other world, and even the same kind of differentiation among other worlds, which we know so well from our own heritage of oral literature.

Parallels throughout the world should no longer surprise us. In Finnish runes the heroes travel to the other world, to Tuonela or to Pohjola or even into the belly of Antero Vipunen as he lies stretched upon the ground with trees growing from him, and the purpose of their journeys is to obtain magical knowledge. Gilgamesh, passing through mountains and over water, travels to the land of the faraway to consult his ancestor Utnapishtim about life and death; he receives, in addition to knowledge, a plant of eternal youth which he soon loses on his return. Odysseus goes to the other world for knowledge from the dead seer Teresias. And there are other well known stories of those who went to the land of the dead to bring back a beloved one—the tale of Orpheus and Eurydice is a symbol for all such myths. But not only a beloved human is sought in the other world—the hero seeks prosperity itself, or that which gives it. So in the *Kalevala's* runes of the Sampo, Väinämöinen and Ilmarinen set out to Pohjola to steal the wealth of the Sampo, are successful, yet lose it upon the return journey. Among the Ovimbundu, similar tales frequently end with death or loss, after the breaking of a tabu, as we have just seen.

However, there is an Ovimbundu story of this type in which the ending seems to indicate that one *can* bring back a boon from the other world—and still live to enjoy it. This story is "Hunger Time," a tale well worth more detailed analysis, since we see in the story what may happen when two tales are mingled together, or are modulated into one another.

"Hunger Time" is a parallel to, or variant of, "Goodhearted Ngeve, Kindhearted Chilombo," at least in regard to a return from another world. In "Hunger Time" the other country is no less clearly the "other world." Although it is not entered through a hole in the ground, its geography is suggestive of another world. It is journeyed to along a path and over rivers, similar to the scenery in the *Kalevala* and in *Gilgamesh;* and the clubhouse is like that in "A Bee Hunter and His Wife." There is, finally, in "Hunger Time" a series of tests through which the protagonist passes with the help of magical assistants. The last test is the same in both Ovimbundu stories, namely the picking out of the thing sought—wife or small animal—from among others of the same kind looking exactly alike. In both cases a fly indicates the answer and thus helps the hero to obtain the object of his search. In "Hunger Time" the hero returns with the small animal and is not laden with tabus. And the man who had been to the other world and returned with the lost animal, together with some wondrous figs, lived more or less happily ever afterward, although he did lose his figs. However, he was not the owner of the little animal, but the younger brother of the owner. The owner also journeys to the other world to fetch figs, but loses his life—though presumably not the small animal, for we hear nothing more of it. Although the first trip to the other country taken by the younger brother was successful, showing that the righteous can obtain the blessing, the second trip, taken by the evil elder brother, was a failure.

The independent existence of the first part of this story, that is to say, the story unhampered by the return of the other brother in order to obtain figs—in fact without any figs!—is indicated by the unpublished "A Tale of Two Brothers" (Folio VII, Tale 6). It is a variant of "Hunger Time" up to the return from the other world with the animal. It begins with the report of a small animal that used to come during planting time to the field of two brothers and eat the seed. A trap was set, the animal was caught in it, but when the wife of one of the brothers went to kill the animal, it first extruded a gourd of water when it was hit, then a gourd of beer, then a bowl of mush, and finally a dish of gravy! Husband and wife enjoyed this animal and its food for a time, and then one morning they left their child at home when they went to work and in the middle of the day the child became hungry. His cries attracted his uncle, who opened the door of the house for him, and was told by the child how to go through the ritual with the small animal and thus obtain food. The older brother was delighted, but while he and the child were eating, the animal wandered away. It will be immediately noted that the loss of the animal is not due to any malevolence or mistreatment by the brother. The animal simply slips away. The second brother thus does not incur the guilt that his counterpart seems to have in "Hunger Time."

"A Tale of Two Brothers" at this point employs the technique of repetition in full of an already narrated incident by two of its participants each in his own words. The child retells, with conversations, what has happened to the animal, and the older brother does the same. After these explanations, the younger brother sends his older brother to find the small animal and bring it back. Like the younger brother in "Hunger Time," the older brother here encounters an old woman with smallpox sores; he cleans her and she gives him two amulets—two horns, Ndundole and Niulole, which he is to whistle on and ask for advice in turn. These of course are like the two horns in "Hunger Time." The first decision he has to make with the help of the horns concerns which path he is to follow at a fork in the road—the well traveled one or the faint trail (the second horn advises the latter; this decision is not in "Hunger Time." Then the crossing of the river at the bridge is advised, as in "Hunger Time"; and also the discovery of the gate to the stockade around the village.

The tests which the brother goes through in "A Tale of Two Brothers" are in part similar, in part different, from those in "Hunger Time," and they present typical multiforms of the same theme of testing and of its several episodes. In the first test the man in "A Tale of Two Brothers" is presented two kinds of food by his hosts, a cock and human brains, and the horn advises him to eat the latter; in "Hunger Time" the little old woman has given him some crabs to eat, and the horn advises him to eat the crabs rather than the cock. The human brains and the gourd of blood in the other tale change back to mush and relish before the man eats them. The next two tests are not in "Hunger Time": the man is asked to sweep all the dooryards (the horn rouses a great wind to accomplish this for him); he is also asked to climb a tree on top of a rock, a tree with delicious fruit, and when a wind rises he stays in the tree as advised by the horn and survives. This tree is undoubtedly the same tree as in "Hunger Time" but the theme is developed differently. The final test is the same in both, except that in "A Tale of Two Brothers" the man has to choose in which box the small animal is located, because the villagers have collected together in one place all the boxes in the village. The means of locating the animal is the same, namely, the fly. When this test is completed successfully the people of the village applaud him and give him presents and he returns with the animal to his brother where he is received with an ovation.

This variant of the story is extremely useful for the study of structure because it shows us the separate parts of the story, and presents us with multiforms of some of them. It helps very much in seeing the structure of "Hunger Time" and its relationship to other tales. In this way we realize that there are groups of tales that are related not merely in that they have the same or similar patterns but often in that they are mixtures of one or more patterns.

A second pattern links "Hunger Time" with another tale in this collection, "The Bride and Her Small Brother." In "Hunger Time" the younger brother encounters an old woman whose boils and filth he licks and who gives him the two magic horns to help him. In "The Bride and Her Small Brother" the brother meets an old man whose scabs he licks and who gives him three magic bananas, the proper handling of which brings him wealth. The theme of the old woman and that of the old man are obviously the same, and they are the link between these two tales. At the entrance of this theme in "Hunger Time" the younger brother becomes parallel to the younger brother in "The Bride and Her Small Brother" and they both then obtain wealth magically, this wealth being represented by the figs in one story and the herds and other real wealth in the other. It is noteworthy that this fruit in "Hunger Time" is in addition to the small animal in this story, although the animal is also a symbol of prosperity and wealth. The small animal belongs to the pattern of returning a lost object from the other world, whereas the fruit belongs to the pattern of wealth gained by a kind deed. Both symbols are present in the story that mingles the two patterns. The stories end alike, with the punishment by death of the greedy brother and of the greedy playmate.

Further light on the role of the little old woman (or man) who needs to be cleaned can be gained from other instances of the theme in these tales. Thus, in "Nightshade Berries," which like "Hunger Time," also occurs during a time of famine, the heroine is lost and the old woman gives the girl squash seeds to plant after her sores have been cleaned. The vines carry the girl home. It is noteworthy that the little old woman does not do anything, but gives some magic to the hero or heroine who cleans her sores. That she is associated with the other world is also clear from this tale, because the girl sings a song as she flies homeward on the vine, and the people in the village recognize from the singing that this is the girl whom they have already mourned as dead. This too, then, is essentially the story of a journey into the other world and return from it.

There is another group of stories telling about a journey to another country to obtain a boon, which have become success stories because of the mingling of patterns. This is the group mentioned above when we were considering series of repetitions, the two in particular which are concerned with obtaining food that must be named or that must not be watched. "Naming Foods in a Time of Famine" and "Omutia Kuvingi" (unpublished Folio IX, No. 1, Tale 5), both of which belong to the Tortoise Saga. Here the journey to seek the food which will save the tribe is repeatedly unsuccessful, because the tabu is broken by one animal after another, and thus the food is useless or it returns to the field whence it came. But the series of repeated incidents is, as we have seen, the framework for a theme which tells of a task performed unsuccessfully by a progression of animals, from small to large, to be solved only by the despised one, tortoise, or by a simpleton. Thus our pattern of the other world yields to the success story of the despised. Examples of this can be found in "Tortoise at the King's Coronation Hunt," in which Tortoise is able to catch Konjombolo after a series of animals had failed, and in a story with human actors, "The Simpleton," in which the simpleton is able to bring the coveted monitor lizard down from the tree for the king, a feat that many others had tried to do but had failed.

In studying the previous story patterns we have noticed that there are a number of instances where the beginning of a tale, which sets the stage and describes the particular situation of the narrative, varies, whereas the pattern of the end of the tale may be the same. We saw this, for example, in "A Girl Believes That Her Brother-in-Law Laughs at Her" and "A Ghost Interrupts the Making of a New Field." The setting for each of these tales is different, although the final scenes are very much alike. It is thus sometimes true that we cannot tell the relationship between two tales from reading or otherwise knowing only the beginning, because the relationship may be apparent only from the ending.

Often the reading of another related tale may be enlightening for the understanding of a tale that one may find puzzling. For example, there is some difficulty in grasping the point of the story, "Chela's Tongue is Slit," partly, no doubt because of the unfamiliar customs of teeth chipping and of the payment of fines. It is the latter theme, that of the payment of fines or of punishment for injustice, that is the moral of the tale. This is especially clear when one meets the theme again in a different setting in Part II or "The Bee Hunter's Family and Their Slave." One of the difficulties with this theme in "Chela's Tongue is Slit" is that Chela, whom we know to be the child of the Queen, speaks of herself in this theme of fines as "a common person" and "a slave." No foundation has been laid, as it were, to justify her calling herself a slave, except perhaps generally the other girls' treatment of her. When we look at "The Bee Hunter's Family and Their Slave" we realize that here the theme of fines and the reference to slave make complete sense. Either we should believe that the theme belongs in the one story and not in the other, or we might be led to re-examine the introductory material in "Chela's Tongue is Slit." Such a re-examination, although it does not solve the problem, does indicate the possibility of a closer relationship between the introductory material in these two stories than one might have thought—a closer relationship than merely that of injustice. In Part II of "The Bee Hunter's Family and Their Slave," the characters consist of two sisters and a slave who go to visit an older sister. The older sister may be thought of as corresponding to the mother of Chela, and it is to be noted that Chela has an older sister who is with her on the tooth chipping trip although she otherwise plays no part. Thus the first part is indicated to be or to have been a story of two sisters, but the role of the slave has been entirely lost, except possibly for the reference in the theme of fines. This may well be because the introductory portion to "Chela's Tongue is Slit" is itself part of a "despised girl," "nuisance of a younger sister" theme, which we find in other stories in this section of the book; for example, in "Gathering Olonjavilili," "Kotunda's Tooth Chipping," and "The Revenge of Chupindiwangonga's Mother."

The theme of the payment of fines is a migrant one and does not "belong" in any one tale. It has two forms, a shorter one, which consists in nothing more than the statement that fines were paid, and a longer and more elaborate form. The latter is especially interesting. We have just seen it associated with two tales, "Chela's Tongue is Slit" and "The Bee Hunter's Family and Their Slave." There is another case of it in a tale in the unpublished Ennis material, "Chinguli Becomes a Bride" (Folio VII, Tale 8). Here it is linked with a variant of "The Woman Who Quarreled with Her Husband." The unpublished tale begins with a bride who is accompanied on her journey to the village of the groom by her bridesmaids and her younger sister, and a slave of her father's named Chinguli. As they are passing over a bridge the slave pushes the bride into the water and she later poses as the bride. In the meantime the bride herself has married a crocodile. Here the resemblance to "The Woman Who Quarreled with Her Husband" becomes apparent. In "Chinguli Becomes a Bride," the person who visits the river for water and stays to spend time with the crocodile's bride is the little girl, the younger sister of the bride. Her visits are discovered, as in the other story, and the bride is captured. At this point the story begins to differ somewhat from "The Woman Who Quarreled with Her Husband" in that the bride requires payment of fines at each stage of her return. This payment-of-fines theme is missing in the other tale, in which the wife simply returns to her husband and child. In "Chinguli Becomes a Bride," Chinguli the slave is herself burned after the truth has been discovered and the real bride returned. It is most interesting and, I believe, significant that the payment-of-fines theme occurs in the variant of the crocodile's bride story in which two sisters and a slave are involved, but that it is missing in the variant in which only a wife and husband and child are the dramatis personae. In other words, it would seem that the payment-of-fines theme belongs with these figures.

This does not mean that every time that these figures appear we also find the payment-of-fines theme. That this is so is clear from another unpublished tale in the Ennis Collection, "Chingulia and Ndombuela" (Folio VII, Tale 11), which is, in its turn, a variant of the story in Part II of "The Bee Hunter's Family and Their Slave." In this story the characters consist of an older sister who is a bride, and a younger sister who is a slave, in addition to several bridesmaids. In "The Bee Hunter's Family and Their Slave," the characters consist of an older sister with a baby, a younger sister, *and* a slave. The distinctive theme that appears in both tales is that of abandoning the older sister on a high place at the order of the slave—in one instance on a high rock where she went for water, and in the other case up in a tree picking fruits. In both tales also the slave takes the place of the older sister, although the timing is not the same in both stories. That is to say, in "Chingulia and Ndombuela" the girl is let down from the tree after the visit in the other village so that she and the younger sister, who has fasted during this time, were very thin when they reached home compared to Chingulia who feasted as the bride. In the other tale the girl is not released from the rock until the discovery of her fate has been made. In this case the theme of the payment of fines comes in at this point, quite correctly. On the other hand the payment-of-fines theme might also have entered the other story at the time of discovery of Chingulia's treachery, or even earlier, when Chingulia gets the bride down from the tree, but it is here omitted. One should add that Chinguli is killed for her mistreatment of her sister.

What we have just been elaborating upon in the wondrous laboratory of Ovimbundu tales has been a woven tapestry of themes and stories, a rich texture of overlapping and interlocking narrative units of varying lengths. This is the kind of panorama that is characteristic of story material in the oral tradition, be it in prose or verse, be it "primitive" or "advanced." For the techniques and processes at work in the Ovimbundu tales, the patterned mingling of themes and thematic sequences that we have just been describing, is the same as those seen in oral epic among the Southern Slavs and in such cultural masterpieces as *The Iliad* and *The Odyssey* of Homer.*

Thus, the Ovimbundu tales show in a clear and exciting way how oral narrative is constructed, composed, and transmitted. We have been able to isolate several themes, independent and recognizable. Further, we have seen these themes relate to the themes about them, forming clusters or patterns which operate as structural or cohesive forces in shaping the narrative. The largest of these patterns are of tale length, but lesser patterns may be joined together by simple addition, by overlapping, or by modulation to form a tale which is essentially a compound. The narrative stories of the Ovimbundu illustrate that mixture of story patterns which we feel must have taken place in both the narrative verses and epics of other cultures, especially in their earlier stages of development.

---

* In a different context—*The Singer of Tales*—I have analyzed similar mixtures of thematic patterns in Yugoslavian oral epic versions of the extremely common story of the return home of a hero after long absence to find his wife about to marry again. The kaleidoscope of variants of this sung tale among the Balkan Slavs is of the same general character as that of the variants we have just been considering from Angola. It is clear that we are dealing with generically similar material in both cases. And in the same context I have elsewhere described the mixtures of story patterns demonstrable in both *The Iliad* and *The Odyssey*.

prologue

1. folk tales about folk tales

the king's endless story

Once there was a king who sent out summons through the whole country, saying: "All of my people! Come to me! Come and hear what I have to tell you of my wish."

When the people had assembled, the king spoke to them, telling them that he was very fond of stories and wished to have someone tell him a story without an end. And he said to them, "If anyone starts a story which finally comes to an end, I will cut off his head." Then he added, "But he who can tell a story that does not come to an end may cut off my head and become king in my stead."

This pronouncement produced excitement among all the tellers of tales. So it came to pass that one of them would say, "I have a story which I can tell in such a way that it will meet the test, and when I have done this I shall be king." Many other tellers of tales were saying the same thing.

One day a storyteller began his story early in the morning, at sunrise. He continued his story until about ten o'clock, at which time it ended. When he had finished, the king said, "Get a sword and cut off his head, for his story has come to an end. My wish is to hear a story which will not come to an end."

Another day, another teller of tales came to the king and said, "Here am I. I have a story which does not come to an end." The king agreed to give him a hearing. This man also began his story at sunrise and he continued the tale until midday; then his story came to an end. When the story stopped, the king said, "Let his head be cut off, for his story had an end. What I wish is a story that has no end."

I

After some days had passed, another storyteller came to the
king saying that he had a story without an end. He began his
story at sunrise also, and in the middle of the afternoon his story
finished. The king said, "As his story is finished, cut off his head
also."

After some days had passed, another storyteller came saying,
"Oh king, here am I. I have a story that has no end. Please be
so kind as to hear it." The king agreed to hear his story.

The storyteller began. "Oh king, listen. Once at Mbangu-
naikongo there was a great grain store house filled with corn from
the floor all the way to the roof. In the roof of this store house
was a small hole. One day a single locust flew down from the
sky through this hole and carried away a single grain of corn. Oh
king, the locusts filled the sky like a cloud. Another locust flew
down from the sky through this hole and carried away a single
grain of corn. Another locust flew down from the sky through
this hole and carried away a single grain of corn. Another locust
flew down from the sky through this hole and carried away a
single grain of corn."

Thus, the storyteller continued saying the same words over
and over again, until the sun went down. Throughout the
evening he continued the same performance. For three days the
storyteller kept this up. Then the king said to him, "Yes, yes, I
have that. Now get on with whatever comes next."

The storyteller replied to this and said, "Oh king, the locusts
have, as yet, cleared out only a small space, and the sky is still
filled with locusts. How can I know what they will uncover?"
Then he resumed saying, "Another locust flew down from the sky
through this hole and carried away a single grain of corn. Another locust flew down from the sky through this hole and carried
away a single grain of corn."

The king became disgusted at hearing the same thing repeated over and over again, and said, "There you go with your
'Another locust flew down from the sky through this hole and
carried away a single grain of corn.' Pass over that part of the
story and let us get on with your story, if you have one."

The storyteller said in reply, "Oh king, oh lion, please listen
patiently, for another locust flew down from the sky through this
hole and carried away another single grain of corn. Another
locust flew down from the sky through this hole and . . ."

Here, the weary king stopped the storyteller, sucked his

tooth angrily, and said: "Here, take this sword and cut off my head." The storyteller took the sword, cut off the king's head, and became king.

mupuiyakalangi

Mupuiyakalangi[1] accompanied his wife when she went to visit her family. They were welcomed joyfully at the village of his wife's family, where even roosters crowed a welcome for Mupuiyakalangi. He considered this to be a sign of things to come.

In the evening they cooked a fowl for Mupuiyakalangi. When he had tasted it, he said, "I have just one thing to say about this fowl: the person who cooked it is a cook." [2]

Dog had listened to Mupuiyakalangi and now said, "Those who eat food with gusto do not offer other praise."

When he had heard this, Mupuiyakalangi said to Dog, "For that insult, I am going to hit you with the broom."

Dog replied, "Do not hit me for telling you that the knotted bunch of meat in your mouth is a testicle."

Mupuiyakalangi gagged and choked until his tongue fell out upon the ground. Just as he was leaning down to pick up his tongue, the rooster rushed in, picked up the tongue, and ran away with it. Mupuiyakalangi chased the rooster, which so frightened the rooster that he dropped the tongue in the ash heap.

Mupuiyakalangi took up his tongue and went with it to the river to wash off the ashes which were on it. When he began to wash his tongue in the river, it slipped from his fingers into the water, and before he could recover it, a fish seized it and swam away with it. Mupuiyakalangi said to himself, "What a day! What weird things are happening to me!"

Mupuiyakalangi looked downstream and saw there a fish trapper. He hurried to him and said, "Brother, I have been unfortunate, for a fish swam away with my tongue. Please be kind enough to do me a favor. Let us open the stomachs of your fish,

[1] This name means: "the rain-maker of Kalangi."

[2] Among the Ovimbundu, the very highest form of praise is to say that a man is "a cook," or "a hunter," etc.

since one of them may be the fish which swam away with my tongue."

The fisherman replied, "Just as you say, master." So they began to open the stomachs of the fish. They finally found the tongue in the stomach of one fish. Mupuiyakalangi took his tongue from the stomach of the fish, and put it back in his mouth without washing it. Then Mupuiyakalangi thanked the fisherman many times for his kindness and help. The fisherman, to indicate his sympathy, gave Mupuiyakalangi some of his fish as a present. Mupuiyakalangi accepted the fish, bade the fisherman goodbye, and walked away along a path.

Mupuiyakalangi had walked but a short distance when he met a little old woman. They greeted each other, and then the little old woman asked him, "Will you trade your fish for some cowpeas?" Mupuiyakalangi agreed and they made the trade. When they parted, the little old woman said to Mupuiyakalangi, "As you go in that direction, you will come to the Plain of Kapule. Those who cross that plain must not look back. If you should look back, you will spill your cowpeas."

Mupuiyakalangi replied to her, "Lady Grandmother, you have warned me. The son has heard."

The little old woman went on her way, and Mupuiyakalangi also went his way. He had gone but a short distance when he forgot the warning given him by the little old woman. He turned around to look back, and as he did this the basket fell from his head [3] and the cowpeas were spilled. He intended to pick them up, but just then a rainstorm came down upon him from the east. He decided that it was best to first take cover from the storm, and then come out to gather up the cowpeas in the morning. So he ran to a nearby village.

In the morning, he returned to recover the cowpeas. When he came to the plain he found that the cowpeas had already sprouted and were growing. He thought over the situation. He decided that although there was some risk in allowing the cowpeas to grow, yet on the whole it was better to leave the cowpeas until they had borne and ripened their pods. Mupuiyakalangi waited and waited, until one day he said to himself, "I shall go and take a look at the cowpeas to see how they are growing." When he came to the place, he found the pods full, all dry and ready to harvest.

[3] The Ovimbundu customarily carry burdens, especially baskets, upon their heads.

He returned to the village and invited the people there to go with him the next day to help him harvest the cowpeas. At dawn the next morning, he and the people he had invited went to the plain to gather the cowpeas. When they reached the plain, they found that an elephant had been there and had eaten the cowpeas, to the last one.

Then Mupuiyakalangi Ukongo Wachimbenje Watelele Ochitachatemo Njundombali Kuvala Nduka Chitilileko[4] said to the others, "You, brothers, go back to the village, while I take my gun with me and track down this elephant." Then Mupuiyakalangi Ukongo Wachimbenje took up the spoor of the elephant and followed it.

He followed and followed until at last he found the elephant out in the wilderness, fast asleep. Because the elephant was asleep, its rear end was open like a fish trap which had been set. One could look inside and see what was there. Mupuiyakalangi stepped softly up to the elephant and looked inside. There inside were his cowpeas in plain sight. Leaning his gun against a tree, Mupuiyakalangi went inside the elephant and began to gather up his cowpeas and throw them out upon the ground. He kept this up until he had thrown out all the cowpeas. When he had finished, he raised his eyes and looked up into the chest of the elephant and saw hanging there the lobes of the elephant's liver. Greed overcame Mupuiyakalangi, so he unsheathed his knife and said to himself, "I shall cut me off some liver."

The cut caused the elephant to move, which caused Mupuiyakalangi to decide, "Now I will get out." But as the elephant was shutting up his rear, Mupuiyakalangi got only his head out of the elephant before the opening closed tight around his neck. The elephant stood up and went away, without stopping for the cowpeas. Thus it happened that Mupuiyakalangi remained in the rear of the elephant for many days. Since the elephant ate many squashes and gourds, Mupuiyakalangi was able to keep himself alive by catching and eating the passing seeds.

[4] Most of the Ovimbundu have very long names. The parts of the names are descriptive, usually condensing the meaning of some proverb. The core of the name often comes from a namesake. If the namesake is still living and acquires additional names, then these are also added to the name of him who was given the namesake's name. Here, *Chimbenje* means "big gun" or "big shot," and *Ukongo Wachimbenje* means "the hunter of the big gun." *Watelele Ochitachatemo Njundombali* means "he who has forged a hundred hoes on two anvils." *Kuvala* means "at the village of the wife's family," and *Kuvala Nduka Chitilileko* means "I am one who was not born at the village of his wife's family."

One day Mupuiyakalangi happened to look up and saw a
hunter stalking the elephant, so he shouted, "O hunter, if you
are going to shoot, shoot it in the other end. Do not shoot it in
the rump, for we,[5] Mupuiyakalangi Ukongo Wachimbenje
Watelele Ochitachatemo Njundombali Kuvala Nduka Chitilileko, are in here."

When the hunter heard this, he was frightened and said,
"Haka! What miraculous thing is this I have encountered today?
An elephant I am about to shoot tells me where to shoot!"

Then Mupuiyakalangi Ukongo Wachimbenje Watelele
Ochitachatemo Njundombali Kuvala Nduka Chitilileko spoke
to the hunter and said, "There is nothing to fear. Do not be
frightened, for it was not the elephant who told you where to
shoot. It was I, Mupuiyakalangi Ukongo Wachimbenje Watelele
Ochitachatemo Njundombali Kuvala Nduka Chitilileko, who
told you where to shoot."

When the hunter heard who it was that directed him, he
shot the elephant in the head and killed it. Then the hunter
went away to their[6] village to summon people to help him cut
up the meat. When the help came, they cut and cut until the
beast was all cut up, and then they took Mupuiyakalangi out.
They found that being so long inside the elephant had bleached
all of his body except his head, so that he was white like an albino.
They were curious and asked him, "Tell us all about yourself, and
how you came to be where you were."

In reply to their question, he said, "I am Mupuiyakalangi
Ukongo Wachimbenje Watelele Ochitachatemo Njundombali
Kuvala Nduka Chitilileko. I went with my wife to visit my
wife's family. When we came to the village of my wife's family,
they welcomed us and rejoiced, and even the roosters crowed to
welcome me. For me this was a portent. In the evening they
cooked fowl for me. When I tasted it, I spoke up and said, 'I
have just one thing to say about this fowl, and that is: that the
one who cooked this fowl is a cook.'

"Dog was listening and said, 'Those who eat food with gusto
do not offer other praise.'

[5] The Ovimbundu indicate a person's importance by referring to themselves or
others in the plural.
[6] English usage would seem to call for "his" here, but the Ovimbundu never say
"my" or "his" village. To them, this would be presumptuous. They always say "our"
or "their" village, in the plural.

"When I heard this, I said, 'For that insult, I am going to hit you with the broom.'

"Dog replied, 'Do not hit me for telling you that the knotted bunch of meat you have in your mouth is a testicle.'

"Then I gagged and choked until my tongue fell out upon the ground. Just as I was about to pick it up, a rooster rushed in, picked it up, and ran off with it. I chased the rooster and he dropped it in the ash heap. I took my tongue and went to the river to wash it. As I started to wash it, my tongue slipped and fell into the water, where a fish seized it and swam away with it. Then I said, 'What a day, and what uncanny things are happening to me today.'

"I looked downstream and saw a man setting fish traps. I went to him and said, 'Brother, I have been unfortunate. As I went to wash my tongue, a fish swam off with it. So if you will do me a favor, please let me slit the stomachs of your fish. It may be that the fish which went off with my tongue is among them.'

"He replied, 'All right, master.'

"We started to open up all the fish, and we found the tongue in one of them. I, Mupuiyakalangi, took it up and put it back in my mouth. I thanked the fisherman, and then he gave me some of his fish as a present. I bade him goodbye, found a path, and started back to the village. I had gone only a little way, when I met a little old woman. We greeted each other. Then the little old woman said, "Will you trade your fish for some cowpeas?'

"I agreed to this, so she took the fish and gave me a basket of cowpeas. As I started to go along the path, the little old woman said to me, 'As you go in that direction, you will soon come to the Plain of Kapule, and there, do not look back, for if you do, what you are carrying will fall and be spilled.'

"I replied, 'Lady Grandmother, you have warned me, and your son has heard.'

"The little old woman went on her way, and I took the path for the village. When I came to the Plain of Kapule, the warning of the little old woman had slipped from my memory. I turned to look back. The instant that I did this, the basket fell from my head, and the cowpeas scattered over the ground. I thought that I would have a job picking them up again, but just then a storm came down from the east. I thought that it was best to run from the rain to a nearby village, and to come back in the morning to pick up the cowpeas. In the morning, when I went out to gather up the cowpeas, I found that they had sprouted and were growing. The plants were strong and fine. Then I thought the matter over and decided that the best thing was to let them grow and bear. So I left them.

"I waited and waited at the village, and when it was time for the cowpeas to have borne, I went to see how they were doing. When I came to the plain, I found that the pods were already dry and ready to be gathered. I went back to the village and called some people to go out with me in the morning to harvest my cowpeas. In the morning, we went to the place and found that an elephant had been there and eaten up the cowpeas to the last one. Then I, Mupuiyakalangi Ukongo Wachimbenje Watelele Ochitachatemo Njundombali Kuvala Nduka Chitilileko, said, 'As for you, brothers, go back to the village, while I go to track down this elephant.'

"From there I followed and followed the elephant until I found him asleep. The elephant, being asleep, was open behind like a fish trap. I could see what was inside, and I saw my cowpeas there, in plain sight. So I leaned my gun against a tree, went inside the elephant, and began throwing out my cowpeas, until I had them all out. Then I saw the liver hanging there. I thought I might just as well have some liver, so I took out my knife and started to cut off a piece. When the elephant awoke and began to move, I said, 'I am getting out of here.'

"The elephant began to shut up, and only my head was out when the exit closed tight around my neck. I stayed inside the elephant for many days, eating only the seeds of squashes and gourds, which the elephant had eaten. One day I happened to look up and see a hunter stalking the elephant. I called to him, 'Shoot him in the head! Do not shoot him in the rump, for we, Mupuiyakalangi Ukongo Wachimbenje Watelele Ochitachatemo Njundombali Kuvala Nduka Chitilileko, are here.' Brothers, that is how this came about."

Then they said to him, "You have already died. You will not die again."

After they had heard his story and given their reply, they gave him some of the meat of the elephant. When he had taken this, he left to go home to their village. Because he had been inside the elephant for such a long time, his body was all bleached and white, like an albino. Thus, he had to go slowly, avoiding the sun.

One day, as he was walking along, he heard the sound of a whistle, "Pee-eep, pee-eep!" [7] From this sound he knew that someone carried in a litter was coming his way. He left the path and climbed a tree. Up in the tree, he hid himself completely in the leaves. It happened that when the king being carried in the litter saw this fine tree, he said, "Stop under that tree. Let us rest there, for it has a fine shade."

The carriers turned aside from the path and stopped under the tree. When this happened, Mupuiyakalangi was much alarmed. The king and his company sat around under the tree for a long time. Mupuiyakalangi, up in the tree, was in great distress. Fear added to his distress, so that he could not contain himself any longer. The king was the victim. The followers were astonished and said, "Where did that water come from?" Then they added, "Let us look up into the tree."

When they looked up into the tree, they saw that there was a person trembling and shaking in the treetop. They called to him, "Today you must pay a big fine for the big breach of good behavior you have committed against a visiting king. Now climb down." He was so emaciated, and in addition so white like an albino, that they looked at him in astonishment.

They asked him, "How did you come to be in this condition?"

Given this opportunity, he began to tell them his story. He said, "Brothers, I am Mupuiyakalangi Ukongo Wachimbenje Watelele Ochitachatemo Njundombali Kuvala Nduka Chitilileko. I went with my wife to visit my wife's family. When we came to their village, they received us very well and rejoiced. Even the roosters crowed to greet me. For me this was a portent. In the evening they cooked a fowl for me. When I tasted it, I said, 'The one who cooked this is a cook.'

"Dog said, 'Those who eat food with gusto do not offer other praise.'

[7] Among the Ovimbundu, whistles and gongs are sounded in front of traveling kings, who are carried by bearers. These sounds are to warn commoners to get upwind from the path, lest they be harmed by the breath and smell of the king, which are believed to be extremely potent, capable of killing a commoner. The king's person, and even its effluvium, are sacred.

"I said to Dog, 'For that insult, I shall take the broom and hit you.'

"Dog replied, 'Do not hit me, for that knotted meat you have in your mouth is a testicle.'

"I gagged and choked until my tongue fell out of my mouth onto the ground. Just as I was about to pick it up, a rooster picked it up and ran off with it. I chased the rooster until he, being frightened, dropped my tongue in the ash heap. I took up my tongue and went to the river to wash it. As I started to wash it, my tongue slipped and fell into the water, where a fish seized it and swam away. Then I said, 'What a day! What weird things are happening to me today!'

"I looked off downstream and saw a man setting traps for fish. I went to him and said, 'Brother, I have been unfortunate, for as I began to wash my tongue, a fish went off with it. If you will do me a favor, please let us slit the stomachs of your fish. It may be that the fish which swam off with my tongue is among them.'

"The fisherman replied, 'All right, master.'

"Then we started to open up all the fish. We found the tongue in one of them. I, Mupuiyakalangi, took up the tongue and put it back into my mouth. I thanked the fisherman for his help. He gave me some of his fish as a present. I bade him good-bye, found a path, and started back for the village. I had gone but a little way when I met a little old woman. After we had greeted each other, the little old woman said to me, 'Will you trade your fish for some cowpeas?'

I agreed to this. She took the fish and gave me a basket of cowpeas. As I was about to go along the path, the little old woman said to me, 'As you go in that direction, you will come to the Plain of Kapule. Do not look back there, for if you do, whatever you are carrying will fall and be spilled.'

"I said to her, 'Lady Grandmother, you have warned me, and your son has heard.'

"The little old woman went on her way. I took the path for the village. When I came to the plain, the warning of the little old woman had slipped from my memory. I turned to look back, the basket fell from my head, and the cowpeas scattered on the ground. I thought that I should have a job in picking them up, but just then a storm came down from the east. I decided that it was best I run to a nearby village and come out in the morning to gather up the cowpeas. In the morning, when I went to the plain to pick up the cowpeas, I found that they had sprouted and were growing. The plants were strong and fine. I thought it over and said, 'The best thing is to leave them here to grow and bear.'

"I waited until it was time for cowpeas to be ripe, and then I went out to see how they were. I found that the pods were dry and the cowpeas were ready to be harvested. I went to the village to get people to come and help harvest my cowpeas. In the morning, we went to the plain to gather the cowpeas. We found that an elephant had been there and eaten them all up, to the last one. Then I, Mupuiyakalangi Ukongo Wachimbenje Watelele Ochitachatemo Njundombali Kuvala Nduka Chitilileko, said, 'Brothers, go home to the village, while I go track down this elephant.'

"Then I followed and followed the spoor of the elephant until I found him fast asleep. Since he was asleep, he was open behind like a fish trap set for fish. One could see all that was inside. There were my cowpeas in plain sight. I leaned my gun against a tree, went inside, and threw out all my cowpeas. When I had done this, I looked up and saw the liver hanging inside. I thought that I might as well have some liver to go with my cowpeas. I took out my knife and began to cut off a piece, when the elephant began to wake up and move. I said, 'Now I am getting out.'

"But the elephant was shutting up, and I was caught around the neck so that my body stayed inside the elephant. I was in there a long time, having only the seeds of gourds and squashes to eat. One day I looked up and saw a hunter stalking the elephant, and already pointing his gun. I called to him and said, 'Shoot him in the other end! Do not shoot him in the rump, but shoot him in the head.'

"When the hunter heard this, he was frightened and said, 'What a marvel! The elephant tells me where to shoot!'

"I said to him, "It is not the elephant who talks to you, but we, Mupuiyakalangi Ukongo Wachimbenje Watelele Ochitachatemo Njundombali Kuvala Nduka Chitilileko, who are here.'

"Then he shot the elephant in the head and it died. After the elephant was dead, he went to their village to call people to come and cut up the flesh of the elephant. They came and cut and cut until they took me out. They found that I had been in the elephant so long that my body was weakened, and my skin all white like that of an albino. They asked me how I came to be there. Then I told them that I was Mupuiyakalangi Kuvala Nduka Chitilileko, and related all that had befallen me.[8]

"Those who listened to the story said, 'You have died already. You will not die again.' They gave me some of the meat of the elephant, and I started out to go back to my village. Because I was weak and white like an albino, I traveled slowly. When I heard the sound of a king's whistle, I was afraid and hid myself in the top of this tree. When the king and his men sat down below, I was terrified and I could not restrain myself."

The king's men marveled at his adventures and said to him, "Brother, you have already died. You cannot die again. You are not far from your village. Just go along home."

Then Mupuiyakalangi Ukongo Wachimbenje Watelele Ochitachatemo Njundombali Kuvala Nduka Chitilileko entered the path and departed. As he went along, he heard funeral drums being played on the path ahead. He felt he had already suffered hardship enough, so he turned aside. He found a cave and went into it and hid. He waited there for some time. Then he heard the drums sounding outside the cave. He thought, "Now what more will happen to me today?"

As he waited and listened, he heard a person say, "Behold, here is a good cave! Let us bury the corpse in here." After they had consulted the corpse itself by divination, and the corpse had consented, they pushed the corpse into the cave where Mupuiyakalangi was hiding. He seized the pole to which the corpse was tied and pushed it out again. Then the people outside said, "Look! The corpse will not agree to be buried in there. Maybe something is lacking." So they took the corpse away and divined once more.

When they had divined the second time, the omens were still the same. Then they said, "Now it is settled. Let us bury the corpse in this cave. Then they pushed the corpse into the cave for the second time. Mupuiyakalangi seized the pole and pushed the corpse out of the cave again. This puzzled the burial party, and they said, "Haka! There is something uncanny here!

---

[8] The narrator may repeat here the entire adventure in detail. In the translation of this story, the informant's and the story's repetition has been retained, as essential to the Umbundu tone and spirit. At this point, the informant himself merely indicated that the previous narrative can be repeated at this point, without actually repeating it.

Let us look inside and find what makes this cave so bothersome."

When they looked into the cave, they found Mupuiyaka-langi. They said to him, "Who are you? How did you come to be in there?"

Then Mupuiyakalangi told them: "I am Mupuiyakalangi Ukongo Wachimbenje Watelele Ochitachatemo Njundombali Kuvala Nduka Chitilileko, who went with my wife to visit her family. When we came to their village, they received us very well, rejoicing over us. Even the roosters crowed to greet me. This was a portent for me. In the evening they cooked a fowl for me. When I tasted it I said, 'The one who cooked this is a cook.'

"When I had said this, Dog spoke up and said, 'Those who eat their food with gusto do not offer other praise.'

"I replied to Dog and said, 'For that insult I shall hit you with the broom.'

"Dog answered, 'Do not hit me, for that knotted meat in your mouth is a testicle.'

"At that, I gagged and choked until my tongue fell out upon the ground. Just as I was reaching to pick it up, a rooster snapped it up and ran off with it. I ran after the rooster and he dropped my tongue in the ash heap. I took up my tongue and went to the river to wash it. As I started to wash it in the river, the tongue slipped and fell into the water. A fish grabbed it and swam away with it. Then I said, 'What a day! What uncanny things have happened to me today!'

"I looked off down river and saw a man who had fish traps in the water. I went to him and said, 'Brother, I am unfortunate, for I went to wash my tongue in the river, and a fish swam off with it. If you will do me a favor, please let us slit the bellies of your fish.'

"He replied, 'All right, master.'

"Then we started to open the fish, and in one of them we found my tongue. Then I, Mupuiyakalangi, took it up and put it back into my mouth. After that I thanked the fisherman. He then gave me some fish as a present. I bade him goodbye, and finding the path, started for the village. I had gone only a short way when I met a little old woman. After we had greeted each other, she said to me, 'Will you trade your fish for some cowpeas?'

I agreed to this, so she took the fish and gave me a basket of cowpeas. As I was about to go along the path, the little old woman said, 'As you go in that direction, you will come soon to the Plain of Kapule. There they do not look back.[9] If you should look back, whatever you may be carrying will fall to the ground and be spilled.'

"I replied, 'Lady Grandmother, you have warned me. Your son has heard.'

"I continued on my way to the village, and the little old woman went her way. Her warning slipped from my mind. While I was crossing the plain, I turned my head to look back. At that very moment the basket slipped and fell. The cowpeas scattered. I thought that I should have a job picking up these cowpeas, but just then a hard storm from the east came down on me. I judged that it was best for me to run to a nearby village for shelter from rain, and then came back the next day to gather up the cowpeas.

"In the morning, when I came to get the cowpeas, I found that they had sprouted and were already growing. The plants were strong and fine. I thought it over and decided that the best thing was to let them grow and bear. So I left them there. I waited until the time when cowpeas should be ripe, and then I went to the plain to see how they were. I found that the pods were dry and ready to be harvested. I went to the village to get some people to come with me to harvest the cowpeas. In the morning, we went out to the plain to pick the cowpeas, and we found that an elephant had come in the night and eaten them up, to the last one.

"Then I, Mupuiyakalangi Ukongo Wachimbenje Watelele Ochitachatemo Njundombali Kuvala Nduka Chitilileko, said, 'Brothers, go home to the village, while I go track down this elephant.' Then I followed and followed the elephant until I found him fast asleep. Since he was asleep, his back end was open like a fish trap set for fish. I could look and see what was inside. I saw my cowpeas there in plain sight. I leaned my gun against a tree, went inside, and threw out all my cowpeas. When I had done this, I looked up inside the elephant and saw the liver hanging there. I thought that I might as well have a slice of

[9] The Ovimbundu are sensitive to the customs of different peoples and places, and are anxious not to violate them. Instead of saying, "Do not do. . . . ," or "You should not do . . . ," the Ovimbundu frequently say merely, "They do not do . . ."

liver. I took out my knife and started to cut off a piece, when the elephant began to wake up and move away. I said to myself, 'Now I am getting out.'

"The elephant was shutting up, and I was caught tight around the neck with my body still inside the elephant. I was in there for a long time. My only food was the seeds of squashes and gourds. One day I looked up and saw a hunter stalking the elephant and pointing his gun at it. I called to him, 'Shoot him at the other end! Do not shoot him in the rump, but shoot him in the head!'

"The hunter was frightened and fell to the ground. He got up and said, 'Oh! What a marvel! An elephant tells me where to shoot!'"

"I told him, 'It was not the elephant who told you where to shoot, but I, Mupuiyakalangi Ukongo Wachimbenje Watelele Ochitachatemo Njundombali Kuvala Nduka Chitilileko, who am in here.'

"Then the hunter shot the elephant in the head, and the elephant died. The hunter, when he knew that the elephant was dead, went off to their village to get help in cutting up the meat. As they were cutting up the elephant, they found me. They took me out and found that I had been inside the elephant so long that my skin was all faded like that of an albino. My body also had no strength. They marveled much over this and asked me, 'How did this happen?'

"Then I told them that I was Mupuiyakalangi Ukongo Wachimbenje Watelele Ochitachatemo Njundombali Kuvala Nduka Chitilileko. I related all that had befallen me.[10]

"Then they said to me, 'You have already died. You will not die again.' They gave me some of the meat of the elephant, and I started out to go to the village. I had to go slowly, for I was weak and since I was white like an albino I had to avoid the sun. As I was walking along the path, I heard the sound of a king's whistle. I was afraid. So I left the path and hid myself among the leaves in the top of a tall tree. The carriers turned aside from the path, stopped, and leaned the pole of the litter against a tree. The king and all his party sat down on the ground under the tree. I, still up in the tree, became very much frightened. Trembling with fright, I was unable to control myself.

[10] Here the entire previous adventure may be related again in detail.

My water fell upon the king. His men said, 'Haka! What is this? Where did that water come from?'

"They looked up into the tree and saw me. They said that there was a person up in the tree, told me to come down, and said that I should have to pay a large fine for insulting a visiting king. When they saw how emaciated my body was and that my skin was white like an albino, they asked me who I was and how I came to be that way. Then I related all that had happened to me.[11]

"The king's men marveled when they heard this story, and said to me, 'Brother, you have already died once. You cannot die again. Since your village is near, just go along home.'

"Then I entered the path and walked along until I heard the funeral drums. I had already had so much trouble that I was afraid, and thinking that I should escape the funeral procession, I left the path. When I found this cave, I went inside and hid. When you pushed the corpse into the cave, I was afraid that you would bury me with the corpse, so I pushed it out again. My brothers, that is what brought me into the cave."

When they had heard this, they said to him, "O brother, you have died. You cannot die again." They told him that his village was near and that he could reach it that same day.

When he came into the village the people were frightened, as well as astonished. Some said that he was a ghost. Some said that it was not he. They all wished to know where he had been and how he came to be two colors. To rid them of all doubts he said, "You know that I am Mupuiyakalangi Ukongo Wachimbenje Watelele Ochitachatemo Njundombali Kuvala Nduka Chitilileko and that I went with my wife to visit her relatives. When we came to their village they received us with rejoicing. Even the roosters crowed with joy to greet me. This was a warning portent for me. In the evening they cooked a fowl. When I ate it, I said, 'The one who cooked this is a cook.'

"When I said this, Dog spoke up, saying, 'Those who eat their food with gusto do not offer other praise.'

"In reply to Dog, I said, 'For that insult I shall hit you with the broom.'

"Dog said, 'Do not hit me, for the knotted meat in your mouth is a testicle.'

[11] Yet another full repetition is appropriate here, and might well be employed by an African storyteller.

"In trying to spit it out, I gagged and coughed until my tongue fell to the ground. I was about to pick it up, when a rooster picked it up and ran away with it. As I chased the rooster, it let my tongue fall into the ash heap. I took up my tongue and went with it to the river to wash it. As I began to wash it, my tongue slipped and fell into the water. A fish came and swam away with it. Then I said, 'What a day! What uncanny things have happened to me today!'

"I looked down the river and saw a man setting fish traps in the water. I went to him and said, 'Brother, I am unfortunate, for as I went to wash my tongue in the river, a fish swam away with it. If you will do me a favor, please let us slit the bellies of your fish. It may be that the fish which swam away with my tongue is among your fish.'

"The fisherman said, 'All right, master.'

"We began to open the fish, and in one of the fish we found my tongue. Then I, Mupuiyakalangi, took it and put it into my mouth. When I had done this, I thanked the fisherman. He gave me some of his fish as a present. I bade the fisherman goodbye, and finding the path, started for the village. I went a short distance and met a little old woman. We greeted each other, and then she said to me, 'Will you trade your fish for some cowpeas?'

"I agreed to this, so she took the fish and gave me a basket of cowpeas. As I was about to go along the path to the village, the little old woman said, 'If you go in that direction, soon you will come to the Plain of Kapule. There they do not look behind them, lest they spill whatever they are carrying.'

"I replied to her, 'Lady Grandmother, you have warned me. Your son has heard.'

"I went along toward the village. The warning of the little old woman slipped from my mind. While I was crossing the plain, I turned my head to look back. The basket fell to the ground and the cowpeas scattered everywhere. I thought that I should have a hard job picking up the cowpeas, when a storm of rain from the east came down upon me. I judged that it was best to flee to a nearby village to seek shelter from the rain, and come out the next day to gather up the cowpeas. In the morning, when I came out to the plain, I found that the cowpeas had sprouted and were already growing. The plants were strong and fine. I thought the matter over and decided to let the cowpeas grow and ripen. I left them as they were.

"I waited and waited until it was time for cowpeas to be ripe, and then I went out to see how they were. The pods were dry and the cowpeas ready to be harvested. I went to the village to get people to help me take in the crop. In the morning, when we went out to the plain, we found that an elephant had been there during the night and eaten up all the cowpeas, to the last one. Then I, Mupuiyakalangi Ukongo Wachimbenje Watelele Ochitachatemo Njundombali Kuvala Nduka Chitilileko, said, 'Brothers, go back to the village, while I go to track down this elephant.'

"I followed the spoor of the elephant until I found him asleep. The elephant being asleep, he left his back end open like a fish trap set for fish. One could look in and see what was there. I looked, and there were my cowpeas in plain sight. I leaned my gun against a tree, went inside, and threw out my cowpeas. When I had finished this, I looked around inside the elephant and saw the lobes of liver hanging there. I thought that I might as well have a slice of liver, so I took out my knife and began to cut off a piece, when the elephant began to wake up and move away. I said, 'Now I am getting out.' The elephant was shutting up, and I was caught around the neck with my body inside the elephant.

"I was in there for a long time. I lived by eating the seeds of squashes and gourds which the elephant ate. One day I looked and saw a hunter stalking the elephant and pointing his gun at it. I called to him, 'Shoot him in the other end! Do not shoot him in the rump, but shoot him in the head.'

"This frightened the hunter, and he fell to the ground. Then he said, 'Oh! What a marvel! An elephant tells me where to shoot.'

"Then I said to him, 'That was no elephant. That was I, Mupuiyakalangi Ukongo Wachimbenje Watelele Ochitachatemo Njundombali Kuvala Nduka Chitilileko, who is in here.'

"The hunter shot the elephant in the head and it died. When he had killed the elephant, the hunter went away to their village to get people to help cut up the meat. They came and cut and cut until they came to me and took me out. I had been inside the elephant so long that I was very thin and my body was all faded like that of an albino. The people marveled much when they saw me, and they asked, 'How did you get in there, and how did it all happen?'

"I told them that I was Mupuiyakalangi Ukongo Wachimbenje Watelele Ochitachatemo Njundombali Kuvala Nduka Chitilileko. I related to them all the misfortunes which had befallen me.[12] When they had heard my story, they said, 'You have died already. You will not die again.'

"They gave me some elephant meat. I entered the path and started for our village. I was weak and had to avoid the sun, so I went slowly. As I walked slowly along the path, I heard a whistle, which meant that a king's party was coming. I was afraid, so I left the path and hid myself among the leaves in the top of a tall tree. When the king came near, he said, 'Stop here, and let us rest under the shade of this large tree.'

"They turned aside and leaned the pole of the litter against the bole of the tree in which I was hiding. The king and all his carriers sat around under the tree. Up in the tree, I was terrified. I was so frightened that I could not contain my water. The water came down on the king, and the king's men said, 'Haka! What is this? Where did that water come from?'

"They looked up into the tree, saw me there shaking, and said, 'It is a man. You there! You have incurred a big fine for defiling a visiting king. Come down quickly!'"

"I came down. When they saw how emaciated I was, and that my body was all faded out like that of an albino, they asked me how I came to be in that condition. I told them about myself, that I was Mupuiyakalangi Ukongo Wachimbenje Watelele Ochitachatemo Njundombali Kuvala Nduka Chitilileko, and recounted all the hardships that had overtaken me.[13]

"The king's men marveled much when they had heard my experiences, and they said to me, 'Brother, you have died already. You cannot die again. You are not far from your village: just go along home.'

"Once more I entered the path and walked along until I heard the drums of a funeral procession. I had already had so much trouble that I did not care to take further risks. I left the path, and when I found a cave, I went into it to hide. The funeral procession came to a halt outside the mouth of the cave. There they stopped and divined. Someone said, 'How about this cave? Will it do for the burial?' The decision was that the cave

---

[12] Of course, the whole story may be repeated again here.

[13] The informant stated that some Umbundu stories take several days to relate properly and entirely.

would serve. They brought the corpse and pushed it into the cave where I was. I was afraid that they would close the mouth of the cave and bury me along with the corpse. So I seized the pole to which the corpse was attached and pushed it out again. Those outside said, 'Look! The corpse does not wish to be buried in there! Maybe something is lacking.'

"They took the corpse out and divined once more. The corpse again consented to go into the cave. Then the people said, 'Now it is settled. Let us bury the corpse in the cave.' The carriers came again and pushed the corpse into the cave once more. I pushed it out again. The burial party was puzzled. They said, 'Haka! There is something uncanny here. Let us look inside the cave to find what it is that makes the corpse so unwilling!'

"They looked inside the cave and found me. They told me to come out. When I came out of the cave, they asked me, 'Who are you? How did you come to be in there? And how did you come to be part albino?'

"Then I said, 'I am Mupuiyakalangi Ukongo Wachimbenje Watelele Ochitachatemo Njundombali Kuvala Nduka Chitilileko.'

"When I had told them all the things which had happened to me,[14] they said, 'Brother, you have died already. You cannot die again. Your village is near and you can reach it today.'

"Then I came along the path until I saw our village. I came in and sat down. Here I am. I have given you the account of my absence. Greetings!"

All his relatives were astonished and rejoiced. They fired guns. They said to Mupuiyakalangi, "As for you, Mupui, we have already held your funeral and mourned for you, for we said that you were dead."

They slaughtered oxen and made a feast. They said to him, "Eat the feast of thanksgiving for a life saved. You have died. You cannot die again."

[14] The last chance for complete repetition of the story!

folk tales of family and kin

2. parents and children

a childless woman

There once was a woman, married and living with her husband, who had no children. Because she had no children, her husband and his family were dissatisfied with her. They said of her, "She does not bear a child." [1]

One day this woman was wandering about in the bush. At a fork in the path she came upon a baby, wiggling about on the ground with its fetal cord still uncut. She picked up the baby and said, "Today I have borne my little baby."

When she returned to her house with the baby, the people who saw her asked, "Whose is this little baby? Where did you get it?"

She replied, "I myself gave birth to this child today. Truly, this is my child."

And the other women said, "When were you ever pregnant? We have never seen you with the belly for this."

And the woman with the baby answered them, "You did not notice my pregnancy because I did not have a very big belly. That is the reason."

The villagers accepted this account of the matter, since there was no report of a missing child, and since a woman who is a true woman would not claim to have borne a child belonging to someone else.

Later in the day the woman sat down on the ground and cut the child's fetal cord. When she had done this, she gave the baby to her stepson, the child of her husband, saying, "Take care of your younger sister while I go to the woods."

[1] The people knew that the woman, and not the man, was barren, because he had been married to a previous wife, who had died after bearing him a child.

21

The woman went away, and while she was gone the baby became very angry. It changed into a little old woman and then gave the boy a sharp slap, saying, "That stepmother of yours did not bear a child. She only came along and picked me up from the path." Then the little old woman put the rattles of a witch doctor around her calves, and went about dancing and singing this song:

> A wife in the village is barren.
>
> She goes tripping about and picks up a hag,
>
> And then she avers, I have gotten a baby.
>
> Now into the village the hypocrite trips
>
> With this tale she is shamelessly telling.

The little old woman had already changed back into a baby, when the woman returned from the forest. When the baby was placed in the hands of the woman, it cried because of the pain in its navel: "Na-a! Na-a!" The woman began to comfort the baby, jogging it up and down and singing softly to it. She asked the child, "Has my baby been crying for long?"

Another day, the woman went to the brook. Before leaving, she said to the boy, "Care well for your little sister. I will come back soon." As soon as the woman had gone, the baby changed into a little old woman again. The little old woman hissed with disgust and asked, "What have the people done to this woman to make her childless? Why must she go out and pick up some other woman's child at the fork in the path?" Then the little old woman gave the boy some kicks, put rattles on her legs, began dancing, and again sang:

> A wife in the village is barren.
>
> She goes tripping about and picks up a hag,
>
> And then she avers, I have gotten a baby.
>
> Now into the village the hypocrite trips
>
> With this tale she is shamelessly telling.

When the little old woman saw the childless woman returning, she hastily changed back into a baby, which began crying,

"Na-a, na-a, na-a-a-a." The woman sat down with baby in her arms and began to nurse it.

These events occurred many times. The boy was weary of staying with the baby and caring for it, for it always changed into a little old woman who kicked and beat him. So one day he went to his father and explained the matter. He said, "This baby is really a little old woman. When I stay with her alone she changes into a little old woman and falls to beating me. She also dances. But when one of you adults comes in, she has changed back into a baby. If you wish to see the truth of what I say, hide outside the house when my mother goes out and leaves the baby with me. You too will see the baby change into a little old woman."

The father had to wait but a short while, for the woman soon said to the boy, "Little father, take care of your little sister for a while. I am going for firewood and shall soon be back." Then the boy and his father looked at each other.

The father went outside, where he hid himself to observe the truth of what his son had told him. He soon noticed that the baby made a disrespectful sucking noise with its mouth. Then it changed into a little old woman, who kicked the boy, donned rattles, and began dancing. As she danced, she sang the same song as before.

As soon as the little old woman had finished dancing, the father came in. But she had quickly changed back into a baby, sitting on the knees of the boy.

When the woman came in later, the man took her aside and explained to her all that had happened. The woman said to him, "This must be your foolish imagination."

The man replied, "If you don't believe what I have told you is true, just pretend you are going out somewhere, but actually stay just outside the house. But first say, 'I am going to the fields,' or 'I shall be back soon.' " The woman did this, instructing the boy to care for the baby while she went out. She remained outside the house peering through a small hole. Soon she saw that the baby was talking, saying, "You people are very foolish. If the woman is barren, why doesn't she get medicine instead of picking up someone else's child and then saying, 'This is my baby?' Now get out of my way before I hit you." With this, the little old woman hit the boy, put on her rattles, danced, and again sang the same song she had been singing on previous days.

When the little old woman had finished dancing, the woman came back into the house, but the little old woman had already changed back into a baby. The woman picked up the baby and said to it, "You are the child of some other woman. It was not I who bore you. I shall carry you back to the place where I picked you up."

Then she carried the baby back to the fork in the path, where she had found it. She put the baby on the ground, left it there, and went away. When she came back to the house, she found the baby had already returned and was again crying, "Na-a-a, na-a-a, na-a-a."

The woman put her hand over her mouth in shocked surprise, and said, "You again! What has brought you here again?" Again the woman carried the baby to the fork of the paths, and once again left her on the ground there. She thought, "I shall hurry back to the house this time." But when she came back into the house, again the baby was there crying, "Na-a-a, na-a-a, na-a-a."

Then the woman said, "Again she is here! Today I have encountered a portent. It seems that I can do nothing. I am helpless. What shall I do?"

To this, the baby could be heard to reply, "Just carrying me back to the place where you found me will not keep me away, unless you also give me a he-goat, a white hen, a rooster, a basket made of the best grass and a long-necked gourd. If you give me those things, then I shall stay at the place from which you took me. If you do not give me those things, I shall not stay at that place but shall stay with you every day."

When she had heard these words, the woman began gathering together the named articles with all possible haste. When she had obtained all of them, she once more carried the baby back to the fork in the paths where she had been leaving the baby. The woman put down the baby along with the articles of payment named by the little old woman.

The baby came to the house no more.

a childless woman's back is wearied

There once was a woman who had borne no children. One day, as she was on her way to the fields, she found a child on a large white ant hill. She picked up the child, placed it on her back, and went off to the fields with it. She spoke fondly to the child, saying, "My child, my child."

When she reached the field, she began to hoe ridges, with the child still on her back. But since she was not accustomed to hoeing ridges with a child on her back, she soon felt an aching in her back and loins. So she said to the child, "For a little time, please sit here."

But the child would not sit, and replied:

> Hoe with me on you.
> Hoe with me on you.
> You thought you had just found an orphan,
> Shall I call my parents?
> Shall I call my parents?
> Old greedy, you heed me.

So she hoed all day with the child on her back, until she stopped working.

She came home to the village very tired. Her back was aching. All the women had now come back from the fields and went to the pounding rocks to pound meal. She went with them, and when she had sat down upon the rocks she said to the child, "My child, please do me a favor. For a little while, sit here on the ground, just while I am pounding meal." But the child refused, singing:

> Pound with me on you.
> Pound with me on you.
> You thought you had just found an orphan,

> Shall I call my parents?
> Shall I call my parents?
> Old greedy, you heed me.

Since the child would not sit on the ground, the woman pounded meal with the child on her back. Because of this, she had difficulty in finishing the pounding. When she had finished pounding meal, she went to the house, and here she made another attempt to have the child come down from her back, saying, "Come now, my child, since I am very tired, sit here on the floor while I go to the stream. I shall come back soon, my child." But the child replied by singing the same song he had been singing before.

This time the real mother of the child was near the village, and hearing the song of the child, she shouted anxiously:

> Bring her, O bring her.
> Sleep not I pray you.

The woman picked up the child, arranged it well on her back, and went with it to the stream, even though she had heard the voice of the real mother outside the village. When she had returned from the stream, she put the pot on the fire to cook mush. Then she said, "My child, now I am not going anywhere else. Just sit here on the floor while I make mush for you." But again the child sang the same song she had sung before. And again the child's real mother could be heard outside the village, anxiously shouting:

> Bring her, O bring her.
> Sleep not I pray you.

Hearing the voice of the real mother, the woman became frightened. She picked up the child, carried her back to the white ant hill from which she had taken her, and left her there.

twins who were sweet and sour

There was once a pregnant woman, who went to the forest to gather firewood.

While she was in the forest, she began to have birth pains and gave birth to twins. She tasted the first baby to be born, found that the baby tasted sour, and so she called her Ngeve. Then when the second baby was born, the mother tasted this baby too, found that she tasted sweet, and named her Njamba.[2]

Then the woman said, "I shall not keep Ngeve, for she is sour." She took up Njamba and carried her away home, leaving the baby Ngeve to wriggle about on the ground by herself.

Soon Mrs. Duyker came by and asked the child, "Are you the child of those who habitually eat us duykers,[3] or are you the child of a goat?"

The baby answered, "I am a kid."

Then Mrs. Duyker said, "Because you are the child of a goat, I shall care for you, but if you were the child of those who eat us, I would pass you by." So Mrs. Duyker picked up the child and carried her to the place where she lived. She cared for the child well. She searched out food for the child of the sort that the child was able to eat, and kept her until she grew up. Later Mrs. Duyker realized that the child was human, but in spite of this Mrs. Duyker cared for her.

One day Ngeve saw her twin sister Njamba come to the pounding rock to pound corn meal. Ngeve said to her, "O young one, let me pound for you." Then Ngeve took over the pounding, and as she pounded she sang this song:

Njamba is sweetish, sweetish.

Ngeve is sourish, sourish.

[2] Twins of the same sex are usually named *Njamba* (elephant) and *Ngeve* (hippopotamus). Where twins are of different sex, the boy is named *Hosi* (lion) and the girl *Ngeve*.
[3] A small African antelope, prominent in Angolan life and lore. Its name, derived form the Dutch *duiker*, meaning "diver or ducker," was given to it because of its tendency to plunge through bushes when pursued.

I was left in the forest wild.
I became the duyker's child.
Ay-ay-ay, ha-a-a-a-ah!

Hearing this song, Njamba asked, "Sister, what is the meaning of the song you sing?" Ngeve replied, "Its meaning is simple enough. Don't question me. Just keep on trusting me to do the pounding." Then Ngeve continued singing and pounding until she had finished pounding all the corn into meal. This meal she gave to Njamba.

When Njamba returned to her mother with the meal, she did not tell her about seeing Ngeve and hearing her song. She just remained silent. Her mother thanked her, saying, "You have really done well. You pounded beautiful meal."

Another day Njamba was sent again to pound meal. Again Ngeve came and pounded the meal, singing the same song. After this had happened every day for five days, Njamba finally explained the matter to her mother, saying, "Mother, every day I meet someone at the pounding rocks, whose name is Ngeve. She is one of us.[4] This is what happens: she pounds and pounds the meal, and I only bring it back to you. While she pounds the meal, she always sings this song:

Njamba is sweetish, sweetish
Ngeve is sourish, sourish.
I was left in the forest wild.
I became the duyker's child.
Ay-ay-ay, ha-a-a-a-ah!

I can hear her singing it now!

Upon hearing this, the mother summoned all the neighbors to come go with her and follow the child when she went out to pound meal. The mother's intention was to catch Ngeve and bring her back to the village, before Mrs. Duyker could take her away again. The neighbors all agreed to accompany the mother, and so she sent Njamba to the pounding rock. Njamba went ahead, and all the people followed her.

[4] "One of us" means "our tribe, our kind, the Ovimbundu."

When Njamba came to the pounding rocks, Ngeve came there again, saying, "Please let me pound for you, young one." Ngeve went to work pounding, singing the same song she had sung before. Then all the people came forward and seized Ngeve.

Mrs. Duyker happened to be feeding nearby. She stopped nibbling, came near, and said to the villagers, "Where are you taking this child you are holding?"

The people said, "Mrs. Duyker, what is it that you wish to have from us?"

To this Mrs. Duyker replied, "As you know, it costs much to bring up a child. Now that I have brought up this child, the only payment which I wish in return is this: that you plant and cultivate a field of cowpeas for me, a big patch which I may nibble from at all times." The people promised to plant such a patch of cowpeas for Mrs. Duyker.

After they had made this promise, the people went away with the child. They reprimanded the mother, saying to her, "On no future day are you ever to do a thing like this again. Deserting a child is wrong, for the bearing of a child is a painful affair."

the child left on a rock in the river

There was a woman who left her child on a large rock in the middle of a river whenever she worked in her field. She always left some mush with the child to ward off hunger.

One day a stranger came along and called from the shore to the child, "Where did you cross the water?"

Pointing, the child answered him, "We crossed at that place."

The stranger crossed over and when he reached the rock asked the child, "Have you any food put away?"

"I have some mush put away here," answered the child.

"Break off some of it for me," directed the stranger.

The child broke off some mush and gave it to the stranger. The stranger ate it. Then he said to the child, "Come with me. Let me take you on my back, and the two of us will walk about for a while." The child agreed to this, and so he went away on the back of the stranger.

After the stranger had walked along the path for some distance, the child began to sing:

> O man, put me down here, for I am a cripple.
> O man, put me down here, for I am a cripple.

When the man did not put him down and when he noticed that the man was taking him far from any place known to him, the child sang another song:

> O my dog, come help me. Njenjelungu!
> Far away hunting, dog, do hear me!

The dog answered this call, came, and was about to bite the stranger, who being wise, dropped the boy. The dog led the child back to the rock.

When his mother returned to the rock, the boy related to her what had happened after she had left him alone on the rock. Yet on the next day she left him on the rock as usual, and went to her field.

The same stranger came again, again asked the child where he had crossed the water, and was again answered by the child, "We crossed there. Cross with care there, and you will get across." Again the stranger asked for food, was given some mush by the boy, and ate the mush. The child's dog was not there, having gone away hunting, as he did every day. Once more the stranger proposed going for a walk with the boy on his back, and once more the boy agreed to this.

After the man had gone some distance the boy sang:

> O man, put me down here, for I am a cripple.
> O man, put me down here, for I am a cripple.

When the child was not put down, and furthermore saw that he was being carried to a strange place, he called for his dog, singing:

> O my dog, come help me. Njenjelungu!
> Far away hunting, dog, do hear me!

Njenjelungu heard the boy's song and ran as fast as he could to save the child. Reaching the stranger and the child, the dog barked savagely at the stranger and was about to bite him, when the stranger dropped the boy and fled. After chasing the stranger a distance, Njenjelungu returned to the boy and led him back to the rock where his mother had left him.

When the mother returned to the child and was told all that happened to him during the afternoon, still she only nodded her head, saying nothing in reply. On another day she again left him on the rock in the middle of the river, leaving him some food, while she went to work in her field. Again the boy's dog, Njenjelungu, went away to hunt for himself.

In the afternoon the same stranger came, asked where to cross the water, was told by the boy where to cross, crossed to the boy, asked the boy for food, was given mush, ate it, and then proposed taking the boy on his back for a walk. The boy agreed and went away on the man's back, but after they had gone some distance he wished to be put down and began singing:

> O man, put me down here, for I am a cripple.
> O man, put me down here, for I am a cripple.

When the man did not put the boy down and it appeared that they were in a strange country, the boy called his far away dog, singing:

> O my dog, come help me. Njenjelungu!
> Far away hunting, dog, do help me!

This day the dog had gone so far away in his hunting that he did not hear the boy's calling. The boy shouted and shouted for Njenjelungu, but Njenjelungu did not hear. The stranger was pleased at this and walked on rapidly, while the boy kept asking to be put down.

They reached a gate, which the man passed through and then locked. They reached a second gate, which the man passed through and then locked. They reached a third gate, which the man passed through and then locked. They went on until they reached a house. Here the man obtained some weak beer and

gave it to the child to drink. When the child had drunk the
beer he was given mush to eat until he was satisfied and happy.

The man went to the king of this place and spoke with him.
The king then made a royal proclamation, saying, "Let all the
people prepare for tomorrow. Tomorrow we shall eat the small
animal which has no tail."

Hearing this, the people rejoiced, saying, "Hear! Hear! Yes,
yes, we hear!"

The next morning they killed and ate the child.[5]

When the boy's mother returned to the rock where she had
left her child, she searched and searched for him, on the rock
where she had always left him. But he was not on the rock. She
went away, asking those she met if they had seen her child, but
no one had seen her child. She did not find him nor hear of him.
She and others of the boy's family began to weep for him and
announced that his funeral would be held.

sons building huts for their mothers

One day two men were building huts for their mothers in a
caravan camp. It happened that one man finished making his
hut quickly, before the other man had yet finished. The man
who had finished his hut put his mother inside it. A heavy rain
came, and the man who had not finished building his hut spoke
to the other man and said, "Friend, please let my mother go into
your hut along with your mother, so that she may take shelter
from the rain."

"No," replied the second man. "Your mother cannot go
into my hut."

Then the woman outside the hut died of exposure to the
driving rain.[6]

[5] Kidnapping and eating of people actually occurred in the past. The cannibalistic feast was usually part of magic rituals performed to secure the success of some
village or regional project. Pregnant women were favorite victims for use in such
cannibalistic success-magic. The scouts appointed to secure a victim usually sought
to kidnap a victim from a distant region.

[6] In the Benguela Highlands the old or feeble, caught without shelter, frequently
perish from the chill and the pelting of the driving rain.

When the rain had stopped, the man whose mother had died took up her corpse and carried it away to bury it where their relatives were buried. As the man went along bearing the corpse of his mother, he met an ogre, who asked him, "Brother, are you carrying meat?"

He answered, "it is true that I am carrying meat."

The ogre took an arm from the corpse. Then the ogre gave him advice, saying, "As you go forward, wherever you hear a small voice, do not go in that direction. Where you hear a great voice, go there."

The man went farther and met another ogre. This ogre was pleased to meet him and welcomed him. This ogre also asked, "Brother, are you carrying meat?"

"Yes," said the man, "meat is really what I am carrying."

Then this ogre took off another arm from the corpse. After the ogre had done this, he advised the man, "As you go forward, wherever you hear a very weak voice, do not go there; but where you hear a great voice, go there." The man listened to this advice.

As the man went forward again, he met another ogre. This ogre also rejoiced to meet him and welcomed him. The ogre said to him, "Brother, are you carrying meat?" The man replied that he was carrying meat. The ogre took off a leg from the corpse and advised him, "As you go forward, if you hear a very small voice, do not go in that direction; but where you hear a loud voice, go there."

The man went on again. As he walked along he met another ogre, who said to him, "Brother, do you carry any meat?"

"Yes," answered the man, "I carry meat."

Then this ogre took the remaining leg from the corpse. All the limbs had now been removed from the corpse, leaving only the head and trunk.

When the man reached the burial place, he buried what remained. After burying these remains, he was given four small bottles and told to return to his village and have a large fine house built. When it was built, he was to open the bottles.

He returned home and did as he had been directed. He built a large, beautiful house. When the house was finished, he began to open the bottles. When he opened the bottles, the house was furnished with furniture and filled with fine clothes. There appeared a fine garden, an orchard with fruits and vegetables, and servants to care for everything. He had become a very wealthy man.

The other man, who had finished his hut quickly and thus saved his mother's life from the fury of the rain, beheld all this prosperity and coveted it. Finally, when his mother died, he thought that he would go and do as the other man had done, and like him become rich.

As he was going along the path with the corpse of his mother, he met an ogre. The ogre rejoiced to see him and said, "Brother, are you carrying meat?"

Hearing this angered the man, who said, "Why do you ask such a question! This is my mother I am carrying, and you are a salted codfish to ask me, 'Brother, do you carry any meat!'"

After hearing this reply, the ogre advised him, "As you go along, if you hear a small voice, go there."

The man did as had been directed. When he came to the place of burials, he was given four small bottles, which he was told to uncork when he had returned to his village and built there a large house. He was pleased to hear this, for he had heard that this was what the other man had been told.

When he had returned home, he built a large house, which was a good one. When he had finished building the house, he went into it and began to uncork bottles. Four large lizards came forth from the first bottle. Toads came from the second, and flies from the third. When he opened the fourth bottle, lions came forth, caught him, and ate him.

a small boy and his little monkey

Once a father caught a little monkey for his young son. After catching it, he brought the little monkey home and gave it to his boy. The little boy loved the little monkey. Every day, skipping and jumping, they played together. And too, the boy petted the monkey. The little monkey was docile, obeying the boy in everything. So long did things go on in this way that the boy forgot the monkey had ever been wild, or might run away.

One day the little monkey heard the cries of other monkeys

coming from a kloof:[7] "Haa-uu, haa-uu, ha-u." The ears of the little monkey pricked up. As soon as the boy was away, the monkey first sneaked toward and and then fled into the kloof where the other monkeys were playing. There it found its relatives, who were happy to see it again. It was also glad to see them. Seeing the little monkey, the other monkeys gave their cry: "Haa-uu, haa-uu, ha-u."

Coming back to the place where he had left the little monkey, the boy found the monkey gone. When he realized that the little monkey had run away, he was sad. He went to his father and said, "Father, the little monkey you gave me has run away."

And his father asked him, "In which direction did it go?"

And the boy replied, "Father, I do not know which way it went."

Whereupon the father made a small drum for his son. When he had finished making it, he gave it to the boy, saying to him, "Take this drum. Go and play it close to all the kloofs. If you are lucky, you will find your little monkey in one of the kloofs."

The boy took the little drum which his father gave him and went away with it. Reaching the first kloof, he began to play on his little drum, which sounded: "Kumbititi-i, kumbititi-i." To this accompaniment, he sang:

> O my father's little monkey,
>
> O my father's little monkey,
>
> The little drum and I,
>
> We are coming for my brother, Ulombe.
>
> For him the drum is calling,
>
> The drum it keeps repeating:
>
> > Kumbititi, kumbititi, aye-way.

When there was no reply from the kloof, the small boy stood up from the log where he had been sitting and went toward another kloof. Near this kloof, he sat down again on another log and began again to beat his little drum: "Kumbititi, kumbititi." As he drummed, he sang this song:

[7] A heavily forested ravine.

O my father's little drum,
O my father's little drum,
It is bound with lily thread,
It is sewn with beard of dwarf,
It is tuned with help of bee.
Nding, dang ho: come dance to the drum.
    Pelengua, pelengua, pelengua.

There was no answer from the kloof, but this time the boy stood up from the log where he had been sitting, in good spirits. He had named the beard of dwarf and not been punished.[8]

When he came to the third kloof, he did as he had done at the second. He began by playing his little drum: "Kumbititi, kumbititi." Then he sought a reply from the kloof by singing:

O my father's little monkey,
O my father's little monkey,
    Are you in there?

In reply, the monkeys in the kloof sang:

In there?[9] He is not in there.
In there? He is not in there.

When the boy heard this, he sang again:

O my father's little monkey,
O my father's little monkey,
    In there, are you not in there?

[8] Naming is important in the magic as well as in the social life of the Ovimbundu. Here, *beard of dwarf*, is a mythical substance of magical powers, and the naming of it could bring either power or punishment to the namer.
[9] The monkeys mimic the boy, saying "there" rather than "here."

Then, dancing, the monkeys sang in reply:

In there? He is not in there.

In there—is a dainty toadstool.

In there—one is summoned by the drum.

Take a look here. There is only one tail.

There are not, there are not, there are not two tails.

Kuta Yongo does not have two tails.

The monkeys continued to dance and sing. And as the boy peered carefully into the kloof, he saw his little monkey dancing and singing among the other monkeys. He ran eagerly into the kloof and took his little monkey up in his arms. When he had his little monkey in his arms, he carried it back to his father in the village.

a father's head

One day a grown man and his son took their hunting gear and went out to their hunting lodge. The father carried his bow. The young man took his bow, and in addition a gun and the powder for it.

So they went, and after they came to the hunting lodge, the first animal that they encountered was a roan antelope. The father said to the son, "Shoot the roan antelope with your gun."

The son replied, "Father, I shall not shoot the animal with my gun for fear of using up my powder." Then the son took his bow and killed the roan antelope with an arrow. They dressed the animal.

When they went on further they found an elephant. The father said to the son, "Shoot the elephant with the gun."

The son replied to his father and said, "Oh no, father, I shall not use the gun, lest we use up the powder." Then the son killed the elephant with an arrow. When the arrow struck the elephant, it went all the way through him and stuck in the ground. This astonished the father. Since the elephant was dead, they cut it up. After they went on hunting.

As they went on they found a bee tree. When they had taken out the honey, the father said, "How are we going to carry the honey, seeing that we have no bark tray for the purpose?"

To this the son replied, "We have plenty of bark trays. There is one on your shin." The son took up his ax and when he had pounded his father's shin with the ax, off came a bark tray. The father was dumbfounded.

Later they were caught in a heavy rain, so heavy that the father was on the point of dying. The son expanded his nose. The nose spread out until it was like a cave. The father took shelter under it, not knowing what it was until the rain stopped. The father marveled still more at this.

They left the hunting lodge and returned to their village. There they lived on the meat they had brought back until it was all gone.

On another day the young man, who had married a wife, planned to visit his wife's family at their village. Soon after he and his wife had left his village to make this journey, the father changed himself so that his head was separated from his body, the head retaining only a miniature body. The young man and his wife walked along until they came to a fork in the path. Here they encountered his father's head with its miniature body. This asked the son, "Where are you going?"

The son and his wife replied, "We are going to visit our relatives."

The head said, "Well, that is where I am going." Then all three of them went on together.

When they reached the edge of the village, the son said, "Honorable sir, from here on your path is that one."

The head said, "I am going into this village also. I shall be a guest along with you." So they went on into the village. When the people of the village saw the wife and her husband, they rejoiced to see them. They at once provided them with a house. When they brought beer to the guest, the head without any hesitation jumped right into the gourd of beer. The beer instantly turned bright red like blood. After this the head drank up all the beer.

The young man and the head stayed in the guest house while the wife went to the kitchen of her mother. Later the people of the village made mush and brought it to the guest house, along with the meat of a fowl. The head came quickly forward, took the food, and ate all of it. The next day food was prepared and brought to the guest house, and again the head seized it and ate all of it.

The wife's family saw that their son-in-law was becoming faint from hunger. They kept watch. When the head went to the bush, leaving the young man in the village, they quickly killed a pig, intending to have their son-in-law eat it before the head returned. They built a high platform, so that when the food was ready they could carry it to the top of the platform for the son-in-law to eat there. When the head came back from the bush, he smelled the odor of food, mush with pork relish. Without delay he leaped up onto the platform and ate all the food, the mush and pork. Again the young man went hungry.

So things went, on into the third and fourth day, until the young man was ravenously hungry. To save him, his in-laws killed another hog and ground a basket of corn into meal. They added a large gourd of beer and gave the young man all this to take with him.

In the morning the young man and his wife left the village. As is the custom, the wife's family accompanied them some distance on their way home. The head went along with them.

When they came to the fork in the path where the head had joined them, the head spoke up and said, "Now we shall share our hog between us. We shall divide the basket of meal and also the beer. In addition we shall split the wife between us." The young man consented. They split the hog in half and divided the meal. Then they split the woman in half. When this had been done, they drank the gourd of beer and buried the woman at the fork in the path. Then the young man went to the village.

As he came into the village, he looked ahead and saw smoke just beginning to ooze out through the thatch of his house. When he came up to the house, he saw his wife inside with all their gifts from her family, safe and sound. Then he saw his father, sound and well.

Later on, the father came to his son to talk with him, and said, "My son, the things which happened to you on your visit were done by me. I did them for this reason: while we were at our hunting lodge, you performed marvels of hunting to amaze me. My son, it is necessary to have mutual respect. When a man is able to perform something, let him keep in mind that the other man may be able to do something else which he cannot do. Do not do the things you are able to do, just to make a boastful show.

filial obedience

A wife died, leaving her husband with a small daughter. As anyone would know, this father was having difficulty caring for this child. The father had no close kinsmen, so he wondered whether the best thing for him to do might not be to move away to another region. In the end this was exactly what he did.

When he had reached another region, he found lodging in a household. The woman of the house had no child of her own. Thus, the woman was pleased to have the child in her house, and she treated this child as though it were her own. Because of this, both the father and the small daughter were well satisfied. There seemed to be nothing wrong with this way of living.

But one day the man began thinking that it is not good to live forever in the house of another, even though well treated there. Though well treated by another, to be in one's own house is to be in one's own house. Following these thoughts, the man went away alone to another region, leaving his daughter behind. He did not say anything to his friend before making this move, not even a "good-by," but left secretly. Nor did he say good-by to his child. Nor did he tell her where he was going. When the man's departure was realized, his friend with whom he had been living searched everywhere for him. He wondered, "Where can my friend have gone that I do not see him any more?" He inquired and searched, but there was no trace of his departed friend.

The man who had left found a good plot of land and cultivated on it a good farm. He planted many things and they grew well. Once more, he began to think about his way of living. He thought, "What am I going to do next?" He decided that his best course would be to go and fetch the child from where he had left her. This he set out to do.

He arrived at the house where his daughter was living in

the middle of the day, while the man and woman were away and had left the child to do the housework. Finding his daughter, the father said to her, "Today I have come to take you to the place where we shall live."

She said to her father, "My father and mother have not come home from the fields. If I am truly to go away, I must wait for them to return, so that I can tell them goodbye."

"Let us just go along," said her father. "It is no longer necessary to say goodbye."

Since leaving secretly disturbed the child, she said again to her father, "Father, let us wait only a little while. They will be here soon."

"Perhaps they have bewitched you," said the man. "We are leaving now, and if you do not obey me, I shall kill you and then go back where I came from."

Believing that her father would kill her if she disobeyed him, the child at this point agreed to go with him and did not try to wait to say goodbye.

When father and daughter reached the region where he had been living, he found that his farm had been ravaged by wild animals. So he dug game pits all about his fields. There were twenty-two game pits. Later, he had a talk with his child and said to her, "I am getting to be too old to go out and examine the game pits. You will have to do this for me. You will go regularly and see if any game has been caught. When some animal has been caught, you are to bring me only the heart of the animal."

The daughter assumed this task, and there was no lack of catches, for it happened that day after day each of the twenty-two pits contained an animal.

Meanwhile their friend, with whom the girl had lived, looked and looked for the child who had lived with him and his wife. In the end, finding no trace of her, they gave up hope of ever seeing her again. One day this man went out to hunt animals. As he was passing along, not thinking of either the girl or her father, he came to the farm of his friend. He had no thought that the girl and her father might be in this part of the country.

As he went along he fell into one of the game pits. But since there were no sharpened stakes in the bottom of this pit, he was not injured. The child was making her round of the game pits, and as usual she was finding that each pit had caught something. When she reached the last pit, she found in it the man who had been as a father to her. She was happy to see him, but she was unable to get him out of the pit, and he was unable to get himself out either alone or with her help. So she left the man in the pit and took the twenty-one hearts back to her father.

When her father had counted the hearts, he said to her. "Where is the other heart?"

"The other duyker did not have a heart," the girl told him.

"There are no duykers lacking hearts," said her father. "Go and take it out, for these hearts are all that I have to live on."

The child returned to the game pit, where the foster father was still trapped. The sight of him caused her to feel a revulsion. She could not think of killing him. The foster father asked, "What did my friend say?"

She answered, "He insisted strongly that I go and take out the heart of the duyker caught in this game pit and bring it to him. But I have thought it over and decided it is impossible for me to kill you."

Then the man in the pit said, "Let it happen as your father commanded. The important thing is that you do not commit any wrong on my account."

"Nevertheless, I shall go to my father again," said the girl.

The girl thought on these things, and decided to explain everything carefully to her father. She did just that when she came to him. She said, "That friend of yours—you remember, the one who kept us so well, and with whom you left me when you came here—it is he who is caught in the game pit. Now, what am I to do?"

Her father said, "Do not argue with me. Go and take the heart out of the duyker which is caught in the pit and bring it to me."

The child returned to the pit. The man in the pit said, "What did your father say when you told him the truth about who is in this pit? What did he tell you to do?"

The girl answered, "He told me, 'I say, go and take out the heart of the duyker that is caught in the pit and bring it to me.' "

The friend said, "Let it be done as your father wills that it shall be done. The main thing is that I will not do anything to bring you into the disgrace of disobedience."

The child considered those words, and would not kill her

foster father, even though she had understood her father's clear command that she should kill him. Seeing that she would not kill him, and thinking it over, the man in the pit said to her, "My child, seeing that you will not kill me, then go and fetch a bird that will summon all the neighbors to come and judge the case properly."

The girl called a bird, and the bird flew and told all the neighbors the facts of the case, even as her foster father had said.

When the folk came together to judge the case, they took only one thing into consideration, and that was that the father had trapped his friend in a pit, so they killed the father. After that was done, they freed the man from the pit.

When the friend had been freed from the pit, he went home, taking with him the child who had refused to kill him. This man had ability to train the child to do that which is right. His wife rejoiced to see the girl back again, and said, "This child has much good sense. She is a true person, much better than her father."

So it happened that the later life of the girl was much better than her earlier life.

3. stepmothers

the brothers kapango and kapango

A man and his woman had a son named Kapango. The woman died while Kapango was still a small boy.

The father later married a widow who also had a son named Kapango. To distinguish the boys the man called his own son Kapango the Elder and called the son of his wife Kapango the Younger.

Some time later the man went to the coast, to Mbaka, to buy cloth. Some of this cloth was to be worn and the remainder of it taken to the interior to be traded for rubber. While the man was away trading for cloth at the coast the new wife stayed in the village with the two boys. During this time the woman secretly dug a deep pit under the kitchen floor, so deep that one could climb out of it only by using a hunter's ladder.[1] The mouth of the pit was concealed under the pounding stone.[2]

When the woman had completed the pit she called her own son, Kapango the Younger, and instructed him in private, "I shall drop my pipe into this deep hole which I have dug next to the pounding stone. When I ask you to go down into the hole and get the pipe for me, you must refuse to do it, answering me, 'I will not go down into that hole.' Then I shall call your older brother by name, Kapango the Elder, and ask him to do it. When he consents I shall lower him into the hole, and he will not be able to get out again. Then when your father returns from the coast he will cherish you and give you all the cloths

[1] A hunter's ladder is made from the trunk of a small tree having many branches, each of which is cut off about ten inches from the trunk.
[2] Where there are ledges of rock above the ground, these are used for the pounding of corn into corn meal. Elsewhere a flat rock is trimmed at the edges and fixed into the kitchen floor, with clay from a white ant hill.

which he brings back. Unless we do this he will not care as much for you as he will care for his own son."

In the afternoon the woman carried out her plan. After throwing her pipe into the hole she called out, "Oh my child, Kapango the Younger, do come here and get my pipe for me. It has fallen into the hole here."

The son, as he had been instructed, said, "I will not do it. I will not go into the hole to get your pipe."

"All right," the woman replied to him, and then called, "My son, Kapango the Elder, will you please go into the pit and fetch my pipe?" The boy obeyed, and she lowered him into the pit with a hunter's ladder. When he had stepped off the ladder she withdrew it and covered the mouth of the pit with the pounding stone.

When next the woman was pounding meal on the pounding stone, "Thump, thump, thump," she called out, "Kapango the Elder, will you take your mush?" And from beneath the pounding stone came the reply, "I am not eating mush any more. Let Kapango the Younger eat my mush for me. I eat only the bran which falls into this hole. The white meal is for Kapango the Younger. My beer is water. Let Kapango the Younger drink my beer for me. My meat is the bones from which Kapango the Younger has eaten the flesh."

This went on from day to day, until the boy in the deep hole became emaciated from hunger and thirst. From lack of sunlight and food he became quite yellow. Yet Suku[3] was with him, for although he lived in great distress, he did not die. Thus he managed to stay alive until his father returned.

When his father returned, the woman was away in the fields. Not finding his son, the father asked the older men in the village, "Where is my son, Kapango the Elder? Where did he go?" The old men related to him just what his wife had been doing, for they had heard about what was taking place, even as they are given to saying, "Even that which goes on under the water will be reported." They also told the father what Kapango the Elder said in reply when the woman tapped on the stone and asked him to take his mush.

To test the truth of these reports, the man went to his house and pounded on the stone, saying, "Kapango the Elder, take your

[3] *Suku* is the supreme ancestral deity, the closest translation of which is "God." See the glossary at the back of this volume.

mush." And from beneath the pounding stone came the reply, "I do not eat mush any more. Let Kapango the Younger eat it. My mush is the hulls from the corn grains. Kapango the Younger has the white meal. Instead of beer I get water. My meat is bones. Kapango the Younger eats the meat off the bones for me."

When he had heard these words, the father rolled the pounding stone away, got the hunter's ladder, and freed his son. Then he washed his son well, placed clean clothes upon him, and put him to bed in the guest house.

When the woman came back from the fields the man asked her, "Where is Kapango the Elder?"

"He went away to visit his mother's brother," she replied. "He was here with me for about two weeks after you went away, and then he went away to the village of his mother's brothers."

This reply angered the man. He sent immediately for the relatives of the woman. When they had assembled, he said to them, "Look at what your relative has been doing, and then you will understand why I have summoned you." He showed them the pit and told them what the woman had been doing, and they were shocked and shamed. They took the woman and went away with her.

The man gave nothing to Kapango the Younger and nothing to the woman, for she had done a very disgraceful thing.

the burial of chinguli

A man's wife died, leaving one child, named Chinguli.[4]

Later the man married again, and this woman had a child, a daughter named Chita.

The man then decided to go to Mbaka, Benguela, to trade for cloth. When he was about to leave, he spoke to his wife, saying, "My wife, I shall not be away long, and while I am gone you are to look after the children well."

After the man had gone, the woman took his child, Chinguli, and went with her to the grave of the dead woman. She opened the grave, put the child Chinguli into the grave, and

[4] This name is pronounced "Chi-ngu-li." Its literal meaning is "great hyena," but it is used euphemistically to mean "lion."

closed the grave again. That is indeed what happened. She put the living child into the grave of her dead mother and shut the grave up again, for she was jealous of the dead woman and her child. She said to herself, "This child Chinguli is beautiful, while my child is ugly. When their father returns he is likely to give fine things to Chinguli and give something ordinary to Chita."

Although Chinguli suffered hardship and despair, still the spirits aided her so that she did not die[5] before some men who had gone to Benguela came near the grave. When these men put down their loads to rest, they spoke to each other, and Chinguli heard their voices. Hearing their voices, she sang:

> My father went to Benguela,
> My mother to Ngumbiyela.[6]
> My mother will stay there forever.
> In here is their daughter Chinguli.
> > He who begot Chita, begot Chita,
> > He also Chinguli Chatembo.[7]

> My father went to Benguela,
> My mother to Ngumbiyela.
> My mother will stay there forever.
> In here is their daughter Chinguli.
> > He who begot Chita, begot Chita,
> > He also Chinguli Chatembo.

The men standing by resting heard this song. When they realized that the voice came from the graves, they took up their loads and went away in haste, saying, "Today we have encountered a great portent: a ghost singing in the full light of day."

[5] According to the native informant, Chinguli's survival illustrates two proverbs or "words of the old men": "He who endures hardship will not die," and "He who plans to go hungry does not eat refuse."

[6] The parts of this artificial word mean literally "shelter me, fence me" and "clean."

[7] *Chatembo* means "Child of a free woman, a woman of standing in the community," i.e., the child of a woman who is formally married and has relatives to protect her rights.

After these men had left, another caravan came along, and the men of this caravan acted the same as the men of the first caravan.

Another caravan came, this one the caravan in which Chinguli's father was traveling. Through everything the girl had continued to sing her song with patience. She thought, "I shall just keep on singing until my father hears me." Thus, when her father's caravan came near, she was singing:

> My father went to Benguela,
> My mother to Ngumbiyela.
> My mother will stay there forever.
> In here is their daughter Chinguli.
> > He who begot Chita, begot Chita,
> > He also Chinguli Chatembo.

> My father went to Benguela,
> My mother to Ngumbiyela.
> My mother will stay there forever.
> In here is their daughter Chinguli.
> > He who begot Chita, begot Chita,
> > He also Chinguli Chatembo.

The father of Chinguli listened. Those with him became disturbed and said: "Listen to that song! Is this place bewitched? Here in bright sunlight can be heard a ghost from beneath a grave. This is a fearful portent. Let us take up our loads and leave this place!"

But the father of Chinguli said to them, "Wait longer, and first keep quiet. Let us listen carefully. There must be a meaning when one hears the voice of a spirit." He spoke thus because he had heard the name of his child Chinguli in the song. He said to the others, "Let us listen carefully once more." As he said this, the child heard the voice of her father and was glad. So she sang once more this song:

> My father went to Benguela,
> My mother to Ngumbiyela.

My mother will stay there forever.
In here is their daughter Chinguli.
He who begot Chita, begot Chita,
He also Chinguli Chatembo.

My father went to Benguela,
My mother to Ngumbiyela.
My mother will stay there forever.
In here is their daughter Chinguli.
He who begot Chita, begot Chita,
He also Chinguli Chatembo.

Her father came near the grave and spoke, saying, "If you are my child, Chinguli, and you are dead, and they have buried you in the grave of your mother, sing the song again." When the child had heard this, she became silent. No sound was heard from the grave.

The father spoke again and said to her, "If it is true that you are my child, and you are alive, and they have buried you alive in the grave of your mother, be sure to sing out the song once more."

The child answered by singing out her song plainly.

Hearing this, the father came and opened the grave. He found his daughter Chinguli in the grave. She had become brown and discolored from being so long away from the light of the sun.

He asked her, "How did this come about?" Then she explained to him everything that her jealous mother had done. When she had finished talking, he took her to the stream and washed her, and then he stirred up some gruel and gave it to her to eat. The food gave her strength enough to walk. They went along slowly to the village, which was not far away.

When they came to the village, the father concealed Chinguli in the house sacred to their ancestors. When his wife appeared, he questioned her, saying, "Now that I am here, where is Chinguli?"

In reply, she said to her husband, "She will be here soon, but now she is away visiting her mother's brothers."

The man became very angry when he heard this lie. He shot the woman, killing her.[8]

a junior wife's jealousy

A hunter's senior wife died, leaving an only daughter as her parting gift to her husband, who had no other children.

The hunter's second and junior wife was a younger woman and had always been jealous of the first wife. The younger woman was still jealous of the senior wife, even after her death.

While the husband was still sequestered, in the period of mourning for his dead senior wife, the younger woman went in secret to the grave of the dead woman, dug up the corpse, cut off the head, carried it away, and concealed it in a pot.

One day, after the man had emerged from mourning, he went to the woods to hunt, as was his custom. He killed a hare. When he came back to the village he put the hare in a pot to cook. The following day the pot was kept on the fire, cared for by the daughter of the dead woman, while the husband and wife went to work in the fields. When they returned from the fields, the man went to the men's conference house[9] and the woman to cook mush in her kitchen. She had the child to carry this mush together with the flesh of a hare to her husband at the men's club-house. She said to the child, "Go, my child, take this food and carry it to your father at the conference house." The child took the food to her father at the conference house.

When the child came back to the house, her jealous step-mother had taken the head of the child's mother out of the pot.

[8] A second wife is often a slave, obtained from her former owner by purchase, instead of obtained from her mother's family by posting a bride-price with them. This woman is apparently a slave, since a man would fear to take violent action against a free woman he had formally married, lest her relatives seek retaliation against him. It is also possible that she is a free wife with protective relatives, and that the husband believes her relatives will approve his killing her in retaliation for her crime against the child.

[9] It is the custom for men to spend the evening with each other in the men's clubhouse, talking and even holding lawsuits, rather than with their wives and children in their sleeping houses. Food is cooked for each man by his wife in her kitchen, but carried or sent to the clubhouse, where the men eat together.

She held the head up before the child and said to her, "Look! Look at the head of your mother."

When she saw the head, the child screamed, "My father! My father! Come quickly and see what your wife is doing. She says, 'Look! Look at the head of your mother.' She says, 'Look! Look at the head of your mother.' "

Hearing the disturbance, the father came and said to the child, "Now then, my child, what is all this about?"

The woman had hurriedly put the head back into the pot, and now she replied to the man's question before the child could speak, "It is nothing at all. Only that she has hurt her foot."

"Is that the truth?" the man asked the child.

"Yes, father, it is true that I stubbed my sore foot," replied the child. The child retired into the house. The woman gave her food, which she ate.

Another day the man and his wife went to work in the field. When the sun was going down they stopped work and returned to the village. As was his custom, the man stopped at the men's clubhouse. While he talked with other men there, his wife prepared food in her kitchen. When it was ready, and she was about to send it to the father, she said to the child, "Go and take this food to your father at the conference house."

The child replied, "I am not going there again."

The woman said to the child, "My child, run along and take this food to your father at the conference house. How will it be viewed by people, if I, your mother, once more go carrying food to the conference house?" Hearing the matter stated thus, the child took the food to her father at the conference house. When she returned her mother was waiting for her in the doorway of the house, holding up the head of the child's mother and saying, "Look! Look at the head of your mother."

The child screamed out, "My father! My father! Come quickly and see what your wife is doing. She says, 'Look! Look at the head of your mother.' She says, 'Look! Look at the head of your mother.' "

The man came from the conference house to his sleeping house and said to the child, "Now what goes on here at my house?"

Again the woman answered first and said, "The child carries on, making a noise, because the hogs were in the doorway. They were in her way when she wanted to come into the house, so she began making this fuss."

"Is this true?" the father asked the child.

"Yes, father, it is so," replied the child. "The hogs were in the doorway." She also added, aside, "Mother, keep still there."

After these same events had been repeated many times the child explained the matter to her father privately. She said, "This is what is being done to me: My stepmother has the head of my mother, who died long ago, and she keeps on showing it to me over and over."

When he had heard this, her father told her, "Today I shall keep watch at the side of the house, at the time when you are to take my food to the conference house. When your stepmother sends you with the food, just go on along and take it there. When you return, if she asks you, 'Is your father still at the conference house, and is he staying there?' you are to say, 'Yes. That is where he is staying.'"

When the time came, the father was keeping watch. The woman prepared the food and then said to the child, "Go and carry the food to your father at the conference house. But first go and see if he is there."

The child went, and when she came back said, "Yes, that is where he is." This was what her father had told her to do. Then she carried the food to the conference house. When she returned she once more found her stepmother waiting for her, holding up the head of her dead mother, and saying, "Look! Look at the head of your mother."

When the woman had said this, the father came out from his place of hiding and seized the woman. He summoned the relatives of this woman and explained to them the harm that the woman had been doing. After he had finished making out his case to her relatives, he expelled her from his house, and she went back to her village and her relatives, returning in disgrace.

a stepmother changes into a lion

Once there was a man whose wife died, leaving him an only child. He married another woman.

Being a hunter, the man one day went away to hunt animals. As he was leaving, he talked with his child and said to her, "My child, I am going away to the bush. I am going away to hunt. You stay with your mother. I shall be back soon."

While the man was away in the woods, the woman said to the child, "My child, crack a few lice for me."

The child said, "Shall I just crack them with my fingernails?"

The mother said, "That will not be good enough for me. Those who crack lice for me do not use their nails; they use only small stones."

Then the child found small stones. When the child hit two stones together, the woman changed into a lion, and the lion tried to catch and eat the child. But the child climbed onto a high rock and yelled out:

> Father, father, dear father, hear me!
> You went hunting, hunting, hunting,
> The hunter went a-hunting for pleasure.
> I cry from fear of my mother.
> Father, you married a lion,
> Thinking her woman.

When her father heard her, he answered, "O my child, I am coming. Cry no more as you have been crying."

The child continued calling, for her father was far away and her mother was still a lion. As she cried the same words again, her father again answered from far away, "O my child, I am coming. Cry no more as you have been crying."

When the lion heard the man's voice, she hit herself with one of the small stones and changed back into human form. She spoke to the child, saying, "My child, come here. What are you crying about? Why did you cry out a little while ago that your father had gone hunting?"

Then the father arrived and asked the child, "My child, why were you crying so loud?"

The mother hastily answered the father, "She was crying for nothing. She simply cries. This child of yours is much too fretful."

So the child also answered, "Father, I was crying for nothing."

These same events repeated themselves for a number of days. Finally, the child explained the matter to her father. She told him, "This stepmother of mine keeps changing herself into a lion, and then she wishes to kill and eat me. When she does this, I flee to that rock there and cry out to you for help in the way that I have been doing."

When her father had heard this, he said to her, "Say no more about it now. Tomorrow, I shall go away only a short distance. I shall wait with my gun, watching. You do just what you have been doing. And it is important that you do not say to your stepmother, 'Today my father is nearby.'"

When it was light the next morning, the father of the child said good-by to her, saying, "My child, today I go to the bush to hunt again, but today do not cry so much as you have been crying. I shall come back early again."

The child said, "Ee-ee-ee."

The father walked only a short distance and then hid in the forest. The woman, thinking that he had gone away, said to the child, "Crack a few lice for me."

The child replied, "Shall I crack them with my fingernails?"

The woman said, "For me lice are not cracked with fingernails, but only with small stones."

The child picked up the small stones which she had used before, saying to her stepmother, "I shall clear your head of lice."

Once more the woman changed into a lion and chased the child, who jumped up onto the rock and began calling out:

> Father, father, dear father, hear me!
>
> You went hunting, hunting, hunting,
>
> The hunter went a-hunting for pleasure.
>
> I cry from fear of my mother.
>
> Father, you married a lion,
>
> Thinking her woman.

This time the father was nearby and saw everything. He leveled his gun and shot the woman who was a lion-witch, the woman who could change back and forth between a woman and a lion.

The father summoned the relatives of the woman. When they arrived and saw that her corpse was that of a lion, they said, "It is all right that you shot her. That is what she deserved."

4. deformed children

the lame girl

A number of girls were together in the kitchen where they regularly slept. One of these girls was lame and limped as she went about. This was because of the many chiggers in her feet. The other girls would not allow her to go about with them, nor would any young man sleep with her. The other girls said, "You make us ashamed before the young men."

One day she came by stealth into the kitchen of the other girls. When they found her there, they were very angry. But finally they relented and let her sit in a corner.

Later, a handsome young man came to the kitchen to get a girl to sleep with him. He looked at all of the girls in order to choose one. He saw the girl in the corner and called her, saying, "Sister, get up, for tonight we sleep together."

The well-groomed girls felt insulted and said, "This man is a fool, for he wishes to sleep with this girl who is lame from chiggers." Although they talked about him this way, he took the girl away.

He slept with her, and in the morning he paid her with the present of a small bird. He said to her, "Take good care of this little bird. If you tap it lightly, the bird will emit something which you will like."

It was a time of famine. The girl tapped the bird lightly, as her lover had directed. The bird laid a whole granary of corn. Then she tapped it again and it laid enough cowpeas to fill a granary. The girl's parents were highly pleased with the bird. They had food for themselves during the whole time of famine. They became wealthy from selling food to those who needed it. The whole family had free food.

As for the girl, her family removed the chiggers from her feet, and she became a beautiful young woman.

How was it with the well-groomed young women? They were called to sleep with young men. What sort of fee did they get? One a wooden ladle, another a pudding stick, and the others some trifles.

legless njombi

Once there was a girl named Njombi, who had no legs. The people of her country decided to move to a distant region. When the time to leave arrived, Njombi's parents talked with her and said, "Since you are a cripple and we are not able to carry you with us, you will just have to stay here in the deserted village. You can sit under the guava trees. When the fruits drop to the ground you will be able to get to them and have something to eat."

Njombi stayed, all alone and enduring much hardship, after all the people of the village had left the country and gone to a distant region. One day an ogre came and begged from her, saying, "Njombi, give me some guavas."

"I have no legs. How am I to give you guavas?" answered Njombi.

Then the ogre said, "Take my legs. Then you can climb into the trees and gather many guavas." Njombi took the legs of the ogre, put them on, and climbed into the tree. She gathered guavas and placed them in two piles. One pile was for the ogre and one for herself. When she had come back to the ground she gave the legs back to the ogre. She gave one pile of guavas to the ogre, saying, "Here are your guavas. Now eat them."

The ogre gulped down his guavas, and turning to Njombi said, "Friend, your guavas are delicious. Give me some more, for mine are all gone."

"Mine are not gone yet. Have you already finished the pile which I gave you?" said Njombi.

"Do hurry and gather me some more, for they taste so good," said the ogre.

"What am I going to climb with, since you have taken your legs back?" she asked.

"Take them again," he said. "If you wish to please me climb quickly."

She took the ogre's legs and once more climbed up the guava tree. Soon she was dropping more guavas to the ground. It happened that in this tree there was a tangle of gourd vines. When she had finished dropping down guavas, Njombi sat down upon the mat of vines. And then the vines lifted up and began to drift away. When the ogre saw this happening he called, "O my legs! O Njombi, what are you doing?"

"Nothing," she answered.

Soon the vines began to fly away. Then the ogre shouted, "Njombi, bring me back my legs! Njombi, bring me my legs!"

She did not reply to the ogre, but began to sing this song:

What helped Njombi climb? O Natenga.

She climbed onto the dragon vines.[1] O Natenga.

Vine, O vine, take, take me to my mother. O Natenga.

The vine it conquered the ovisonde.[2] O Natenga.

The ovisonde they vanquished the onganga.[3] O Natenga.

I go riding, riding on the tongs to the rock of Zebra. O Natenga.

Thus Njombi flew away. She flew on and on throughout the night. About eight in the morning she reached the village of her parents, in the new country of her people. The people in the village and those out by the pounding rocks heard the song Njombi was singing and were alive with astonishment. They said to each other, "Listen to that song! What Njombi is that? Is it the cripple that we left far away in our old village? Can it be she? This one singing now, is she that Njombi? Is she with us again?"

When she came close to the ground they saw that it was the same Njombi. Then all the villagers came running to her, giving her a boisterous welcome, greeting her over and over again, asking if she were well, and asking where she got her legs.

[1] A vine of especially snake-like appearances may be indicated by "dragon vine."
[2] Driver ants.
[3] A witch.

She explained to them that she had stayed on in the deserted village, what she did there, and how the ogre had come and lent her his legs so that she might climb the guava tree. She told how the gourd vines had flown away with her.

Her family were very happy that she had arrived and had come with legs. They presented her with a slave and killed an ox in honor of her coming. Later Njombi married, became queen of the country, and had a voice in all things.[4]

nehova's ulcer

A girl named Nehova had remained unwed. No young man wished to have her because she had a great ulcer which could not be cured.

One day an ogre came to her parents and said, "I wish to marry this girl, Nehova, even though she does have this ulcer. I shall cure her of the ulcer." Her parents consented to this marriage with the ogre, since he promised to cure her.

After they were married the ogre took Nehova away to his village. He cleansed the ulcer and cared for her until she was cured and they were truly married.

The ogre was a hunter and it was his custom to kill animals, which he then brought and fed to Nehova. He did this with the intention that when she was properly fattened he would eat her. Nehova was very happy, since she was having plenty to eat, and

---

[4] The young man who supplied this story went on to offer this interpretation, which is interesting for its mixture of Umbundu and Christian ideas, and for its use of traditional lore as a justification of young people's revolt against authority of the elders:

"The moral of this story is: the wise fight each other, and the fools inherit.

"In thinking of this story as it applies to the Kingdom of God, one sees that the privileged, because of their position of privilege, think that by continuing to use the system now in use, they will be able to deal with every problem. This is not true at all, for when some small new challenge presents itself, they will refuse to recognize it as new.

"Some adults, in the presence of the younger ones, whom they consider to be their inferiors, are doing that which is wrong. If it should happen that a youth has the right of some matter, he is condemned by his elders, who will not admit that a youth can have the right.

"It happens sometimes that the children have difficulty in getting on with the old folks, and as a consequence it follows that the children are they who first find life."

this of the best. She did not know that the ogre intended to eat her when she had become sufficiently fattened. No thought of this entered her mind.

One day Toad came along and talked with Nehova. He said, "Listen to me, Nehova. The thing for you to do is flee. This ogre is feeding you well, so that he may eat you when you are fat enough. But when you flee you should not travel on the ground. If you do the ogre will track you down, and when he finds you he will eat you on the spot. Since I am a relative of yours, agree that I swallow you. Then I shall travel all the way to your country and you will arrive there safely."

Hearing this made Nehova very sad. Even though she was being fed abundantly, she could no longer be happy after hearing this. Because Toad insisted that if she stayed there she would surely be eaten, she agreed to have Toad swallow her. He succeeded in swallowing her completely. When he had finally gotten her down he started out along the path.

In the afternoon the ogre came back to his village. When he did not find Nehova there he began shouting:

> Nehova-e-e, O my Nehova,
> Take back your ulcer.
> My intention is to grab you,
> To cook you and eat you.
>   Nehova-e-e, O my Nehova,
>   Take your ulcer back.

The ogre continued shouting this until he came to Toad. He asked Toad, "You there, have you seen Nehova?"

Toad answered, "I have not seen her," so the ogre continued singing:

> Nehova-e-e, O my Nehova,
> Take back your ulcer.
> My intention is to grab you,
> To cook you and eat you.

This the ogre went on singing and shouting until he came to the village from which Nehova had come. Then he stopped shouting, and did not go into the village.

When Toad came, he went into the village and into the house of Nehova's parents. When the parents saw Toad they did not recognize him, and so they started to keep him out of the house. But he persisted, went inside the house, and vomited out their child Nehova. Her parents saw that she was quite well and strong, and no longer had an ulcer.

The parents of Nehova rejoiced greatly. When Toad related all that had happened, they thanked him profusely. Also, they heard the ogre outside the village, singing:

> Nehova-e-e, O my Nehova,
> Take back your ulcer.
> My intention is to grab you,
> To cook you and eat you.

In the end the ogre went away leaving Nehova, who had been saved by Toad.

5. girls

gathering olonjavilili

Once a group of girls said to each other, "Let us go to gather olonjavilili[1] fruits." They all agreed to this. One of the girls had a younger sister who had a hunchback, and this hunchback child said, "I too am going along."

The other girls said, "That is impossible. Let her stay at home. We will not take a hunchback along with us." And they whispered to the hunchback's sister, "Sister, let us hurry so that we shall give her the slip. She will not be able to see us and will have to stay behind. This will teach her a lesson." Then they all hurried and quickly went away.

When they arrived at the place where the fruit grew they picked it rapidly and then returned by a different path.

The hunchback had followed after them. As she walked along she found some ripe olonjavilili and began to shout, "Look! There are olonjavilili here. Olonjavilili are here!" There was no reply. She was standing beneath a tree under which drops were falling, which she thought were from overly ripe olonjavilili. But in the top of this tree was the corpse of a dead person.[2] When she looked up she saw the corpse in the tree, and that the drops were falling from it. Seeing this, she left that place hurriedly, crying out, "Water! Where can I go to bathe? For Kalunga[3] has burst upon me."

Embelengenje[4] answered her, "Come here and bathe. Come, bathe in running water."

[1] The tasty fruits of a tree.
[2] It was formerly the custom of the Ovimbundu to wrap the corpse of a suicide in a mat, bind it in the top of a tree, and leave it there.
[3] The dark, mysterious place to which the dead go; not a place of punishment. The dead may punish those still living, but are not themselves punished.
[4] The mythical great hunter.

When she heard what he said, she went to meet Embelengenje. He showed her the water, and she bathed herself it it. Then Embelengenje called to her saying, "Come, go with me." She followed him. Embelengenje removed the hump from her back, and they lived together. They lived together for a long time and later they had a son whose name was Chinyama.[5] The sole employment of Embelengenje was hunting animals in the wild.

One day, after Chinyama had grown to size and understanding, he spoke to his mother, saying, "Mother, the path to the country from which you came, have you forgotten it?"

"I have not forgotten it," she said.

"Lead the way to it," he said. "Let us go to that country, for I do not know it." One day the woman took her basket upon her head and the child upon her back and started to go toward her home country. She had gone a little way when Embelengenje returned from his hunting and found her gone. He called out across the forest to them, "Chinyama, take on the hump that came off from your mother's back!"

"Mother, he has put the hump on my back," said Chinyama.

Then they called back and forth to each other until they came together. Embelengenje asked, "Where were you going with my child?"

"I went with him to the fields to look for food. Eating only meat is not good for him," she answered.

"You are not allowed to go away with my child," Embelengenje said to her. For some time, their lives continued as formerly.

Then one day the mother and child again thought that they would flee. The woman took her basket upon her head and the child upon her back and set out. They had gone but a short distance when Embelengenje, returning home early from his hunting, found them gone and went back out to look for them. Once more he called out, "Oh Chinyama, take the hump, the hump of your mother!"

"Oh mother, he has put the hump back on my back," cried Chinyama to his mother.

She returned home to Embelengenje, who asked her, "Just where were you going?"

[5] *Chinyama* means animal. It is seldom used as a name for a person, since it is insulting to call a person an animal.

"I have been to the fields for food," answered the woman.

These same events repeated themselves four times. The fifth time that the mother and child attempted to escape, Embelengenje had gone hunting far away. The fugitives traveled fast over the beaten paths, fearing that Embelengenje might find their scent and thus track them down quickly. When Embelengenje did return home, he went out looking for his wife and child, but did not find them. Once more he called out, "Chinyama, take the hump of your mother." No one answered this call. Then he tried to follow their scent, but since they took many different paths, he could not find them, so finally he returned home.

When the mother and child had finally gotten free, they traveled hurriedly, going on until they came to the country of the mother. They stopped in the bush outside the village. When a child passed, the woman asked the child, "Is my mother Ngandi[6] in the village? And is my father Ngandi in there?"

"They are there, in the village," replied the child.

"Go and tell those I have named to come here," the woman said to the child.

The parents were alarmed when they received this message and said to each other, "Now who can that be who summons us to meet outside the village? Could it possibly be our child who strayed away and became lost in a foreign country? The one for whom we have already wept?" In this state of mind they went into the bush and discovered that it was indeed their child awaiting them there. Her hump had come off and she was no longer a humpback. They rejoiced greatly, shouting and shouting with joy. Then they said to her, "Now let us go into the village, where we may talk with you properly and at length."

But the girl replied to her family, "I came out from the village a humpback. Since I am not that now, I cannot go back again."

Then they gave her an ox in payment of their fine,[7] so that

---

[6] *Ngandi* is a generalized proper name. The Ovimbundu use this expression much as we use "John Doe."

[7] All losses and indignities are settled by the payment of fines, virtually the entire law being civil rather than criminal, as we use those terms. One who has suffered insulting treatment, such as being sold into slavery or being treated as a humpback, will demand a fine from those who inflicted the insult, when opportunity presents itself. As in this story, the payment of a fine usually involves elements of ritual, exchange, pleading, journeying or entering, and ascent to higher status by acquiring more possessions.

she might be persuaded to enter the village again, and she went with them into the village.

When they reached the house they said, "Let us go into the house," but she answered, "The house that I left as a hunchback, I cannot go into again." So they presented her with a hog as their fine, after which she went into the house.

Then they said to her, "Sit down in this chair," to which she replied, "The chair that I sat upon as a hunchback I cannot sit upon any more." So her family gave her a rooster, and when she received the rooster she sat down.

Later in the day they prepared food and brought it to her. She refused to take the food, saying, "The food which I ate as a hunchback, I cannot eat again." To meet this objection they gave her a goat, after which she ate the food.

When she had eaten, they talked to her and asked her where she had been and what she had done in the land of the strangers. She related to them all the events which had befallen her. When night came, they said to her, "It is now time to sleep. Will you please use this bed?" She replied to them that the bed which she had slept upon as a hunchback, she could not sleep upon again. So the family gave her a sheep.

She went to bed and slept. After that she did not require the payment of any more gifts.

chela's tongue is slit

A group of girls of a certain village said, "Let us go and have our teeth chipped." [8] They all agreed to do this.

One of the girls had a younger sister named Chela, who wished to go along. Chela was a peculiar child, considered by the other girls to be feeble-minded. Even her sister disliked her, and none of the girls wanted her to accompany them, so they told Chela to stay at home.

Chela insisted, "I am going with you. I shall go on my own legs. No one will have to carry me." The other girls, even her own sister, became vexed with Chela. They rebuffed her with

[8] The Ovimbundu chip out a V-shaped notch between their upper incisors as a tribal mark and consider untrimmed teeth to be ugly.

ridicule, saying, "You remain here. Stay away from us. How could you expect to be made beautiful?" But Chela still pleaded to be allowed to go with them. Since they would not allow her to go with them, she followed behind them when they went.

The girls traveled along in this way, ahead of Chela, until they reached the house of one who chipped teeth with a small tooth ax. While their teeth were being chipped the girls said to the tooth chipper, "We shall pay you to work on the girl Chela, but you are not to chip her teeth the way that you chip ours. When she arrives, just cut her tongue. The little imbecile lagged behind and is not here yet, but she will surely come and you must not forget to cut her tongue." Chela's sister was party to this plot.

The operator recognized Chela when she arrived. He asked her if she had come to have her teeth chipped while the other girls' teeth were chipped, and she answered, "Yes sir."

"Open your mouth and I shall quickly attend to it," he said. Chela opened her mouth. He took out his knife instead of his tooth ax, and began to slit her tongue.

Chela cried out, "Have mercy! You are hurting me terribly!"

He told her: "Brace up. This is what I did to your comrades." He finished mutilating her tongue, while she yelled until finally he let her go.

Chela then went to the kitchen where the other girls were gathered together. When she entered they said to her, "Oh Chela, please let us see how he fixed your teeth." Since she could not speak, she kept her mouth closed and just hummed and shook her head to indicate that she would not show them her teeth. Later her sister joined the other girls in scolding her. They said to her, "Please, Chela, let us see how he chipped your teeth. If you do not show us, we will beat you for being impudent." Still Chela only shook her head, for her tongue was so damaged that she could not speak.

The next morning her tongue was swollen. That day the girls went home to their village. Once more Chela lagged behind, for she could not travel well. As the girls approached their village along the path they began to sing:

> Those who chipped our teeth so finely
> Cut the fat tongue of fool Chela.

Those who chipped our teeth so finely
Cut the fat tongue of fool Chela.
The child of the king is young Chela.
Cut is the tongue of fool Chela.

Chela would have sung this song with the other girls, but she could not. Her tongue was so swollen that she could not sing, and only went, "Mumble, mumble."

The mother of Chela was out in a field through which the path led, and Chela's mother was the queen. Hearing the song, Chela's mother said with surprise, "Who is named in that song?"

When the girls heard her question they said to each other, "Let us sing it again, much louder. Sing out!" And they sang the same song again.

When Chela's mother heard the song again she began to worry, thinking, "The Chela they sing of must be my child Chela. If it is true that her tongue has been cut, what kind of tooth trimming are they doing over there?"

Once more the girls said to each other, "Once more! Let us sing it again and sing so loud that the mother will understand it." And they sang the song again:

Those who chipped our teeth so finely
Cut the fat tongue of fool Chela.
Those who chipped our teeth so finely
Cut the fat tongue of fool Chela.
The child of the king is young Chela.
Cut is the tongue of fool Chela.

The girls went on singing the song until they reached a stream at which they confronted Chela's mother. All the girls except Chela crossed the stream, and when it was Chela's turn her mother said to her, "Now cross over the bridge."

Chela said to her mother, "I will not cross where the children of nobles have crossed, for I am just a common person." Then the queen chose a girl from among those who had already crossed and gave her to Chela as a slave.[9] Chela then crossed the stream.

The girls continued until they reached the village gate. The other girls entered, but Chela said, "I cannot enter here, for this is the gate through which free people pass, and I am a despised slave." The queen gave her another one of the girls as a slave, and Chela passed through the gate into the village.

They came to the house of Chela's family, and Chela's mother said to her, "Enter the house." But Chela refused to enter, saying to her mother, "I cannot go in through that doorway, since it is the entrance for children of the free, and I am a despised slave." Then another girl was given her as a slave, and she went into the house.

After she had entered the house, her family said to her, "Sit down on the stool." This too she refused to do, saying, "I cannot sit on a stool in which free people sit, for I am a despised slave." Then they gave her an ox, and she sat down.

Later in the day food was cooked for Chela, and her family invited her to eat. But Chela refused the food, replying to their invitations to eat, "I can no longer eat the food eaten by free people, for I am a despised slave." She was given a hog, and when she had received this she discovered that her tongue was cured sufficiently for her to be able to eat.

When night approached her family prepared Chela's bed and said to her, "Now come and go to bed."

But she answered them, "I cannot lie on that bed, since it is a bed for free people to sleep upon. I will not sleep on that."

This time the family gave her a goat, and thus induced her to go to bed.

The next day Chela made no further complaint. Later she too became queen.

kotundu's tooth chipping

One day a group of girls were leaving their village to have their teeth chipped [10] in another village. A knock-kneed girl

---

[9] Slavery is not always permanent; a slave can be ransomed by his family for an ox, a large hog, or a bale of rubber, equal in value to the slave.

[10] The teeth are chipped with a small ritual ax, used only for this operation. The corners of the upper front teeth are chipped in differing patterns, sometimes indicating the person's tribe.

whose feet were covered with chigoes[11] and whose head was crawling with lice wished to go with them. Because of her defects, the other girls did not wish to have her accompany them. They told her that she was too repulsive. Although they felt this way about her, still she tagged along after them.

When they came into the middle of a wood, they finally stopped and scolded her, using harsh and ugly words. After this reproof, she ceased following them and started walking on another path.

As she traveled along she came upon a little old woman with rheumy eyes, whose body was filthy. This little old woman said to the girl, "I wish to have you clean me up." Although much disgusted with the condition of the old woman, the girl consented and attended to the woman with such care that she became quite clean.

When the task was completed, the little old woman asked the girl, "Now, tell me where you are going?" The girl replied that she was on her way to a village where she would have her teeth chipped. The woman said to the girl, "Please, let me chip your teeth." The girl consented, and the little old woman trimmed her teeth so that above they resembled the sun and below they were like the moon. When she had finished the operation, she said to the girl, "When you meet your friends, do not tell them or show them how your teeth are trimmed, not even if they urge you to do so."

At the village where the other girls had gone, some of them had their teeth chipped in the style of Vachokue, some in the swallow-tail style, and others in other styles.

On their way back to their village they met the girl who had taken the other path. When they met her they said, "Now girls, let us show her our teeth." This they did, but she would not show them her teeth. She walked apart from them by herself and did not even speak a word to them, to avoid showing them her teeth. They showed their teeth to each other, but did not see hers. They teased her, saying, "Come now, let us look at your teeth so that we may see their style. You have seen the styles of your friends."

After a time, due to their insistence, she agreed and showed the other girls her teeth. When the other girls saw how her

---

[11] A species of small flea, also known as *jiggers* and *chiggers*. The female burrows under the skin of human feet and hands, causing painful and reddened sores.

teeth were chipped, that the upper teeth were like the sun and the lower ones like the moon, they fell to the ground from the light of the sun and the moon. After they had recovered they arose from the ground and went apart from the girl, saying to each other, "What shall we do with this girl? If we walk on with her, everyone will praise her for having her teeth so well chipped. Worse yet, all the young men will be attracted to her."

They concluded, "It is best that we kill her. Then when we go back to the village and they question us about her, let us say, 'She parted from us and walked alone on another path. We do not know where she went.' " When they had agreed to this decision, they went back to her, took her aside, and killed her.

When they reached the village and were asked about the girl, they said, "We did not see where she went. She took a different path and went alone."

Later on, there came a day when people noted that a little bird came to the mother of the girl, whose name had been Kotundu, and sang this song:

O Kotundu, O Kotundu, tia-a-a.
O Kotundu, above there is the sun, tia-a-a.
O Kotundu, below there is the moon, tia-a-a.

The bird then went to the men's clubhouse and sang the same song there.

When the attention of the villagers had been attracted to the little bird, it flew away from them a short distance. As the people followed after it, the bird flew before them, flitting from tree to tree, continuing to sing the same song about the sun and the moon, until it reached the place from which it had come. Reaching this place, it stopped singing and waited for the people to come there. In the group of villagers were both men and women, and the entire family of Kotundu.

All of these people came to the place where the little bird had stopped singing. There was here a patch of nettles, and in the nettles they found the body of the dead Kotundu. The nettles and surrounding ground had been scorched.

When the parents of Kotundu looked at her and saw that she had been murdered, they wept. But they did not attempt to name anyone as guilty of her murder, for they said to themselves, "A thief is caught in the field, he is not caught on the path." Then the parents took up Kotundu's body and buried it.

the revenge of chupindiwangonga's mother

One day the big girls of a village were talking among themselves, planning and saying, "Let's go out into the woods today and dig for beer roots."

There was a smaller girl in the village, Chupindiwangonga, who said to them, "I will go along with you."

But since she did not have an older sister to bring her along, the older girls said to her, "You must stay here, for if you come with us you might delay us."

"I will not slow you down," said Chupindiwangonga. "I will run fast along the path."

The big girls would not consent to take her along, but she kept teasing them to allow her to go, and finally she followed them when they left. Out on the path, the older girls threw sand into her eyes and left her on the path alone.

When they returned to the village, Chupindiwangonga's mother asked them, "Where did you leave your little companion who went away with you?"

Then all the girls in the village replied, "We did not see where she went, for she walked away by herself." The mother knew that they were lying and had purposely left Chupindiwangonga alone somewhere, for they had all left the village together.

The mother dealt with the matter thus: she begged a little piece of beer root from each of the girls.[12] She put all these pieces of beer root into a mortar, pounded them together, and sang:

> The girls of this village,
> Today may they perish,
> Perish for my daughter,
> Beloved Chupindiwangonga.

[12] The efficacy of Ovimbundu witchcraft and black magic often depends upon procuring some article from the intended victim.

Soon all the girls of the village did die. Not one escaped. But the woman kept right on pounding beer root in her mortar, now singing:

> The children of this village,
> Today may they perish,
> Perish for my daughter,
> Beloved Chupindiwangonga.

Then all the children of the village died. Not one escaped. Still the woman kept right on pounding her beer roots, now singing:

> Young men of the village,
> Today may you perish,
> Perish for my daughter,
> Beloved Chupindiwangonga.

All the young men of the village died. The woman continued mashing beer root. As she pounded, she sang:

> Old men of the village,
> Today may you perish,
> Perish for my daughter,
> Beloved Chupindiwangonga.

The older men of the village died, and not even one of them was left alive. Still, the woman kept right on mashing beer roots, and as she pounded, she sang:

> You women of the village,
> Today may you perish,
> Perish for my daughter,
> Beloved Chupindiwangonga.

All the women of the village died, and no one was left alive in the village: no man, no woman, no child. Still the woman kept right on mashing beer roots. As she pounded, she sang:

> The hogs of the village,
> Today may they perish,
> Perish for my daughter,
> Beloved Chupindiwangonga.

All the hogs in the village died, and not one hog was left alive. Still the woman kept pounding beer roots and singing. She named all the animals and all the fowls of the village, and all of them died.

She alone was left alive in the village. Soon she began to reflect, "What shall I do with all these corpses, all that is left here in the village?" She decided to carry all the corpses out into the forest. She moved all the corpses of commoners out into the forest. By the time she was ready to move the queen's corpse into the forest, the queen's body had become soft. When she tried to carry the queen's body, the queen gushed out all over her, covering her from head to foot. Her eyelids were stuck together. She was like a blind person. In this great distress, she began to shout:

> Where shall I bathe me?
> Water!
> Where shall I bathe me?
> Water!
> Now all the woes of Njembo[13] engulf me!
> Mercy!

Then all the girls of the village who had died replied:

> Bathe here in water.
> Polluted, O come to the waters of mercy! [14]

[13] See the Glossary at the back of this volume.
[14] There is irony in this "mercy" toward her who had no mercy.

The woman stumbled on searching for water, seeking the place from which the girls of the village had called to her, but she could find no water. So she shouted her same call for a place to bathe again, and this time all the children of the village who had died replied, calling:

Bathe here in water.
Polluted, O come to the waters of mercy!

The blinded woman searched for the place from which the children's voices had come, but she found no water there. So again she shouted for water in which to bathe, and this time all the young men of the village who had died answered her, promising water for her where they were. But she could not find water at the place they had called from either.

As she groped about, she searched for water where she heard the voices of the women of the village, and then where she heard the voices of the old men of the village, but still she found no water. So she shouted again for a place to bathe:

Where shall I bathe me?
Water!
Where shall I bathe me?
Water!
Now all the woes of Njembo engulf me!
Mercy!

This time, after she sang, the king of the village, who had also died, called to her:

Bathe here in water.
Polluted, O come to the waters of justice.

She went in that direction and really found a deep pool of water.
Finding water, she said, "Now I shall bend down and bathe myself." When she tried to bathe in the water, she fell into the

pool. She sank beneath the water and died. She was never seen again.

the humbi-humbi feather

In a country having a year of great famine, a group of girls were discussing the situation. They said, "Now that this hunger has come upon us, let us do something about it while we still have legs." [15]

The girls agreed that their best course was to go to a certain region where it was rumored food was still to be had. By doing this, they might be able to help their parents to live, as well as save their own lives.

The small brother of one of the girls said to her, "I am going with you."

"You cannot go with us, for among all my friends there is not one who is taking a child with her," his sister told him.

"Though that be true, still it is certain that I myself am going along. I shall go on my own legs," the boy replied to his sister. She went to a bush and broke off a switch with which to whip him, but even as she did this he said, "Even if you beat me, still I am going along."

At this point the other girls took the boy's side and said, "Sister, you may as well let the boy go with us."

But the sister came back at them, saying, "You can talk this way now, but just let us get out into the woods and you will be singing a chorus to me of 'There is your young brother far behind us, slowing us down.' I will be pained continually by the blame for this. Am I going to suffer it? Therefore, let him stay with his mother." Though the boy begged and begged to be taken along, still his sister would not agree for him to join their journey.

Then the other girls, all of them except his sister, agreed that they would take him along. They began the journey, and when they had already slept twice along the way they came on the third day to a village. Here they found the men's clubhouse filled with men, young men, boys and children; the houses filled

[15] One able to travel well "has legs." A feeble person says, "I have no legs."

with women, girls and children.[16] They were warmly welcomed
by the villagers, who, old and young, followed the custom of
eating all strangers who came to them. For this reason, the
villagers were all plump and fat. They were happy when they
saw these strangers arriving, thinking, "Today we shall seize
these girls and later eat them all."

The villagers provided a house for the girls to sleep in. In
the afternoon the villagers cooked corn mush and relish for the
girls. This they did to quiet suspicion in the minds of the girls,
and make them believe they had found peace. The girls did not
suspect that this was a village of cannibals.

Meanwhile, and before the villagers had brought the food,
the boy had gone away from the village to search for wild
squashes. Having found some, he returned with them and divided them among the girls, giving one squash to each. To his
sister he gave only a quite small one.

When food was being brought by the villagers, the boy said
to the girls, "Do not eat the food which comes with a meat relish
or with beans, but eat only the corn mush which has egg plant or
bean leaf greens with it. It is only that which you may eat." The
girls ate as he directed, but he himself did not eat at all. He was
prepared to lie down for the night hungry.

The boy went outside, found a piece of cane stalk, picked it
up from the ground, and sat down with the cane stalk in his
hand. Later, after it had become quite dark, he noticed people
coming his way. The girls were all lying down inside the house
asleep, but the boy was sitting outside the house fully awake.
The men he had seen coming arrived and said to him, "Have you
already slept?"

"I have not been asleep," he replied.

Then they asked him, "Father, what is it that you wish to
have?"

He answered them, "What I wish to have is food that I can
eat in our own village. Sleep would not come because I thought
of this."

They said to him, "Rest your mind. We are going to give
you a whole bin full of corn and another full of beans," thinking
to themselves that he could not carry these things away, since

---

[16] The bachelors' house or men's clubhouse may be entered freely by small children and by all males, but is a forbidden place to girls and women, who are expected
to spend most of their time close to their kitchens.

when he slept they would kill him. Their way of killing was to wait until the victims were asleep, for it was taboo with them to have even the victim himself witness a killing.

While they were preparing the corn and beans they had promised the boy, he was inside the house digging furiously in the ground with his piece of cane stalk. But when he heard them coming toward him, he stopped digging and sat quietly on the ground. They arrived and delivered to him the bins of grain, saying, "There you are, father. Now you can sleep on it." The boy said, "Ee-ee."

After going away and waiting a short time, the men came back to the house once more. They thought, "By this time the boy will be asleep, for we have given him what he desired."

Reaching the house, they asked, "Are you asleep?"

And the boy replied, "I am not asleep."

So they asked him, "Father, why is it that you do not sleep?"

And the boy replied, "O, I do sleep when I can sleep, but in this region it is much too cold for me to sleep. I have nothing with which to wrap myself against the cold, so how can I sleep?"

So they said to him, "We understand and we are going to open some bales of bedding and bring a wrap to lend you, for young people are always feeling a chill."

Again they went away, and again the boy resumed digging. He kept up his digging whenever the men were not with him. When he heard them coming again he sat down by the fireplace. They came in and loaded him down with cloth and blankets, saying, "Now you can sleep." But when they had left, he continued digging.

Soon the men came again, saying to each other, "Now he will be asleep, for he was reaching the point of drowsiness." And to him they said, "Have you been asleep?"

"I have not slept," he answered them.

Now the men began to scold him, saying, "What more do you want?"

"A herd of cattle," he told them.

They went outside and said among themselves, "All right, let us fetch cattle. Does the insolent boy believe that he will derive the benefit from these things he is begging of us? Let us give him the things he asks, so that he will fall asleep soon. Let him make us toil some more. In the end we shall eat him."

While they were talking thus, the boy was making a tunnel

under the ground to his own country.

When they returned with the cattle, they said to him, "We have brought this herd that you asked for, and now you must go to sleep. Do not let us find you keeping watch again."

They went away for a time, and then came back and asked, "Have you been asleep?"

"I have not yet been asleep," he said to them.

This time the men became angry and said to the boy, "You insolent youngster! We shall whip you! What more do you want? Young fellow! Aren't you going to sleep at all tonight?"

He answered, "Once I was really drowsy, on the point of falling asleep, when I began wishing that I had a feather from Humbi-humbi[17] and another from Kachimbamba." [18]

At this, the men went away and later returned with the feathers. As they gave him the feathers, they said to the boy, "If we come once more and find you still awake, you will be clubbed. We shall come and beat you with knobkerries[19] in a way that will frighten you."

The boy asked for nothing more, but said, "Yes, truly. Now I will fall asleep."

The tunnel still lacked a short distance of being completed, so the boy resumed digging. The men departed and waited a short while. They said to each other that he was surely asleep now. When they came again to his hut, they asked if he was asleep, and he answered from behind the closed door that he was not yet asleep. As they pounded on the closed door they asked what desire was still on his mind that kept him from sleep, and he answered, "I wish to have a boy and a girl."

While the men were going to get these, the boy loaded the herd of cattle and everything else that had been given to him onto the feather of Humbi-humbi. Then he awakened the girls and added them to the feather's cargo. His own sister he placed on the feather of Kachimbamba. They left in the house the wild squashes which he had given to the girls in the afternoon. Then they began traveling on the feathers through the tunnel, which reached about as far as one could walk in a day.

[17] A heron which circles high in the sky, soaring without apparent effort.

[18] A nighthawk which during its mating season acquires decorative feathers, causing it to fly heavily and frequently alight. Decorative feathers make the wing tips squared instead of pointed, and plume-like feathers two feet long trail from each wing.

[19] Clubs with many knobs and points on the larger end, which is usually a root.

The villagers returned and asking, "Now are you asleep?" received no reply. There was silence. So they said to each other, "This time he is really asleep. Now we shall end their lives." Then the villagers set fire to the house, saying, "When they are burned we shall take them out, and if they are well done, we shall eat this cooked meat."

As the house burned down, the wild squashes which had been left inside began to burst open—"Bang!"—and as each exploded a different man would say, "That one is mine." They counted the bursts and the last one was a small one. When this was heard, they said, "That one was the youngster who caused us so much toil. Now he has had his punishment."

While the house burned, the escapees were flying fast. They were hardly visible, since they were flying high up in the heavens. However, the boy's sister, riding on the Kachimbamba feather, was not making such good time. The feather of Kachimbamba sought to alight after every short flight. Whenever she felt the feather sinking toward earth she had to spur it onward and keep it aloft.

When the roof of the house fell in, the villagers began poking the ashes, but found no one. Even when they had finished looking, they had not found the hole through which the boy and the girls left, for it was now completely filled.

In this way all the girls escaped the village of cannibals, and the villagers were unable to follow them. When they approached near to their home village, the feathers lowered down to the earth. The boy said to them all, "If it had not been for me all of you would now be dead. Is that not true? What is my reward to be? What are you going to give me in return for saving your lives?"

To this the girls replied, "O brother, let us go further with you. Since you have already done so much for us, you will be well rewarded."

Then he said that the girl who had carried him on her back would not have to give him anything in payment, but that the other girls would each have to give him something in payment.

At the village they carefully explained to their parents everything that had happened. The parents of the girls gave to the boy a large hog for each girl he had saved. The boy's father was made prosperous by the grain and cattle flown back by his son. This prosperity was increased by the hogs.

6. *boys and men*

a boy encounters an ogre

One day some children went into the woods to search for guavas. Among the children was a small boy named Ulombe.

When the boys found the guava trees, the larger boys picked guavas with a red pulp. The small boy, Ulombe, gathered only green guavas. When they later sat down to eat the fruit, they said, "Let us show our fruits to see who has picked the best."

They showed their fruits, and it appeared that Ulombe had gathered only green guavas. Seeing this, the other boys laughed and laughed, and they said that Ulombe was a fool. Ulombe called on his older brother and said to him, "Come and go with me, so that I may learn to gather good fruits."

To this, his older brother replied, "In the village I am your elder brother, but out here in the woods I am not your elder brother."

When his brother refused to accompany or help him, Ulombe asked his cousin to go with him. His cousin replied to Ulombe, "In the village I am your cousin, but out here in the woods, I am not your cousin."

All the older boys refused to help Ulombe choose the right fruits. So Ulombe said to them, "Since none of you will accompany me and teach me, I will go gathering fruits in the forest all alone."

Ulombe went into the woods, and when he came to the guava trees he climbed up into one of the trees, and was busy choosing fruits when an ogre came that way and saw Ulombe.

"Drop down onto this knife," said the ogre to Ulombe.

"I will not drop down onto your knife, lest it cut me," replied Ulombe.

Then the ogre said, "Drop down onto my spear."

And Ulombe answered, "I will not drop down onto your spear, lest it pierce me."

"Then drop down across this ax," commanded the ogre.

But Ulombe refused, saying, "I will not drop down across your ax, lest it cut off my head."

After waiting a short while, the ogre said, "There is some mush for young brother in this bag I have. Just drop down into this bag."

Hearing this, Ulombe dropped down into the ogre's bag. The ogre tied the mouth of the bag and started for his village. As they traveled along, the boy sang over and over from within the bag this refrain:

> You ogres are rumored to put down your load
> And then go away into the bush.[1]
> Yet you do not put down your load.
> You do not go into the bush.
> Yet you do not put down your load.
> You do not go into the bush.

The boy continued singing this song, from within the ogre's bag, until they came close to the ogre's village. Then the ogre said, "I have now arrived at my village. Now I shall go into the bush. Shall I stop here?"

"Do not go into the bush here, so near the village, for the dung of an ogre stinks," said the boy.

So the ogre continued walking, carrying the bag with the boy in it, until they were far from the village. Finally the ogre said, "I am stopping here." The ogre put down the bag with the boy in it, and went to one side of the path, in the bush, and squatted down.

While the ogre was squatting behind the bushes,[2] the boy untied the sack and got out. Then he found a stone and a bumblebee. These he placed in the sack.

[1] Common Umbundu idioms for defecation are *to go into the bush, to visit the bush,* and *to squat,* all of which occur in this story.

[2] *Squatting* here indicates both what the ogre is doing, and the fact that the boy is temporarily out of his sight.

When the ogre came back from the bush, he asked if the boy were still in the sack, and the bumblebee in the sack went, "Loo-oo-oo." So the ogre picked up the bag, and as it still weighed much the same at it had before, he thought that the boy was still inside.

As the ogre walked along he began to sing a song to alert his wife for his coming:

> O Nambimbi, put on the pot.
> Fill it with water and get it hot.
> The hunter is coming with what he caught.

The ogre sang this song several times, until his wife heard it and put on the pot. The water in the pot was already hot when the ogre arrived at his house. Coming into his house, he untied the bag, and emptied its contents into the pot. The stone broke the pot, the broken pot spilled the water, and the water put out the fire. Seeing all this, the woman scolded her husband, saying to him, "Now why did you do what you have just done? You are a fool to bring home a stone."

To justify himself, the ogre said, "Truly, I was carrying a person. He must have escaped and put that stone into the bag, while I had put down the bag to go into the bush. I am returning to that place before long. And this time I shall not come back home without bringing something that can be eaten."

On another day the ogre went hunting again, and on that same day the boys once again went into the woods to gather guavas. Again the boys plotted against Ulombe, saying that on this day they were all to pick green guavas, and no one was to pick guavas with red pulp.

When the boys came to the guava trees, the older boys all went to one side where they picked guavas with red pulp. Ulombe followed their instructions and picked only green guavas. Later, when they came together again to show the fruits which they had gathered, only Ulombe had picked green guavas. All the others had picked guavas with red pulp, good to eat.

Once more, Ulombe asked his kinsmen to go to the guava trees with him, and once more they all refused to accompany him or teach him. So Ulombe went back to the guava trees, once more all alone.

At that very time the ogre came back to the guava trees looking for the same Ulombe. As he had done before, the ogre asked Ulombe to fall down onto his knife, then his spear. Ulombe, as he had done the first time, refused, answering that the knife would cut him, the spear pierce him. Then the ogre said to Ulombe, "Come down into my bag where there is some mush for my young brother."

When Ulombe heard this invitation, he went down into the bag. The ogre tied the mouth of the bag, and taking it over his shoulder started for home. As they traveled along, Ulombe sang this song:

> I have heard from the rabbit
> That you ogres have a habit
> When out on the road
> Of putting down your load
> To go and pay a visit to the bush.
> Now you, on the road,
> Aren't you putting down your load,
> To go and pay a visit to the bush?

But this time the ogre did not put down his load, the bag with Ulombe in it. He continued walking along. When he came near his village, he began to sing, to alert his wife for his coming, the same song as before:

> O Nambimbi, put on the pot.
> Fill it with water and get it hot.
> The hunter is coming with what he caught.

Nambimbi heard this song, for when the ogre came into his house he found that his wife had put on the pot, and the water was already warming. The ogre untied the bag and emptied the contents into the pot. Thus, into the pot went Ulombe. When the wife saw Ulombe fall into the water, she was well pleased and began to pluck off his clothing and otherwise prepare him to be cooked for the next meal. The woman called her own child near, and giving him a long needle, said to him, "Take this needle, and watch the pot. If it begins to boil over, stick the needle into the bottom of its contents."

The child took the needle, and sat by the pot. From the pot, Ulombe said to the child of the ogre, "Do not stick me. Do you stick needles into your kinsmen?"

The child ran to its mother, saying to her, "Mother, the pot insulted me!"

"You did not try to keep the pot from boiling over into the fire," replied the mother.

When the child had returned to the pot, it soon insulted the child again, saying, "I am a kinsman of your mother. I also belong to your father's family."

The ogre's child hurried off to his mother and told her about this. While the ogre's child was away from the pot, and as the water in the pot was getting hot, Ulombe jumped out of the pot. Then Ulombe caught the ogre's child, cut it up, and put it into the pot. Then Ulombe sat down by the pot and looked after the cooking very carefully. In the dim interior of the hut, Ulombe seemed to the ogres to be their child. Ulombe called to the woman and said, "O mother, I do not wish to eat meat today. All I want to eat is some beans."

"All right," replied the woman. "Cook some beans for yourself. But tend to your job of seeing that the pot does not boil over into the fire."

When it came time to eat that evening, Ulombe would not touch the meat stew. He ate only beans.

Some two days later Ulombe spoke to the ogre, saying to him, "Father, please hew from wood a small drum for me." The ogre agreed, carving a small wooden drum for Ulombe. When Ulombe had the drum, he played upon it and sang this song:

> Kumbiti, kumbiti, kumbiti-i-i,
>> The ogres have eaten their son.
> Kumbiti, kumbiti, kumbiti-i-i,
>> The ogres have eaten their own.
>
> O little drum! O little drum!
>> Come carry me home,
>> Home to my little brother,

> O little drum, come carry me,
> Carry me home.

Several times Ulombe sang this song. As he was holding the drum between his knees, playing on it and singing, the drum rose into the air and soared away toward his own village. Soon, the people of Ulombe's village heard the sound of drumming and singing in the distance. The song named Ulombe. Then the villagers saw Ulombe flying toward them through the air. Although Ulombe's parents had already wept in mourning for him, they now rejoiced. When Ulombe riding his drum came down to the ground, all the people of his village came to see him, rejoicing with singing and dancing.

a hunter tests ties of family and friendship

One day a hunter went out to hunt. He found a roan antelope, shot and killed it. Then he returned to the village. When he came to the village, he went to the compound of the headman. The hunter found his uncle there, for that was where his uncle lived. He greeted his uncle by clapping his hands. His uncle said to him, "One stands his gun outside." When he had done this, he went into his uncle's house. His uncle spoke to him and said, "Did you just happen to come along here at midday?"

The hunter said, "Honored sir, I shall tell you about the matter that has caused me to show up here. It is that when I went to hunt this morning, I went along the edges of the fields. When I saw a duyker,[3] I shot at it. When it fell to the ground, I ran quickly to catch the duyker. When I came near the place where the duyker had fallen, I heard a person scream: 'Oh father, Oh! Oh father, Oh! You shot me. You shot me.' When I heard this I ran away."

When the uncle had heard what his nephew told him, he became angry and picked up his staff. The nephew hastily ran

---

[3] The duyker is an antelope small enough to be mistaken for a person in the bush. The roan antelope, which had actually been killed, is so large and imposing that it could not conceivably be mistaken for a person, even in underbrush.

out of the house, for his uncle was about to beat him. He took his gun from the place where he had leaned it and ran. He ran until he came to a village where his friend lived. When he came there his friend saw that the hunter was in a sweat and asked, "What is chasing you?"

The hunter said, "Oh dear friend, I am lost."

His friend said, "Tell me about it quickly so that I can do something about it."

The hunter told him, "This morning I went out to hunt. When I came between the fields, I saw a duyker. I shot at it. It fell to the ground. When I came to the place where the duyker fell, I heard a person scream: 'Oh father, Oh! Oh father, Oh! You shot me. You shot me.' Hearing that, I fled. When I came to the village, I went to the headman's compound, and I went into my uncle's house. When I told him all what I did in the woods, my uncle was angry. He took up his staff and was about to beat me, and he said, 'Now, get out of here. I want to see no more of you, lest you frighten the children.' I got out of there in a hurry and came here. Now, are you going to put me out, or what are you going to do?"

His friend spoke without any hesitation and said, "Let us make an end of your trouble. If it means death, let us go and die. If it means a lawsuit,[4] let us go and pay the fine." Then the friend called his young men and said, "Come. Let us go and attend to the burial." When they had equipped themselves, they set out and went to the place.

When they came to the roan antelope, the hunter said, "There is the person that I shot."

His friend spoke to him and said, "Why have you acted this way?"

The hunter replied, "I did it to test the ties of family against the ties of friendship. Now I have found that family ties are weaker than ties of friendship."

They cut up the antelope and carried it away to the village of his friend. The next day he asked for the help of his friend's servants, to go and fetch his possessions. He moved to the village of his friend.

[4] In the law of the Ovimbundu, death is usually reserved as a punishment for sorcery. A killing is settled by the payment of a fine determined by the action of a special court, the family of the accused paying damages to the family of the victim.

7. courtship

a young man and the girl who slept with him

A young man liked a girl, who came to sleep with him nights.[1] Each night he sent a messenger to call for her.

One day he spent the time cooking some mushrooms in a small pot, since he had sent a messenger to fetch the girl, and did not expect her to arrive for some time. He added to the cooking mushrooms some lard, which made them taste delicious.

He was eating the mushrooms when the girl came. He said to her, "Come over here and try some of these mushrooms I am eating. They taste very good."

She refused, saying, "I am not going to eat anything."

Again he said, "Do come and eat some of these mushrooms which I am eating, for they are very good. I would not offer them to you unless they were good."

Still she would not eat, and said, "I will not eat anything. Even if you leave some of it uneaten, I will not touch it."

The young man continued to eat, and at last said, "All right, I am going to leave some of these mushrooms to eat early tomorrow morning, myself, before the other boys come around." Then he went out, saying to her, "I shall be back soon, after I have been to the house of my friend."

While he was gone, the girl began thinking about the mushrooms and wondering how they were seasoned. She thought, "Haka! [2] What did he put in to cook with them, that made him

---

[1] *Uvaisi* is a custom of the Umbundu. Unmarried men and women sleep together, with the knowledge of the girl's mother, who receives from the man some payment. Preliminary arrangements are made through third parties, and the girl is coached by her aunts on how she should behave when sleeping with a man. Sexual relations are not supposed to occur, since virginity at marriage is highly valued and publicly announced.

[2] See the Glossary at the back of this volume.

so eager for me to taste them?" So she got up, went to the fire,
and tasted the mushrooms. They tasted good. They tasted so
good that she went again and again to the fire to taste them.

The pot in which the mushrooms had been cooked had a
very narrow top, and as she reached her hand into the pot, the
bracelet she was wearing on her arm slipped down to her wrist
and wedged into the narrow neck of the pot, so that she could
not get her hand out of the pot. She was afraid that if she pulled
her arm too hard she might break the pot, which belonged to
another. So she went back to bed with the pot stuck on her
hand. She drew her cloth up over her left hand and the pot.

She did not go to sleep, but lay there worrying about the
pot stuck on her hand, and thinking, "What will I say to the
young man when he comes back? I would not touch the mushrooms when he offered them to me, and now I have my hand
stuck in the pot." Her body lay quiet, but her heart was disturbed.

After a time, she saw that the young man had returned and
was in the house. He said to her, "Dear one, have you gone to
bed already?" She remained silent, so he said, "Dear, what is the
matter with you?"

Still she did not reply, so he blew the fire in the fireplace up
higher, and then came over to the bed and lay down. He spoke
to her several times, but she still remained silent. Then he said
to her, "What is the matter with you? Every other night we have
talked to each other." She said nothing, so he put his arm
around the girl and discovered that she was trembling. He said,
"What are you trembling for? Hold my hand." She would not
hold his hand.

A little later he said to her, "Haka! What is this on your
arm, next to me?"

She replied, "I have a sore arm, and cannot lift it."

He touched her arm and perceived that the little pot of
mushrooms he had cooked was stuck on her hand. Then he said
to her, "Are you trying to hide that little pot of mushrooms
which you have on your hand? See! Didn't I say to you, 'Take
a taste of it. Take a taste of it,' and you would not taste them?
Now get up so that I can get the pot off your hand. It does
not matter if I break the pot, it is not valuable."

He got his knobkerry, placed her arm on a stool, cracked the
pot with knobkerry, and the mushrooms spilled out on the

floor. Then he comforted her, saying, "Let us talk. This is nothing at all. We will spend the night pleasantly as we have been doing on other nights. There is nothing to worry about." Then they went to sleep.

Early the next morning the girl awoke and went home. The young man again sent a messenger for her, but she would not come to sleep with him any more, for whenever she thought of him she was ashamed of what she had done.

a young woman's three lovers

Once there was a young woman who had three lovers. The young men were enamored of the girl. Each wished to marry her. She liked all three of them and would have agreed to marry any one of them. Since a woman may not marry three men, she made them this proposition: "I will marry the one of the three who goes to Mbaka[3] and brings back to me something which has never before been seen in this village."

The three youths agreed to her proposal. They set out together to go to the coast to look for things new and strange. They came to Mbaka and went into a trading house. The first of the three brought a metal bow together with arrows for it. The second one bought a casket of dreams. The third bought a metal snuffbox and the magic snuff that belonged with it. When they had completed their purchases, they left for home.

On the first night out they stopped in the desert to sleep. The young man who had purchased the casket of dreams had a dream in the night. He dreamed that the girl they wished to marry had died.

In the morning he told the dream to the others. He said to them, "What are we going to do? By the time we get to the village she will already be rotting."

The young man who had the metal bow spoke up and said, "Let us all mount one of my arrows and we shall arrive there immediately."

They did as he suggested. When they came to the village, they found that the dream had been true and the girl had died.

[3] *Mbaka* is the Umbundu name for Benguela.

The people were about to bury the corpse. The three of them, including the one who had bought the snuffbox with the magic snuff, spoke to the burial party and said, "Undo the box. We just wish to look at her with our own eyes."

At first some of the people objected to this request, while others sided with the plea of the young men, saying, "Let them see the corpse, for they were her lovers."

When the box had been opened and the corpse unwrapped, the young man with the snuffbox opened it, took out some of the powder, and applied it to the nose of the corpse. Then the corpse began to sneeze. This astonished the people assembled for the funeral. After the corpse had sneezed, she opened her eyes and looked around. Someone gave her some gruel. She ate it and soon gained strength. They helped her to sit up, but she was unable to speak yet. Two days later she recovered and began to talk.

The people of the region were astonished by the girl's return from death. Soon they began to gossip, saying, "When she is well again, perhaps she will marry the young man who brought back the snuffbox from Mbaka, for his snuff brought her back from the dead."

Hearing this gossip, the young man who had brought back the casket of dreams objected, "She should not marry him, for I dreamed the dream. If I had not dreamed of her death, we would have returned to the village much later and found that her corpse had been buried and begun to rot." The young man who had brought back the metal bow and its arrows said, "Neither of the others should marry her. Even though we knew of her death, yet we should have arrived long after her funeral and burial, if we had not flown here on one of my arrows.

There was much dispute and wrangling over the claims of the three men to marry the girl. The people said, "What are we going to do about this case?" They decided to take the dispute before the king in the head village and ask him to judge the case.

The king heard the arguments and took the case under consideration. He weighed the arguments for some time. When the time came for the king to give his decision, he announced: "All three of the youths have performed marvels in the great work of bringing the girl back from the dead. The three are equals. Each of their claims to the girl is canceled out by the marvelous things brought back from Mbaka by the other two. There can be justice only if none of the three marries the girl."

After the king had announced this decision, he looked well at the girl. He saw that she was very comely, so he added this further announcement: "I shall marry her myself." He did.

suse selects a bride

There was once a handsome young man named Suse[4] who did not wish to hurry into marriage.

The village girls were fond of Suse. They kept coming to him and showing themselves off, hoping that he would choose to marry one of them. Whenever they went near him, they first made themselves beautiful. They carefully washed their legs,[5] arranged their hair, and put on their best cloths.

When the girls had finished making themselves beautiful, they would go to Suse's house and visit with his mother. She would call to Suse, saying, "O Suse, come welcome your friends who wish to see you." But Suse would always reply:

Those! Chatter, chatter, chatter.
That's not what I'm seeking.
They needn't tarry.

And so Suse's mother would say to the girls, "Run along. He is not interested in any of you." The girls would go away.

Later other girls would come. These would have taken even more care than the first girls to make themselves beautiful, and would say to each other, "How can he resist choosing one of us?" They would walk near where Suse was working, and then call on his mother. She would invite them in to sit down. Then she

[4] This is not a traditional Umbundu name, but is derived from "Jose," which in turn is derived from "Joseph."
[5] Umbundu girls wash their legs in cold water and then let them dry in the air, a process which produces a glossy skin, considered beautiful.

would call to Suse again, "O Suse, come welcome your friends who wish to see you." But again he would say,

> Those! Chatter, chatter, chatter.
> That's not what I'm seeking.
> They needn't tarry.

And so Suse's mother would tell them, "Run along. Suse is not interested in any of you."

Later many other girls came to show themselves off to Suse. But he did not even look to see whether any of them were beautiful. And he chose no girl.

One day a group of girls called on Suse's mother, one of whom had many chiggers under her skin. Also, every part of her body was awkward. The girls who came with her jeered at her, saying to her, "Don't come with us, for we may be shamed if we are seen with you, since your appearance is disgraceful. You cannot walk with important and well-dressed girls who are calling on a man who has not yet chosen a wife. Do you think that you could be chosen, as filthy as you are? Keep away from us, sister." Such insults made the girl with chiggers follow behind at a distance.

When the girls came to Suse's house, they talked to his mother, who called to Suse, "O Suse, come welcome your friends who wish to see you." And again he replied,

> Those! Chatter, chatter, chatter.
> That's not what I'm seeking.
> They needn't tarry.

And so Suse's mother dismissed them, saying, "Run along. Suse is not interested in any of you." The girls went away.

After the girls had gone away, the girl with the chiggers, who had followed behind the other girls, came into the house to Suse's mother. Suse's mother called to Suse, "O Suse, come and greet the girl who spreads chiggers!" And Suse answered:

> She, she's not the one who chatters.
> Now bring her hot water
> And hasten to bathe her.

Then the woman bathed her and rubbed her with palm oil so that her body glistened. When this had been done, Suse said,

> She, she's not the one who chatters.
> Now hurry and give her
> Both pomade and brushes.

Then the servants brought brushes and combs, combed her hair, and braided her hair in style. When all this had been done, Suse said:

> She, she's not the one who chatters.
> With pins and needles
> Now dig out her chiggers.

Then the helpers carefully removed all the chiggers from the girl's skin. When they had removed all the chiggers, they washed her feet. When this had been done, Suse said:

> She, she's not the one who chatters.
> Bring dresses and ribbons
> And shoes to adorn her.

Then the mother brought out fine clothing, underwear, shoes and ornamental combs. When beautiful combs had been placed in the girl's hair, Suse said:

> She, she's not the one who chatters.
> Bring oxen for riding.
> To visit her parents.

The family brought oxen to ride, and both Suse and the girl mounted the oxen to go and visit the parents of the girl, to formally arrange the engagement.

When they reached the village of her parents, the villagers stood and stared at them. They were frightened, for they had heard it said that the approaching man and woman were white people. When Suse and his bride reached the house of her parents, the parents were frightened and said, "A white man and his lady[6] have come to our house. What are we going to do?" No one prepared to welcome them, or went out to greet them.

After Suse and his bride had waited some time, and still were not 'greeted, the girl called out and said, "Mother! Don't you come out to greet your own child?"

When her mother heard this, she said, "Who is this? She is the size of my daughter, but she has no chiggers. She calls to me, 'Mother.' Is she my daughter or not?"

The girl said, "Look at me well, and you will know who I am."

The mother looked at the girl carefully. Then she knelt down to the ground and said, "I cannot look at you, for it makes me embarrassed."

The girl related in detail everything that had happened to her. When she had finished telling everything, her family began to celebrate, and all the people of the village came to greet Suse and his bride. The family provided a good guest house for Suse, and began to talk with him about the engagement. Suse paid them the money, both for the engagement and for the marriage.

The marriage celebration was held, and Suse became the son-in-law of the family. The parents were highly pleased and said, "Truly, our child has married well."

kalende the speechless marries

A family had a child, a girl, who could not speak. Her name was Kalende. Her family cared for her well while she was still a child, and cared for her well until she grew up to become a young woman. She became an adult, but still could not speak.

* The native word translated as "lady" is derived from the Portuguese *dona*, "lady of the house," and is used by the Ovimbundu to refer to white women.

There came a time when a young man wished to marry her. He said that he loved her very much, but her parents would not agree to the marriage. They said, "Our daughter does not speak at all. How can you live with her in marriage?"

The young man said, "I can live with her and get on with her very well, for I love her very much."

The family replied to him, "This marriage may take place and begin well, yet in the end it will prove a failure, for you are a rich man and she is poor." But in spite of all their objections, the man would not give up Kalende.

In the end he married her, against her parents' objections. Because he loved Kalende so much, the marriage was very successful. They lived together in their home for a long time without talking to each other.

Then a friend of the husband advised him, "Go down to the river and set some fish traps. Place a catfish in the last trap." The man agreed to his friend's plan. He prepared some fish traps and put them in the river, placing a catfish inside the last trap.

In the morning the man called his wife and asked her to go with him to examine traps in the river. She was agreeable and went with him. They walked along the bank looking into the traps. When they came to the last trap, the woman went to look into it. She saw the catfish, became terrified, and screamed out loudly. After screaming, she went on talking about her fright. Realizing that she was talking, she said to her husband, "Let us go to my village, so that my parents may hear me speak."

Then they set out for the village of Kalende's parents. When her parents saw their daughter who had been mute and heard her speaking, they asked, "Who cured you?" She related to them how she had found her speech. They were much pleased listening to her, and cooked some meat to celebrate the event.

too long a separation during courtship

Once there was a young man who wished to marry a girl. He had not yet acquired the wealth to pay for the marriage, so he spoke to the girl about this. He said to her, "I am going away to get a job, so that I can earn enough to pay for that which is needed in getting married." He went away and worked for wages for two years.

During this time other young men in the village courted the girl. These said to her, "Come now, marry one of us. That one who went away to get work is not coming back any more." The girl wrote a letter to her boy friend, saying, "Hurry and come back, for if you do not come, I shall have to marry someone else."

The young man wrote and said in reply: "Be patient with me. Wait just a little longer. I shall return soon." Then the young man continued working for another two years. The other young men kept teasing the girl during this time. They said to her, "If you wait longer to marry, you will become undesirable. You will not be able to get married at all. One of us will marry you now."

Then she sent another letter to the young man, saying, "Now things have come to the point that I am going to get married if you do not come back immediately."

The young man replied to this, "Please wait, for I am coming in a month's time." However, the young woman did not wait, but married another.

The young man was walking on his way home. He did not know that she had married another man, nor know of the village to which she had gone. It happened that when he came near that village he met the girl herself returning from the fields. At the sight of him, she made sounds of joy, saying, "Oh-h-h! Oh my elder brother, he has come at last! I am lucky!" Then she explained the matter to the other women with her, saying, "This man is my older brother who went away to earn money by working. Now he is on his way back home. Truly, he is your brother-in-law."

Then the young man said to her that he was not stopping for the night, since he had to hurry home. The young woman protested, "It will not do at all for you to go on without stopping. Since we have been separated so long, you must spend the night here." In the end the young man agreed to stop for the night, since he was carrying a large box, with a large bundle on top of that.

When they came to the village, the young woman explained to the people, "This man is your brother-in-law." It happened that her husband was away that day, visiting other villages.

Late in the day a shoat was killed and cooked, and some

fowls also. These foods were prepared to honor the guest. When evening came, people of the village paid visits to the guest. After many of the villagers had visited with the young man, they began to bid him good night, knowing that he was weary from his journey. One by one they left the house of the guest, saying, "Now we are going to our house to sleep."

The young woman stayed on talking with the young man, after all the others had gone. Finally she said to him, "Let us go to our house to sleep."

But he objected, "That will not be right, for now you are a married woman with a husband."

But the woman kept insisting and teasing. She said, "It will not be right for you to stay away from my house. You must come and sleep at our house." Finally he yielded to her insistence and went with her to her house.

When they had entered her house, the man said to her, "I shall sleep here on the floor by the fire. I do not need a bed."

But the woman would not agree to this, and said, "No, no, friend. Do not sleep on the floor. You know that I am your fellow villager." In the end they both slept in her bed.

It happened that in the middle of the night her husband came home. He knocked on the door to get in. The man inside the house was frightened and thought, "This night I die."

The young woman said to him, "Now do not be afraid at all. Just leave everything to me." She got a large white towel.[7] She had the man lie down on the floor beside the fire. She covered him with the towel. Then, after she had unlocked the door with the key, she sat down by the young man, keeping him between her feet.

When the husband came in he asked, "What is this that I see here in my house?"

"Elder one," she said, "don't disturb me. Do not take my brother away from me in my own house."

Her husband answered, "I am going to take that towel away."

She screamed at him, "Elder one, just let your brother-in-law alone!"

---

[7] Those who can afford to own a large white towel use it around the house as a table cloth, a chair cover, a shawl, and in other ways. It is a sign of affluence and prestige to possess several of these large white towels, which come from the coast, through trading.

Then the husband left to fetch his older brother.

While the husband was away, the wife shut the young man up in the granary, covered him up, and locked him in with a key. She went back into the house and laid down. Then she snored, pretending that she was asleep.

Soon her husband came back, bringing his older brother with him. When they came up to the house, she pretended that she had been asleep, and went through the motions of waking up. She said, "Who is this? By my father! What is happening? Who is this going about in the night?" She went to the door and opened it, still asking, "What is the matter? Why are you coming around in the night talking with brother-in-law?"

Then the husband asked, "What was that thing I found there on the floor? Where is it?"

The woman replied, "Perhaps you are sick. At what time did you come here? People who wander about in the night fall into the habit of talking in a strange way."

These words made the husband angry, and he slapped the woman. When he did this she screamed, "O brother-in-law! Hold your younger brother, before he kills me! He is sick and crazed with jealousy. Don't you realize that he is talking about something he did not see?"

This made the husband even more angry. He began to beat his wife. Then the woman shouted, "Brother-in-law, hold your younger brother, before he kills me!"

Then the older brother restrained her husband. This made the husband still more angry, and he fought back violently. While this was happening, the woman shouted and called for the neighbors, saying, "Wake up! Come here! Our brother who has been wandering about in the night is crazed with jealousy." All the neighbors came in, and they helped catch him and hold him.

The villagers called a witch doctor. When the witch doctor came, he shaved the man's head and put cupping horns[8] upon the shaved head. The woman advised them: "Tie him up, and keep him tied for four days. If you do not, he will kill me, for he will not yet be well for four days." The witch doctor agreed, and her husband was tied.

[8] Cupping horns are two to three inches long, usually made from goats' horns, hollow on the inside and pierced at both ends. The witch doctors use cupping horns to suck blood from small incisions made in the scalp.

When the guest in the granary heard this disturbance, he feigned to wake up, and to be astonished. He said, "Sister! What has happened? Haka! Did brother-in-law come back in the night?"

To this the woman replied, "Your brother-in-law is crazed with jealousy." The guest was given his breakfast. Later on he left for his village.

When the husband had had time to think matters over, he said, "Let this woman go back to her village. Let someone go and bring back my money." Accordingly, the family did just that.

Later on the woman married her former fiancé.

the maiden and the lion

Once there was a young woman who would not permit young men to court her. Many young men attempted to court her, because of her beauty.

There came a time when the inhabitants of the region moved away to a far country. Her father and mother went with the other people, but they would not permit their daughter to go with them, saying to her, "Since you will not agree to marry, we are leaving you here all by yourself."

So when all the people moved away, her parents went with them and left her behind. She said, "How am I going to live here alone, all by myself?"

This young woman, whose name was Chitunda, cut down trees and built five stockades, one inside the other. She shut herself up in the center stockade. She did not go out in the morning until the sun was high.

One day a lion came and called: "Oh Chitunda! Oh Chitunda!" Then Chitunda replied to the lion by singing:

That is I. I am Chitunda Changanga,
The woman who will not yield to men.
Oh my father, in the village you may sleep.
I sleep not—Death is calling me.

> Oh my mother, in the village you may sleep.
> I sleep not—Death is calling me.

The lion broke through the outer stockade. When he came to the second stockade, he called: "Oh Chitunda! Oh Chitunda!" Once more Chitunda replied to the lion, singing:

> That is I. I am Chitunda Changanga,
> The woman who will not yield to men.
> Oh my father, in the village you may sleep.
> I sleep not—Death is calling me.
> Oh my mother, in the village you may sleep.
> I sleep not—Death is calling me.

The lion broke through the second stockade. When he came to the third stockade he called: "Oh Chitunda! Oh Chitunda!" Once more Chitunda replied to the lion, singing:

> That is I. I am Chitunda Changanga,
> The woman who will not yield to men.
> Oh my father, in the village you may sleep.
> I sleep not—Death is calling me.
> Oh my mother, in the village you may sleep.
> I sleep not—Death is calling me.

The lion broke through the third stockade. When he came to the fourth stockade he called: "Oh Chitunda! Oh Chitunda!" Once more Chitunda replied to the lion, singing:

> That is I. I am Chitunda Changanga,
> The woman who will not yield to men.
> Oh my father, in the village you may sleep.
> I sleep not—Death is calling me.
> Oh my mother, in the village you may sleep.
> I sleep not—Death is calling me.

The lion broke through the fourth stockade. When he came to the fifth stockade he called: "Oh Chitunda! Oh Chitunda!" Once more Chitunda replied to the lion, singing:

> That is I. I am Chitunda Changanga,
> The woman who will not yield to men.
> Oh my father, in the village you may sleep.
> I sleep not—Death is calling me.
> Oh my mother, in the village you may sleep.
> I sleep not—Death is calling me.

Then the lion broke through the fifth stockade. When he had entered, he asked Chitunda, "Shall I wed you or shall I eat you?"

Chitunda replied to the lion: "You may wed me." So the lion took Chitunda for his wife.

The lion spent the days hunting animals. In the course of time the lion and Chitunda had six children. Five of the children were like their mother. The sixth child was a lion. After the birth of this child, Chitunda planted some gourd vines. The vines grew well and bore gourds.

One day she thought things over carefully and then said to herself, "Now I know what I am going to do. I shall flee to the country where my father's family went." She called together her five children who were like herself, and had them mount the gourd vines. The gourd vines rose up and began to fly away. The vines flew until they came to the country where her parents were. When she came there, the family received her and her children with great rejoicing. Her parents welcomed the children, greeting them again and again.

the maiden who would not marry the eagle

Once there was a maiden whom the eagle courted. He came to her and said, "Please consent to marry me." The girl would not accept him.

After that, other animals came to her wishing to marry her. All the animals of the wild came to her. She would not accept any of them.

One day there came another suitor, the lion, wearing his fine clothes. The maiden consented to marry him. When they had been wed the lion carried her away to his den. The woman carried with her her younger sister, for companionship and for help in the housework. In the lion's house the work of the woman was to keep the house clean, prepare the food and perform other house work. The master of the house, the lion, was away all day hunting animals in the wilderness. The thought of the lion was, "When this woman becomes thoroughly fat I shall eat her."

One day an old lioness came and talked with the woman. She said to the woman, "Perhaps you do not have any family[9] of your own?"

"I do have a family," answered the woman.

"Then by all means go back to your family, if you still have one," said the lioness. "Just go out behind and look at the pile of skulls that is there. They are the skulls of women of your folk.[10] Even as you are, so were they." When the woman had heard this, she went behind the den, took a look, and became frightened.

The woman thought, "By my father, I am not stopping here to die a miserable death. I shall take my sister and go back to our family." She gathered together all the things which she had brought with her to the den: gourds, bottle gourds, the foods which humans eat, and other things. The baskets of both sisters were heaped high with their belongings. When all was ready they departed, the older sister singing this song:

> I would not marry the eagle.
> I would not marry the cutworm.

[9] Umbundu kinship stresses the importance of the mother and the maternal uncle: "family" here would mean mother, mother's brothers and descendants of mother's brothers, and of course does not mean a nuclear or marital family.

[10] "Your folk" means Ovimbundu. The Ovimbundu regard themselves as one race, people or folk; whites as another; unrelated tribes as another; birds as another, etc.

So I went and married the plover,[11]
The lover that came from the mountain,
And he only wanted to eat me.

Come eagle, come, and help me get away.
Come eagle, come, and take me to my father.
Come eagle, come, and take me to my mother.

The eagle flying in the sky
To the maiden made reply:
What have I been telling you,
    Over and over?

Later in the day the lion came back from the woods where he had been hunting. He thought he would come home to his wife and his sister-in-law. When he arrived he called out, "Wife, where have you gone?" When no one answered him, he sniffed about until he found their scent, which led to the path. He said to himself, "They have run away." He intended to eat them on the spot when he found them.

The lion followed swiftly along the path until he overtook them. Then he thought that all that remained for him to do was to grab them. The woman looked back and saw him. She took a gourd of sesame from her basket, dropped sesame seeds on the path, and ran on. When the lion reached the spilled sesame seeds he stopped, and began to gather up the sesame and eat some of it. As he did this he thought, "It cost someone much work to cultivate these seeds. It is not right that they should be wasted."

While the lion was licking up the sesame the woman and her sister were running on. At the same time the eagle was flying

[11] Although the lion is intended, the Umbundu word, *okakelekele*, clearly names a bird, a plover which struts about on the plains, calling attention to itself by its strutting and its shrill whistle. Such a metaphorical substitution is common in these Umbundu stories and songs. Here it seems that the lion is depicted as an exhibitionist, since the next line goes on to mention "the mountain," connoting "high plains" or "a place to show off."

above them. As they ran the older woman continued to sing the same song she had been singing.

When the lion had finished eating the sesame, he again followed them in haste. He overtook them once more and again thought, "Now I shall catch her." This time the woman threw down a small gourd of corn meal. The gourd broke and scattered the meal upon the ground. When the lion came to the meal he stopped, lowered his head, and began to lick up the meal. As the lion did this he thought, "Much work was required to cultivate the grain from which this meal was made, and it should not be wasted."

While the lion was eating the meal the woman and her sister ran on, the woman still singing her song.

When the lion had finished licking up the corn meal, he hurried after the woman and her sister. Once more he caught up to them, and once more he thought that he now had them. But before he could catch the woman she threw down a gourd filled with millet. The gourd broke and the millet seeds were scattered. The lion broke his stride, and then stopped to lick up the millet. As he was doing this he thought, "It costs much effort to grow millet, and it is wrong to waste it."

While the lion was gathering up the millet the two women were still fleeing, one still singing:

> I would not marry the eagle.
> I would not marry the cutworm.
> So I went and married the plover,
> The lover that came from the mountain,
> And he only wanted to eat me.
>
> Come eagle, come, and help me get away.
> Come eagle, come, and take me to my father.
> Come eagle, come, and take me to my mother.
>
> The eagle flying in the sky
> To the maiden made reply:
> What have I been telling you,
>   Over and over?

After the lion had gathered up the millet, he came leaping along again. Just as he saw them again and thought, "This time I shall catch that woman," the eagle flew down very swiftly, lifted up the woman and her sister, and flew with them to the top of a tree. He alighted on the tree in order to secure a better grip on the two women, for he had lifted them up in haste and did not have a good grip on them.

As the women were sitting in the tree with the eagle, the lion came to the tree and cut it down. When the tree said, "I am about to fall," the eagle rose up and flew away with the two women. The lion followed them, running along on the ground below. The lion called to the eagle and said, "Eagle, if you will not let me have my wife, at least drop her sister down to me, so that I may eat her." The eagle refused his consent to this, and flew on.

The eagle flew until he came to the home of the woman's parents. There he settled in a tree. The lion was watching from the top of a rock, to see where they came to earth, so that he might go there to get the woman. The people of the village, when they saw the eagle alight in the tree, were on the point of shooting him.

"Do not do that! Do not shoot!" called the woman.

The people were astonished to hear this and said, "Look! Is an eagle able to talk? Let us listen to what he has to say."

The woman resumed, saying, "We are your children. The eagle brought us here. If he had not brought us, we should have been eaten. Look outside the village, over there, and you will see who is lying in wait for us. First shoot him, so that we may come down from the tree and tell you about the harrowing escape we have made."

The people got a gun and shot the lion so that he died.

When the lion had been killed, the eagle came down to the ground with the woman and her sister. The woman then related to her family all which had happened to herself and her sister during their stay with the lion.

When the parents had heard the story they spoke to the eagle and said, "We are not able to pay you enough for what you have done, unless you will marry her, as you wished to do in the past."

The eagle, after listening to what the parents had to say, replied to them, "It is true that I did wish to marry this woman in the past. But since she did not consent at that time, I am no longer willing to marry her. The service that I have done her sprang only from my desire to help her. For she was weeping, and this caused me to have pity." The eagle, when he had said this, flew away.[12]

swallow and toad go courting

One day Swallow said to Toad, "Friend Toad, come now, and let us go to the sky to look for our women, so that we may marry." Toad agreed to the plan.

When it was light the next morning, Swallow came to call on Toad. He said, "Friend, it is now day. Shall we be on our way?"

Toad came out of his house and said, "Yes, we shall go." Then he asked Swallow, "Have you been to the clubhouse yet to let the elders know?"

Swallow said, "No. I have not been there."

Toad said to him, "Go along and say good-by to them for me too. Since I do not have good legs,[13] I shall go on ahead. You will overtake me on the way." Since Swallow was able to travel quickly, he flew off at once for the clubhouse. He left his traveling bag behind, putting it down by Toad's house. Toad climbed into Swallow's traveling bag, and left for the sky. Without looking in his traveling bag, Swallow flew straight for the sky.

When Swallow reached the sky, he put his traveling bag down by the door post outside the clubhouse. Toad came stealthily out of the traveling bag, and no one saw him do it. He was sweating because of the heat in Swallow's traveling bag. Wiping his face, Toad said to Swallow, "Have you just arrived? I came a little while ago and have been waiting for you over there."

---

[12] The telling of this story often is extended by specifying the dropping on the ground of additional items of the local diet: dried mushrooms, dried locusts, sauce made from tomatoes and peppers, peanut butter, small red eggplants, squash seed, etc.

[13] The phrase literally translated "good legs" is a common idiom meaning "health," and by analogy applicable to any strength or ability.

The men of the village greeted them warmly and asked them what had brought them there. Swallow and Toad explained that they had come to the sky looking for women to marry. When evening came, the people of the village sent them girls, such as they wished.

They spent the night with the girls, talking. In the morning they told the girls, "Someday you will see us again." This was the way that they courted girls, preliminary to becoming engaged to marry. They told the girls, "We are not going to wait until next year. We shall be here again very soon to become engaged."

Later in the morning, Toad said to Swallow, "Since you are the older, it is for you to go to the elders at the clubhouse and present our farewells. Let us not sneak off without farewells." Swallow was about to take his traveling bag with him, but Toad said, "Leave your traveling bag here. It makes shame to carry your traveling bag in your hand when you are stopping with your in-laws." Swallow left his traveling bag at the guest house.

As Swallow was leaving, Toad said to him, "I shall go on ahead. When you fly along, you will overtake me on your way."

When Swallow had done his duty he got his traveling bag and flew straight down to earth. When he came to the[14] house, he left his traveling bag on the ground while he went to fetch the key from the place where they had hidden it. Toad stealthily got out of the bag. He was wiping the sweat from his face as he said to Swallow, "You must have taken a long detour in the sky."

Swallow was astonished and said to Toad, "Have you been here long?"

Toad said, "I came some little time ago."

Swallow said in amazement, "Well, Toad does have legs! Yes sir, Toad has jumped up to the sky and already back down again."

Swallow hurried about and raised the money for his marriage. Then he came to talk the matter over with Toad. Swallow said to Toad, "How is it with you? Shall we go and marry our women now?"

---

[14] The phrase might be translated into English as "his house." However, this would alter the tone, since singular personal possessive constructions are almost never used in the Umbundu language. Instead, ownership is expressed as residing in some group, or else it is implied or omitted.

Toad replied, "The money is lacking. I have not made the arrangements yet. If it is all right with you, and you are willing to wait, put off our marriages for the time being."

Swallow said to this, "I cannot put this off any longer, for I have the money already." Swallow flew to the sky and married his woman. Toad stayed behind.

Later, when Toad had the money, he was not able to marry the woman, for he had no one to carry him to the sky. In the end he did not get married at all.

elephant, toad and white man's daughter

There was a white man who had several daughters. The white man said of one of his daughters, "No one may marry this daughter of mine, unless he can name her name." [15]

After the men had heard this, many of them came to court this daughter, but none of them won her, for they did not know her name.

One day Elephant came to woo her. The father told Elephant what he had told the other men, "He who marries her must first name her name." Elephant was disturbed to hear this statement, for he did not know her name.

On his way home, Elephant passed close to the house of Toad. As Elephant passed by Toad's house, he rumbled [16] and grumbled as he ruminated over the situation.

Toad hailed Elephant and asked him, "Uncle Elephant, what are you rumbling about?"

Elephant replied, "Nephew Toad, I wished to marry the white man's daughter, but the white man said to me, 'He who weds my daughter must first name her name.' Since I do not know her name, I am thinking about the matter and grumbling over it."

[15] The principal ethnographic study of the Ovimbundu, Wilfred D. Hambly's *The Ovimbundu of Angola*, published in 1934 by the Field Museum of Natural History in Chicago, states that the Ovimbundu do not have secret names. That study was based chiefly upon the statements of two or three Ovimbundu informants. Various Ovimbundu informants supplied the collector of these folk stories with five or six stories dramatizing secret names.

[16] Elephants, in digesting their food, make a rumbling sound which can be heard for some distance and is therefore useful to the hunters of elephants.

Then Toad said to Elephant, "Uncle, that is easy. Can naming an ordinary name worry you?"

Elephant said in reply, "Nephew, if you know her name, do tell it to me."

Toad answered, "Uncle, what will you pay me if I tell you the name?"

Elephant said, "Well, what do you demand that I pay?"

Toad replied, "All that I ask is that you furnish me with a few mushrooms."

Elephant said, "That is too easy! Perhaps you want more than mushrooms, and you say 'mushrooms' meaning something else."

Then Toad said, "In truth, all that I wish is mushrooms. Ordinary mushrooms. If you promise to furnish me with mushrooms, I shall name her name. Come back again tomorrow, and I shall name her name."

When Elephant heard this, he went off rejoicing. He thought he would go to the white man and name the name of the white man's daughter. When he had done this, he would marry the very beautiful girl.

When Elephant had gone, Toad dressed himself up and went to the house where the girl lived. Toad went through a hole and got himself into a corner of the house. As is the way with children, the children in this house were in the habit of calling each other by name. Soon one of the children of the house called, "Oh sister Julia, let us go to play." And the mother said, "Oh Julia, heed your brother." Toad repeated the name "Julia" over to himself, came out, and went off home.

At daybreak the next morning, Elephant was at Toad's house and said, "Nephew, come now, tell me the name right away."

Toad was ready with the answer and said, "Her name is Julia, but do not forget to bring me my mushrooms." Elephant promised to do this. But Elephant was so pleased with knowing the girl's name that he started for the girl's house, repeating as he went along, "Her name is Julia, her name is Julia."

Elephant came to the house and named the name. Her father agreed to the engagement, saying, "You may marry her, for that is her name. I shall keep my promise, which was made to all the suitors." Then the two of them, Elephant and the girl, conversed pleasantly and with much satisfaction.

Elephant came away from the house, and as he was passing Toad's house, Toad said to him, "Oh Uncle, where are my mushrooms? Didn't I tell you the right name?"

Elephant replied, "You seem to have a craze about mushrooms. Just wait a bit. If I think of it, maybe I shall bring you some in the morning."

Early the next morning, as Elephant was passing, Toad spoke to Elephant once more and said, "Uncle, perhaps you do not mean to give me my mushrooms after all!"

Elephant gave Toad a small bit of mushroom, saying to him, "While people are busy with really important affairs, why do you add to their difficulties talk about a few mushrooms?"

After Elephant left, Toad went to the house where the girl lived. When he came there he spoke to them and said, "I myself wish to wed this girl, for I love her."

The father of the girl replied, "This girl is already engaged to Elephant, for he named her name. This is in accord with the promise which I made to many previous suitors."

In reply to this statement Toad said, "Nonsense! Elephant has a great snout and bad legs. Among the people who did not know the name, he was one. He did not know it until I told it to him. Then he came here and repeated it to you. In addition, he is my grandfather's slave."

When the girl's family heard these statements, the family said, "When he comes here again, we shall withdraw our consent to the engagement."

On a later day, Elephant came to talk with the girl, and she said to him, "I no longer consent to marry you, for you are not a worthy person. You are not acquainted with prominent people, and besides you are the slave of a freeman, Toad's grandfather."

When Elephant heard these words, he became angry, very angry, and said, "I? Am I rated as a slave of the Toads? Today I will go back to look for Toad and pulverize him, so that there will not be left a speck of life in him. He has shamed me, the king, before men by saying that I am a slave." In great dudgeon, Elephant came to Toad's house and shouted, "Come out, Toad!"

Toad answered and said, "Is that you, Uncle?"

Elephant's reply was, "What was it that you said to that girl? That Elephant is the slave of your people and an ordinary person?"

Then Toad spoke softly, "Now, now, now, Uncle. Listen

carefully to what I am saying. Was it I that said those words? Now Uncle, if I had a bad heart, would I have told you the name of the girl at all? Consider this: you Elephants are big people, and they do not repeat idle gossip but deal with the truth. As I am your nephew and because of the past, it is impossible for me to do you any harm. So Uncle, tomorrow you go and take me to my elder brother, Duyker. We shall pass by the girl's house, since it is on the way to Duyker's."

Elephant, who had been very angry, calmed down when he heard this, and was angry no more. Then he said, "It is necessary that we go, and that we pass along the road which runs by the girl's house." After this conference Elephant went on his way.

When Elephant left, Toad dressed himself up and went to the house of the girl once more. When he arrived there, he began by saying, "Elephant passed by my house yesterday, and I bawled him out plenty. In order to make it quite clear to you that Elephant is our slave, I shall come along by here mounted on Elephant." After dropping this word, Toad went back home.

Early the next morning, as soon as it was light, Elephant came to Toad's house and called, "Toad, come out and let us go."

Toad replied, "Right, Uncle, but for us to get there quickly, it will be better for you to carry me on your back. I thought over what you told me yesterday, and it made me angry. When we come to the girl's house, let us go right on by without stopping."

Elephant agreed to this and said, "Climb on and let us go without delay."

After Toad had climbed up, he said, "Uncle, when we are about to pass their house, it would be a good thing for you to go by on the run, doing your best, so that your in-laws may admire you and say, 'My! Can't father run fast!' Then they, as well as the girl, will have great respect for you."

Elephant said, "Yes, that will be good! Today, those who have ridiculed me will see how fast I can run." When Toad was well seated, Elephant began to run.

When they came near the house where the girl lived, Toad said to Elephant, "Uncle, now is the time to run. Run so that they shall marvel, for up to this time, they have never seen you run." Then Elephant began to run still faster, and as he was running by the house, Toad was shouting: "Look at the slave of my grandfather! Look at the slave of my grandfather!" All in the house came out to look, and agreed that Elephant was Toad's slave.

Later in the day, when they were about to return from Duyker's, Toad said to Elephant, "Uncle Elephant, due to the rate at which you have been running, you have sweated much, so that it will be best for us to go right on past the girl's house without stopping. It will be best to wait a few days before going there to talk over your marriage with the woman. You would not have noticed it, because you were running so fast, but while we passed their house I heard your in-laws when they came out to look. They were astonished, and they praised you highly. They said, 'Big people, even if they are strong, yet have speed.' For that reason, they will not break their promise to you, even though they have objections, for they are afraid of you."

Once more Elephant agreed to what Toad said, so Toad added, "It is important that you do not forget to run hard when we are passing your in-laws."

When Elephant passed the house again, he ran at his best speed. Once more the people of the house said, "He? Sure enough, he really is a slave." Their impression was strengthened, for as Elephant was speeding, Toad was once more shouting, "See the slave of my grandfather! See my grandfather's slave!"

The family of the girl said, "We certainly will not give him our daughter."

When Elephant and Toad came to Toad's house, they stopped. Later, Elephant went off to his house. After Elephant had gone, Toad went to the girl's house again that very afternoon, to explain matters.

Toad said to the family, "Did you see how I rode our slave?"

They replied, "We saw it. We no longer agree to the marriage." When Toad had this assurance, he went back to his house.

The next morning, Elephant arose with much pleasure. He said, "Today I shall go and visit my young lady, for yesterday her relatives were impressed when they saw how fast I can run." When Elephant came to the house, the family talked with him and told him, "We no longer consent to have you marry this girl, for yesterday we saw how Toad rode you. Now we know that you are actually their slave."

Elephant became very indignant when he heard this, and

was angry with Toad. He said, "Today I shall say nothing more to Toad, but just go and smash him."

When Toad saw Elephant coming, he began to shout: "Oh Uncle, Oh mother's brother, did she rebuff you again today?"

Elephant replied, "Toad, you have been doing me dirt! Today you will not escape."

Toad said, "Now, now, Uncle, since the sun has already set, let us come back to this some other day, for I see that hatred wishes to come between us. To avert this, I will go and fetch my father's sister and talk it over with her. Let us skip the rest now, since it is already dark. Just go home and sleep on it. Then in the morning let us go to the house of my father's sister and settle this once and for all. It is right that a big man like you should have a wife." Elephant agreed to the proposal made by Toad, and went away home.

The next morning Elephant came to Toad's house and said, "Let us get going." Toad came out of the house and said to Elephant, "To get this matter settled quickly, you will have to carry me on your back. Otherwise things are going to be held up while I am getting to the house of my father's sister." Elephant saw that this was the case, so he said, "Climb on, and be quick about it." Toad climbed up onto Elephant's shoulder hump, where he could readily be seen by all whom they passed. As Elephant was going along, he passed under a tree. Toad broke off a branch to use as a whip.

When they were approaching the house of the white man, Toad said to Elephant, "Run hard, so that when they see you, it again will be to your advantage." Once more Elephant ran hard and fast. As Elephant went running by at great speed, Toad was shouting in the language of the white man, "Look! The slave of my grandfather! Look! The slave of my grandfather!" While Toad was shouting this, he was plying the whip.

Finally, Elephant understood what Toad was shouting. This made him very angry. He began to jump up and down with all his might. He thought that Toad would fall off, and then he would trample him to death on the spot. Toad hung on tight while this was going on.

Finally Toad caught hold of the leaves of a branch on a tree which came his way, and he climbed off onto the tree and got away. Elephant searched and searched, but could not find Toad.

When Toad came down out of the tree, he went to the driver ants and said to them, "When next you find Elephant lying down on the ground, kill him. When you have done this, come to me, and I shall pay you two oxen." The driver ants accepted his offer, and they began to watch along the paths where Elephant usually passed.

Later the driver ants found Elephant lying down. They attacked him through every opening, front and rear. They went inside and killed him.

When Elephant was dead the ants went to Toad and said, "We have killed Elephant, now pay us." Toad paid them for the job. Then Toad took his gun, went out and shot the corpse.

Toad spoke to some people going along the path and said to them, "Go and summon the white man to come here and cut up the elephant which I have killed. I shot him because he was impudent to me and wished to bring me into disrepute." When the white men came with their servants to dispose of the carcass, they were astonished and said, "Sure enough, Toad is powerful! See—he has killed an Elephant!"

the recluse

There was once a young man, a Catholic, who did not wish to marry. He did not care to eat food cooked by women, nor to be where women were. When he thought about his problem, he said, "What am I going to do? It seems to me that the best thing would be to go off by myself and live alone." So he went away and built a house in which he lived all alone. He lived this way for four years.

One day it rained. The rain fell heavily all day long. Late in the day a woman who had been out in the rain came into his house to take refuge from the rain and the storm. The rain kept falling as night and darkness came on. The young man said, "Woman, it is time for you to be going, for I am not accustomed to have women stay with me."

The woman said, "I am not going, for the rain has not stopped."

The young man prepared food and gave it to the woman, she ate it. Later, when it was quite night, the young man said, "I am not in the habit of stopping with women. Where are you going to sleep?"

She said, "I shall sleep on the floor, and you can sleep in the bed."

He said, "I am not going to stay in the same house with a woman. You may sleep here in the house, while I go to sleep in the granary." Then the young man went to the granary and locked himself in with a key. He went to sleep.

He wakened later and noticed that the woman was lying behind him. He asked her, "Now then, why did you come here?" and she answered, "I am cold." Then he put two blankets over her, and he himself lay down on the floor.

Later when he went to turn over, there was the woman at his back. He sat up and said, "Why did you come here?" She said, "I am still cold." Then he added to her cover and climbed onto the bed.

Later when he started to move, he found that he had already made connection with the woman. He was very warm and felt satisfied with himself. Then he had a change of mind. He said, "I have been cheating myself. Women are fine."

Then the woman said, "Now that you have sinned, and since you have had experience, go and marry."

The woman changed into a python and the python said to him, "Look—you have committed a sin. That which you avoided you have done. What are you yourself? Were you not born? Was it not a woman who bore you? Go now and get married."

The young man went away happy, but repenting the years he had spent alone. He said, "I have wasted my time. It is a good thing to marry." So he went to the village and married a wife.

8. married life

a woman and her husband's dogs

Once there was a woman, the wife of a man who was fond of dogs and kept many of them.

All of the woman's children had died, so there were no children to keep her at home. But her husband wished her to remain at home to care for his dogs, so he would not permit her to go away anywhere during the day.

One day a beer drinking festival was to be held in a nearby village. The woman decided that she would disobey her husband's command to stay at home. So she addressed the dogs thus: "I have no children to keep me at home, and I am not going to be the slave of you ordinary dogs. Today, go and pound meal for yourselves. Go and make your own corn meal mush." Then the woman went away to the beer drinking.

After the woman had gone the dogs decided to go off to the woods hunting. As they were leaving, the dogs saw a woman whom they did not know standing in the doorway of the house. This woman said to them, "When you come back from the woods, come back by way of the plum tree."

On their way back from hunting, the dogs came by way of the plum tree. They found the same strange woman they had seen in the doorway, now standing by the plum tree. The woman knocked down some plums from the branches and then asked the dogs, "How do you dogs eat this fruit?"

The dogs answered and told her, "We gnaw and gnaw them."

Then the woman said to them: "Go off into the woods and join your relatives, the jackals."

The dogs went away into the woods, and the woman who had refused to care for them never saw them again.

a hunter takes his beautiful wife away from the village

Once there was a man, a hunter, who married an unusually beautiful woman. Her beauty set him thinking. He thought in these words, "Now that I have married this exceptionally beautiful woman, I must take thought for myself. If we stay here in the village, I shall probably be known only as the husband of this great beauty. What can I do?" He decided that it would be better for him if he took her away from the village, and they should live alone in the woods.

The woman disliked this plan and said to him, "Even if I am beautiful, still I am really yours. The main thing to be considered [1] is this: you have married me, and therefore I cannot marry some other man. So let us just live on here in the village."

But the man replied to her, "It is useless to argue[1] this, for I have spoken my word, the word of the man who married you." So the woman consented to his plan, and they went to live in the middle of the woods. There were just the two of them. When they were settled, the man built a stockade with a gateway and put in a gate that fastened.

One day the man told his wife, "I am going away to hunt in the woods. When you hear my voice, you are to come to the gate and open it. You are not to open the gate unless you hear my voice." The woman consented, and they both did as he had proposed. Whenever he had been away hunting, he returned to the gate and sang:

Nambelengenje, Nambelengenje,[2]
'Tis your husband, who has long been out hunting.
Nambelengenje, open up the gate now.
Nambelengenje, open the gateway.

[1] The Umbundu language favors the use of impersonal forms, even when verbs imply a specific subject. In these cases, it is clear that "to be considered" means "for you to consider," and that "to argue" means "for you to argue."

[2] The great hunter of Umbundu myth is *Embelengenje*, and his wife is *Nambelengenje*.

And whenever the woman heard this song she came to open the gate and help her husband through the gateway, for it was too narrow for a man carrying an animal to pass through. They would get the animal through the gateway, carry it into the house, and leave it on the ground. Then the husband would rest while his wife prepared the food. After he had eaten, they would skin the animal, the wife helping him to do this. After they had dressed the animal, the woman would cook the viscera for the morning meal. Then the man would go hunting again on some later day, for he was a hunter. Whenever he went hunting, he left meat for his wife to cook, and he instructed her, "If you hear a voice other than mine, do not answer. Only when you hear my voice are you to answer." Then he would go away into the woods.

An ogre was spying on the man and woman, and the ogre heard the song which the husband always sang when he returned from the woods. One day the ogre tried singing the song, in a high pitched voice:

Nambelengenje, Nambelengenje,

'Tis your husband, who has long been out hunting.

Nambelengenje, open up the gate now.

Nambelengenje, open the gateway.

When the woman heard this, she kept silent, for she knew that it was not the voice of her husband.

Later her husband returned. He sang in a deep strong voice, as he always did. The ogre listened carefully as the husband sang:

Nambelengenje, Nambelengenje,

'Tis your husband, who has long been out hunting.

Nambelengenje, open up the gate now.

Nambelengenje, open the gateway.

The woman recognized her husband's voice and sang in reply:

Today the prey is what

Of beast with hoof or horn?

And the hunter answered her by singing:

> Onguluve[3]
> Makes the gravy.

So that he might get through the gate on another day, the ogre was listening carefully to the singing.

The woman opened the gate, the man passed through the gateway, and the two went to the house together. The hunter threw the onguluve down upon the ground. He rested, and the wife brought him food, which he ate. This food included the flesh of an animal he had killed on a previous day. When they had scraped and dressed the onguluve, they put the intestines on to cook.

Meanwhile, the ogre was trying to copy the voice of the hunter. As he did this, the ogre realized that his voice was too high pitched. The ogre began to keep pebbles in his mouth, to develop a heavy voice, like that of the hunter.

One day, when the hunter was about to go to the woods in the morning, he said good-bye to his wife and reminded her again, "Wife, do not forget to do as we have been doing in the past." She promised.

Later in the day, but before the time when her husband was in the habit of returning from the woods, the ogre came, and imitating the voice of the hunter sang:

> Nambelengenje, Nambelengenje,
> 'Tis your husband, who has long been out hunting.
> Nambelengenje, open up the gate now.
> Nambelengenje, open the gateway.

The woman was deceived and thought that the voice was the voice of her husband. She answered:

> Today the prey is what
> Of beast with hoof or horn?

[3] Wart hog.

To this the ogre responded:

> It's a duyker
> Makes the gravy.

Then she opened the door and went to unfasten the gate, as she had done on other days. When she opened the gate, she found that it was not her husband, but an ogre. The ogre seized her and carried her into the house. There he killed her, dismembered her body, and ate it. He took the head and placed it above the doorway. He also saved the blood, put it in a broken gourd, and put this on the top of the partly open door.

Later in the day the hunter came and began to sing:

> Nambelengenje, Nambelengenje,
> 'Tis your husband, who has long been out hunting.
> Nambelengenje, open up the gate now.
> Nambelengenje, open the gateway.

There was silence. He became frightened. He thought, "Haka! What shall I find here today?" Then the hunter repeated his call, singing:

> Nambelengenje, Nambelengenje,
> 'Tis your husband, who has long been out hunting.
> Nambelengenje, open up the gate now.
> Nambelengenje, open the gateway.

There was only silence. He threw the animal he carried to the ground, and then he found the gate unfastened. He said, "Now I shall go into the house."

He pushed the door to enter, the gourd fell, and the blood splashed down before him. Then he peered into the house and saw before him the head of his wife, the eyes not yet closed. When he saw this he cried out, "Oh my mother, help me! Oh my father, help me! Help me! Help me! What is this that I am seeing today? Sons of free men, help me! What shall I do now? My heart is red within me, like a fire. Oh-h! Help me!" Then he blew his nose. For some time he just stood there, weeping and crying out.

When he had stopped weeping, he went out and brought in the animal that he had killed. He skinned the animal, packing the flesh along with the household equipment, took up the load, and went off to the village. There he summoned people to the funeral.

He never went back to the place again.

the woman who quarreled with her husband

Once there was a woman who had quarreled with her husband and said in her prayers, "Even death is better than this."

Later she went to the river for a drink of water and was caught by a crocodile. The crocodile asked her, "Do you choose to be cut up by my teeth, or do you choose to marry me?"

The woman replied to the crocodile: "I choose to marry."

The woman's husband searched and searched everywhere for his wife, but did not find her. In addition he was worried about the care of the child she had left. For the woman had left in the village a child which was quite small and still nursing.[4]

One day the child came down by the river to play, and was dipping up water with a little gourd. As the child dipped water she made a sound: "Mbui, mbui, mbui."[5] The mother heard this and she said, "Who are you, making that 'mbui, mbui, mbui' sound as you dip water? Are you my child Chilombo?"

"Yes, mother, it is I," said the child.

"Are your father's cattle well?" asked the woman.

"All of them are all right," answered the child.

Finally the woman said, "My child, the sun is going down. Go on home now, my Chilombo."

The child replied to this: "I wish to nurse."

[4] Ovimbundu women often nurse a child into its fourth or fifth year, when it is already running about, talking, and playing.

[5] *Mbui* is onomatopoeic for the sound of water when it is disturbed. See the Glossary at the back of this volume.

So the mother came out of the water and nursed the child. She also braided the child's hair nicely. Then she put her down, saying, "Now my child, go along to the village." The child went away much pleased, for she and her mother had met again, and she had nursed. As she came into the village she was very happy.

When her father saw Chilombo he asked her, "My child, who braided your hair so nicely for you?"

She said, "My mother."

He said, "Where is she?"

"She is down there in the river," the child answered.

The father thought, "Isn't it always that way with small children? They imagine many things." Having thus settled the matter, the father forgot about his child's answer.

Another day the child went to the river again. She was fond of the place, for it was there that she had found her mother. Her sadness had departed, her heart had cheered, her fears had vanished, and her troubles were gone. She came to the river and began dipping up water with her little gourd: "Mbui, mbui, mbui."

Her mother heard this and said, "Who is that going 'mbui, mbui, mbui'? Are you Chilombo?"

The child replied, "Yes, mother, it is I."

The mother asked, "Are your father's cattle well?"

Chilombo answered, "They are all well, and all the animals are well."

When it became late in the day the mother said, "My child Chilombo, the sun is going down. Now run along home."

The child said to her, "Mother, I would nurse some."

Her mother came out of the water and nursed the child, also braiding her hair nicely and rubbing her with oil. Then she put her down and said, "Go along to the village now, for the sun has already gone down." Her previous joy now increased, the child went back to the village again. The mother went back into the water once more. Whenever the child had been to the river she was happy.

When her father again saw Chilombo he noticed her braiding and was pleased. He asked her, "My child, who has made your hair beautiful in this way?"

She said, "My mother."

He asked her, "Where is she?"

The child answered, "She is there, in the river."

The father now believed her and was pleased, thinking, "This must be the truth. Since the sun has gone down I cannot go to the river today. It is best for me to sleep first. Tomorrow I shall follow my child at the time when she usually goes to the river."

They slept that night, and in the morning the father followed his child until she went to the river. When they came to the river the child began to dip up water with her gourd: "Mbui, mbui, mbui."

The mother made no response. But the father said to Chilombo, "Keep it up, my child. Keep it up, my child." So she kept dipping water; going "mbui, mbui, mbui." Still the mother did not respond, for she had seen that the father came along with the child. The child said, "Father, she will not come forth."

The father went back to the village, and the child remained by herself at the side of the river. Once more she dipped water, going "mbui, mbui, mbui," and now the mother spoke to her, saying, "Who are you, going 'mbui, mbui, mbui' that way? Are you my Chilombo?"

"Yes mother, it is I," said the child.

After waiting for a time the mother asked, "Are your father's cattle and the other animals well?"

"They are all well," answered the child.

Then the mother said, "Chilombo, my child, go now, for the sun is getting low."

The child said to her, "O mother, let me nurse some."

The mother came out of the water and nursed the child, also braiding her hair beautifully once more.

When the child returned to the village the father saw from the child's braided hair that her mother really had been there in the river. He surmised that the mother had heard his voice and not come out of the water because he was there. He talked with all the men in the village and secured their help.

The next day they all followed the child until she went down to the river. They followed her at a distance. The father said to the other men, "There must be complete silence this time, when we go near the river. No one is to speak." When they came to the river they lay down on the ground to watch what the child would do, and also to see if the mother would come out of the water. When the child made the noise, "mbui, mbui, mbui," the mother said, "Who is that making the noise, 'mbui, mbui, mbui'? Are you Chilombo?"

The child said, "Mother, it is I."

After waiting a time, the mother asked, "Are your father's cattle and other animals well?"

The child answered, "They are all well."

Later the woman said to the child, "Chilombo, my child, go along home now, for the sun has set."

Chilombo said, "Mother, let me nurse some."

The mother came out of the water to nurse the child.

When she did this the men came quickly and seized her. As the woman struggled against them, the crocodile came out of the water to drive the men off. In spite of the crocodile, the husband himself pulled at the woman until he overcame her struggles, and then he carried his wife and her child back to the village.

an unfaithful husband

Once there was a man who would leave his wife to woo another woman in another village. This other woman became his regular mistress.

One day strong beer was being brewed at the village of this other woman. The man was there with the woman on the day that the beer became almost ripe, and she said to him, "To-morrow the strong beer will be ripe, and you are to stay away. Do not come here tomorrow." The man assented to this and went home. But late in the afternoon of the next day the man had in his heart a longing for strong beer. So he decided, "I am going over to that village, in spite of her telling me to stay away today." He took up his gun and cartridge box and went out.

When he came to the village of the woman he went to the woman's house and went in. There he found a sleeping child and some of the strong beer. He drank some of the beer and then went to sleep himself.

Later he heard cries coming from the village dance floor: "Tchah! Tchah!" Then the dancing villagers began to flee from the dance floor. The woman who had ordered him not to come to the village during the beer drinking and dancing had changed herself into a lion. She was half human and half lion. The man awoke and saw her coming into her house, bringing a large hog with her. She did not notice him. He was very frightened until she changed herself back into human form.

That night the woman scraped the hog. When she had finished the whole scraping job she looked into the bed, and there was the man. She said to him, "I told you not to come here. Why did you come?"

"Oh, for nothing," replied the man.

Then the woman said, "You have spied on me. Get up and go to your own village."

The man would not get up and go. The woman grew very angry over his staying, until he went out of the house and started away. When he had left the woman turned herself into a lion again and came following the man. When he saw her coming after him he climbed into a tree. When the lion-woman came to the tree she saw the man up in it. She began to jump and jump trying to get at him.

Then the man said to her, "Go away and change back into a woman again. When I wooed you did I not pay you at the time? Did you not eat of my meat and salt? Since you ate this regularly and repeatedly, you are now at fault, and I shall shoot you." When he had said this the woman jumped again, and so high that she caught the man and began to drag him down from the tree to kill him. Then the man shot her and she died.

The man came down out of the tree and went away to his own village. When he arrived there, his wife said to him, "What did I tell you?"

The man replied to her, "From now on I shall heed what you say."

To teach the child of a goat, put its head in a pot.

the hunter who changed himself into a great bird

Once there was a hunter. He was married. He and his wife lived together happily and got on together well.

Every day the woman worked in her field, growing food for the house. The man went to the bush to hunt.

Whenever the man killed an animal he would return by way of his wife's field, and the two of them would go back to the village together. When he was late she would wait for him, even if the sun was going down, so that they might go back to the village together.

One day the man fell to thinking, "Although I am eating meat, yet I am not well nourished. It would be good for my health to go back to the village during the day and get something to eat. To do this, I shall change myself into a bird." He mulled this over all during the day, while he did his usual hunting. That day he and his wife returned to the village late in the afternoon, the man carrying a duyker he had killed and the woman carrying a basket of food from her field. The man skinned the duyker and put its viscera in the pot to stew, while the woman prepared other food. When all was cooked they ate.

The next morning they went away as usual. They charged their son, who was left behind in the house, to keep putting water into the pot so that the duyker meat would cook without burning and would be cooked well when they returned from the fields and the bush. After the man had walked with his wife to her field he went off into the woods to hunt, as was his custom. Out in the bush he killed a duyker and hid it in the forest. He then changed himself into a large bird and went to the village. When he came to his house he went in and began eating meat from the pot that was on the fire.

The child began shouting for his father, crying, "Father, come! A great bird is here. A great bird is here eating up our relish!"

To this the great bird answered, "Chu-chu, chu-chu, chu-chu," meaning by this: "I, the hunter, have swallowed meat."

After he had eaten, he returned to the woods, changed back into a hunter, and picked up his duyker from where he had hidden it. He came to his wife's field late, but still found his wife waiting for him, although the sun had already gone down.

When they reached the village they found that nearly all the meat which they had left cooking had been eaten. There were only bones, with a little meat attached to them, left in the pot.

They asked the boy, "What has happened today? Where is the meat? Tell us, son, who ate all this meat?"

The boy replied, "I shouted and shouted for father, for a great bird came in here and ate all the meat."

Hearing this, the boy's mother and even his father became very angry. They said to him, "What are we all going to eat today?" Then they and the others who ate with them ate the little meat that was left in the pot. They explained to the others who ate in their house, "Today there is no relish, for some great bird came here today and ate all the meat."

These same events occurred every day for six days. The woman became irritable and cross. The man too became grouchy and complained much.

Finally the woman had a thought. She said, "I am going to look for a small bow with arrows, and I shall give them to the boy, so that when the great bird comes again he can shoot it." Even he who was the great bird thought this a good idea. He believed that he would not be harmed by any arrow-shooting the small child could do. Believing this, he gave the boy a small bow and charged him: "Today, if you see the great bird come, you are to shoot it with these arrows if you can."

The parents went away to the fields. When they had reached the wife's field the hunter left her and went off into the bush, saying to her, "Since the great bird keeps eating our meat, I must go hunting again." When he had gone into the woods he killed an animal. He hid it in the bush, went back into the village, and began eating the meat in the pot, as he had done on previous days. While he was eating the meat the child took up his small bow and shot the great bird with an arrow, so that the great bird died. The boy dragged the great bird to the back of the room, into a corner. Although the body was changed into that of a bird, the thighs seemed still to be those of a person.[6]

The woman was in the field. When the sun was about to set she saw that the man still had not come. So she picked up the basket of food she had gathered in the field and started home, thinking, "Now what could have happened to him?"

When she reached the village she found that the meat relish was all there. It had not been eaten by the great bird.

She asked the boy, "My child, how have you been today? Have you seen your father?"

The boy said, "I have not seen my father, but today the great bird came, the one that has been eating our meat every day, and I killed it. I shot it with my arrow. Mother, do you not see that all the meat is still in the pot today?"

[6] The thigh of an ostrich resembles that of a man.

The mother said, "Where is the bird? Let me see it."

The child pointed to the corner. As the woman looked at the great bird she realized that it was really her husband. Then she began to weep and grieve, crying, "Oh! My husband is dead. It was he who was eating the meat!"

a hunter seeks meat for his wife

Once there was a hunter who married a wife. The woman had meat hunger, so after a time she said to her husband, "Husband, I cannot endure my meat hunger. Can't you go and kill something for me? I am seized with a great hunger for meat." This sent the man to the woods to hunt.

One day he was setting a snare and did not have a good grip on the trigger. The spring released, caught the hunter himself, and jerked him into the air, where he hung and died.

He had been a hunter who hunted with dogs. His dogs knew that he was dead, and began to howl loudly. After they had howled, the dogs tried to carry away the corpse of their master. They kept dragging him some distance and then resting. Soon a little bird began to sing this song:

> Tee-ay, tee-ay, tee-ay. Tee-ay, tee-ay, tee-ay.
>
> Tell the hungering wife
>
> Her man was caught in a snare
>
> And the snare has taken his life.
>
> His dogs tried to carry the corpse.
>
> Because they cannot do it, they wail.
>
> O wail, wail, wail for your master, wail!

The dogs joined in the song and howled their part of it. The little bird sang on, to lead the song for the dogs:

> Bird: Tee-ay, tee-ay, tee-ay. Tee-ay, tee-ay, tee-ay.
>
> Dogs: Go tell the hungering wife.
>
> Birds: Tee-ay, tee-ay, tee-ay. Tee-ay, tee-ay, tee-ay.

Dogs: Go tell the jealous wife,
              Corpse is too much for dogs to carry.

Bird: Too much to carry, too much to carry, to carry.

Dogs: To carry, to carry home our master.

Bird: Wail, wail, O wail! Wail, wail, wail!

When the dogs later came into the village dragging their burden, all the people in the village were astounded, but especially the woman. Then she confessed her fault and said, "If I had not had meat hunger, my husband would not have died."

a bee hunter and his wife

One day a hunter went out to place a beehive in its tree.

He came into the woods, and when he had bound the two halves of the beehive together, he fastened his braided rope to the hive and the other end of the rope to his belt, and climbed the tree until he came to the place where the hive was to be fixed. Then he pulled the hive up. When he had it up with him, he started to place it where it belonged. Before he had finished placing it well, he looked down and saw a herd of wart hogs running toward his tree. Before he could reach the ground, the wart hogs arrived at the foot of the tree, picked up his gun, and ran away with it. When the hunter reached the ground he ran very fast after them. When he neared them, the wart hogs went into a burrow.

The hunter dropped down on his hands and knees and crawled into the burrow after them. As he advanced into the burrow he saw a gate before him. When he went through it he came to a men's clubhouse. There he found many men, even some of his own relatives. Among these was his uncle, who spoke to him and asked, "My son, what brought you here?"

The hunter answered, "The wart hogs grabbed my gun and ran away with it. I ran after them. They came here, and I came after them to this village."

His uncle said, "Haka! They are insolent! They were sent

to another place, but instead of going there, they went and grabbed your gun. It does not make any difference, for tomorrow you shall have your gun."

When it became dark in the evening, the hunter's uncle said to him, "Let us go now, and I shall show you into the house where you are to spend the night." When they came into the house, the uncle told him, "When you lie down, wrap yourself up well, including your head. When it becomes light in the morning, and your fellow sleepers have gone out, then you may get up and come out to the clubhouse, where you will receive your gun."

At daybreak, he uncovered his head. Then he saw that his fellow lodgers were bones, nothing but bones. He covered his head again. When it was quite light, he uncovered his head again, and when he looked, there were no bones there. He came out and went to the clubhouse. His uncle gave him his gun and said to him, "Take your gun. Since you slept with hunger, take this tick-bird hen. When you come to your village, eat it all by yourself, and do not give any of it to anyone else. Moreover, if on any day you tell anyone what you have seen here, on that very day you shall die."

He took his gun and the heron and left. When he came to the mouth of the burrow, he dropped down on his hands and knees and came out through the hole.

When he came to the village, he killed the tick-bird hen and put it on to cook. His relatives, who had searched for him in the woods, rejoiced to find him safely returned. When his wife came back from the fields and found her husband home and cooking a fowl, she was pleased and said, "This evening, we shall have chicken gravy." When the fowl had been cooked, the man ate it all and shared none of it with anyone else. His wife became angry that her husband had shared none of the chicken with her. She said to him, "Now tell me why you cheated me out of the chicken."

The man said, "I did not do it for any reason."

The wife scolded her husband, saying to him, "If you do not explain this to me, I will kill myself as a protest against you. From the time that you married me, I have never been stingy with you at all, in anything."

The man said to her, "Now dear, do not let this be a source of trouble. Go and fetch your relatives, so that all of you may hear about it at once."

The next morning, the woman went to summon her relatives. They came that evening. The man killed a large hog, cut it up, put it in a pot, and cooked it. When it was daylight the next morning, he called all the guests, including the women[7] guests, to come and have breakfast. When they had finished eating, they assembled to hear the case. The man began by stating his side of the case. He said: "Now listen, and I shall tell you why I deprived my wife of her share of the fowl. On the morning of the day that I went hunting, I left the village, and when I came to the woods, I bound up my beehive and climbed a tree to put it in place. Just as I was doing this, a drove of wart hogs came along under the tree. They picked up my gun and ran off with it. I came down from the tree and ran after them, until they went into a hole in the ground. I got down on my hands and knees and went after them into the burrow. I went along until I came to a gate. I went through the gate and to a men's clubhouse. At the men's clubhouse I found a crowd of men, among whom were some of my relatives. Among these was my uncle, who asked me, 'Why did you come here?' I told him that the wart hogs picked up my gun and came with it into this village. My uncle said, 'Stop for the night, and you will get your gun in the morning.' That evening my uncle took me to a house. He said to me, 'When you lie down, cover yourself up, including your head. When it is daylight, you may uncover yourself again.' At daybreak I uncovered my head, and I saw nothing but bones and bones in the house. Then I covered my head again. When it was broad daylight, I came out and went to the clubhouse. My uncle gave me my gun, at the same time saying, 'Take your gun. And since you slept with hunger, take this tick-bird hen with you, to eat when you come to the village. When you eat this fowl, do not give any of it to anyone. If you do, or if you tell what you saw here, you shall die.' That is why I was stingy with my wife." When he had said this, the man died.

The relatives of the man seized the family of the woman, and all her relatives became slaves.

[7] It is the custom among the Ovimbundu for men to eat at the clubhouse, apart from the women.

goodhearted ngeve, kindhearted chilombo

Some villagers were holding a three-day festival for beer-drinking and dancing.

A man came to the festival, looked at a woman standing apart by a fence, saw that she was beautiful, and said to her, "Do we sleep together tonight?"

"Yes sir," replied the woman, promising to sleep with him.

The man gave her his umbrella to hold for him, and later in the evening he returned to her and took her with him to the house where he was sleeping. Here they lay together talking, and the man said to her, "Perhaps it is possible that you will agree to marry me?" The woman quickly agreed to this.

Later the woman told him that they must postpone the marriage ceremony for some time, since there was not time for her to go home to her village now. It was already planting time and her village was so far away that she must stay and cultivate a field in this village during planting time. After that, she could go home to her village for marriage ceremonies. And so they planted a field there.

One day the man noticed that termites had eaten part of the broom in their house. He said, "Mba! [8] These termites! I shall burn up these termites."

The woman heard this and said to him, "Never dare to say that you will burn up white ants."

Another day the woman had cooked a pot of relish. After the relish had cooked, she set the pot aside to cool. Later, a spider spun a web across the top of the pot. The man saw this and said, "This miserable spider here! I shall throw it in the fire, for it has become a nuisance."

The woman heard him say this and again she spoke to him, saying, "Never, at any time, are you to say, 'I shall throw a spider into the fire.'"

On another day the woman took corn to the pounding rock to pound it into meal. When she had pounded the meal, she spread it out to dry on the rock. She sat down to rest, while she

[8] See the Glossary at the back of this volume.

kept watch over the meal. She looked up and saw a whirlwind
approaching. She watched it, hoping that it would pass either to
one side or to the other, but she saw that the whirlwind was
heading straight for her meal. When it came to the rock the
whirlwind sucked up the meal and carried it away.

When she came back to the village, the man asked, "Where
did the meal go?"

She replied and said, "The meal went with the whirlwind."

When the man heard this, he was very angry and said, "I
am going to go and punish that whirlwind."

The woman admonished him: "Never dare to be angry at
a whirlwind. It is the nature of things that they do some in-
convenient thing to us at some time. On another occasion things
will do something to please you."

At another time they had planted a field. The shoots came
up after seven days. Three days later, when the plants were well
started, an ant-bear came in the night searching for termites and
destroyed the whole field of corn. The man was angry when
he discovered this and said, "As for this ant-bear, I shall dig it
out and kill it."

Once more the woman spoke to him and said, "Dear, do
not do that, but love it. Some day you will see what an ant-bear
can do for you."

Another day there were many flies about, and they were
alighting on the man's food. This also irritated him. He said,
"I shall kill these flies."

The woman quickly advised him, "Never try to kill flies,
for some day you will see what flies will do for you, and then
you will be glad to have them." The man followed the advice
which the woman so frequently gave him.

Finally there came a day when the woman announced, "I
am going to our village right away."

The man replied, "What about me? When you have gone
away, how shall I know whether you have gone to stay or will
come back? How am I to follow you, in case you do not come
back?"

She answered him, "I shall not stay. I plan to stop there
only two days. If you see that three days have gone by and I
have not returned, then come for me. Just go along the path
asking for the village of Goodhearted Ngeve, Kindhearted Chilombo. The people along the way will give you directions, so

you will not get lost, but will come to it." The man agreed to
do this.

When he had waited the three days and the woman had not
returned, he set out to follow her. After he had traveled far
without receiving any satisfactory answer when he asked directions, he became tired and sat down upon a log lying beside the
path. As he sat resting, he noticed a white ant running about on
the log. The white ant asked him a question: "You, sitting there,
where are you going?"

The man replied to the question of the white ant: "I am
going to the stem of the giant mushroom where Goodhearted
Ngeve, Kindhearted Chilombo lives."

The white ant replied, "Behold, you have come there already. Just climb onto my back." The man mounted the termite's back, and the termite went under the ground. When they
came into the underground, the man saw a large and extensive
village. The termite had him dismount. After he had waited
there for some time, he saw a boy coming his way. The man
asked the boy, "Is this Ketaholua Kelanga Landambi, where
Goodhearted Ngeve, Kindhearted Chilombo lives?"

The boy answered, "Yes indeed. This is the place. But
what brings you here?"

To this question the man replied, "I come here because
Goodhearted Ngeve, Kindhearted Chilombo is my wife, and I
have come looking for her." The boy ran to the men's clubhouse and told the elders that a man waited outside. The elders
said, "Fetch him in."

When the man came inside, the elders asked him, "Where
do you wish to go?"

The man said to them, "I am going to Ketaholua Kelanga
Landambi where Goodhearted Ngeve, Kindhearted Chilombo
lives."

The elders said, "You have arrived. Indeed this is the place,
and you are our guest." They took his small bundle and lodged
him in a storehouse.

Then the head of the village summoned his servants and
told them to go and kill one of the fowls[9] reserved for guests. As
the servants had been told, they went and killed the ox which

[9] It is the custom to serve chickens and other fowls to guests, but kings and
wealthy men might have an ox or a hog killed for a person they wish to honor, and
call the ox or hog "a fowl."

had been indicated by the king. Now this fowl was a large and very fat bullock. They cooked the whole ox, even the hide and horns. The mess filled four very large pots. They built a big hot fire about the pots so that the meat would cook quickly and be ready by afternoon. Just before sunset they stirred up corn meal, to make mush to go with the meat. They filled three large basins such as are used for bathtubs with this mush. Assuming that the guest would be very hungry by this time, the king said to the servants, "Go and take this little food to the guest."

When the servants presented this food to the guest, he gave hearty thanks for it. But he was disturbed to see such a heap of mush and the flesh of a whole ox. He could think of no way to eat all this food. While he puzzled over this, an ant-bear came into the hut and dug a great burrow in the ground under the hut. Then the ant-bear said to the man, "Do not be discouraged. Just dump all the food into this burrow. Save a little of the mush and some of the liver to eat, and dump the rest down the hole. Then I shall fill up the hole and tamp down the earth. When you wash your hands, let the water fall on the spot and then pat it down well." After the man had done all this, he sat down and waited.

Later he sensed that the servants of the king were coming. They came to the house and said, "The king sent us, saying, 'Go fetch the dishes, so that you may wash them, for the sun has set already.'"

The man said to them, "That is good." Then he gave them the containers. The servants looked around to see if he had put any food on the floor, or if there was any mess. They could see no food or mess.

When they returned to the king, he asked them, "Did you find nothing in the containers?"

They answered the king, "We could find nothing in the containers. We looked about the house, but saw nothing. We did not find even a bone there."

Later in the evening, the men of the village plotted against the guest. They said, "Tomorrow let the stranger be asked to fell that big tree of ours. Everyone knows that it is the despair of all. No one has ever touched it with an ax, for even to look at it is frightening."

Shortly after this a fly came to the guest and said to him, "I come to give you information. I was in the men's clubhouse when they made a plot against you, saying, 'Tomorrow morning when it is light, we shall test our guest.' This is what they will ask you to do: You will be asked to fell a real ox of a tree, a tree so large that the people think it can never be cut down. The ax that they will give you for this is a small ceremonial ax that is not even sharp. When they summon you to this tree-felling test, they will look upon you as a person who has already struck his last blow. When you come to the tree, first look for a spot where the tree borer has dropped its droppings. Aim the blow of your little ax at that spot. You will see that the tree will fall down. When you are felling this tree you must strike only once, for they have sworn to kill you if you hit the tree twice before it falls down."

When it was light in the morning, the king ordered a royal proclamation: "All persons, hear ye well! All persons will remain in the village today, to accompany the stranger when he goes to our famous tree to see if he can cut it down. We have always thought that no one could cut it down."

To this all the people answered: "Indeed that is the truth. If he fails we shall kill him."

When the guest left the village all the people of the village followed him. When they had come outside the village, the people pointed out the tree of the test. The girth of this tree was equal to that of a really large baobab tree. They gave the guest the ceremonial ax to be used, and told him to hit the tree only once, for if he hit the tree a second time his fate would be decided. The man took the ceremonial ax and went around the tree looking for the place where the tree borer had dropped its droppings. When he found this place, he took the handle of the little ax in both hands and struck the tree at that place. When he struck it, the tree fell down. All the people shouted, "Hoo-oo-oo!" Then they all went back to the village together. The man rejoiced. He said, "Today I escaped death."

Later, when they talked the matter over in the men's club-house, the men of the village said, "What are we going to do next?" They deliberated and finally said, "Let us have him named to go and put a bridge across the river for us, a bridge across the river which we have never been able to bridge." This river was as large as the Katombela River.

That evening the fly came to him once more and said, "They plan to say to you tomorrow morning, 'The guest must go and build a bridge across the river. We shall cross the river at the ford, and at the time for returning we expect to have the bridge completed. If we do not find the bridge ready, we shall kill the guest.' "

As soon as it was light in the morning, the king made a formal announcement: "Today let all the people go down to the river and cross it at the ford. At the time for the return we shall expect to find a bridge built by the guest."

Then all the people shouted and said, "This is the thing to do! This is the right thing for the guest to do!"

When the guest came to the river, he found Spider, who said to him, "Do not be excited over nothing. Set two strong posts in the ground at this side of the river, the right distance apart for supporting a large bridge. Then take me on your back and carry me across to the other side of the river, and there set up two other strong posts in the same way. Just leave the rest to me." The man immediately did as Spider directed. Then Spider went to work spinning, coming and going. When the time came for the people to return from the fields, the bridge was completed.

When the men gathered in the clubhouse that evening, they prepared another plot to test the guest. They announced: "Tomorrow the guest may rest, but first he must sweep the whole village for us. Sweep it so clean that we cannot find any trash at all inside the stockade." Soon a whirlwind came from the east and swept the whole village, taking away the trash. The whole village was swept clean, just as the villagers had demanded.

That same afternoon the men of the village took counsel together, and this time they said, "Tomorrow we shall have the guest point out the house in which his wife, Goodhearted Ngeve, Kindhearted Chilombo is."

When this had been announced, the fly came to him again, and told him, "They have plotted this against you: You must point out the house in which your wife is. Do not be concerned about this, for tomorrow I shall go and roll in the ashes at the clubhouse. When you go out for this test, I shall sit on your nose. When I leave your nose, and go and alight on a house, then and only then, point to that house."

In the morning when it was light, the men of the village came to the guest and said, "Today you are to go and point out for us the house in which your woman is." The village was very

large, as broad as from Elende to Chinjenje.[10] The villagers and
their guest went out and began to walk among the houses. As
they walked, the man noticed that the fly left his nose, went to
a certain house, and alighted on it. The man pointed to that
house and said, "Goodhearted Ngeve, Kindhearted Chilombo,
come out."

The woman came out. Then they all went to the clubhouse
where the men presented the man with a shovel, a hoe and an ax,
telling him: "Take your wife. Here she is. But if she should
die, do not bury her."

After this ceremony, the two, the man and his wife, left
the place. When they came to their[11] home country, they found
that the people had deserted the village and built in another
place. When the two of them came to the abandoned village,
they went to their house to sleep for the night.

In the morning the man tried to awaken his wife, but found
that she was dead. Then he took the hoe, spade and ax, dug a
grave, and buried her. After the burial, he decided to return to
his house.

When he came back to the house, he found that the corpse
of his wife was already there before him. Then he went and
buried her once more. After he had repeated this three times, he
mounted his ox and fled away to rejoin his own people.

[10] About eighteen miles, certainly a fantasied width for a village.
[11] It is his and not her village to which they return, since a married couple resides
in the man's village. "Their home country" means "the home country of his people
and family." Only plural pronouns are used in such cases, since the individual speaks
of himself as a member of his people.

9. jealousy between wives

a man's two wives

Once there were two women, the wives of one man. One of these women died.

One day the woman who remained went to the grave of the dead wife, knocking on the grave, "Tap, tap, tap," and challenging the dead: "Come out and let us revile each other with the words of our mutual jealousy. As you are a woman, come out!"

The dead woman replied from the grave: "I left the young men in the conference house to you. I left the girls in the kitchen to you. Let us bow to the ultimate decisions of fate. O whirlwind [1] mine, come and whip this woman for me!" A whirlwind of great force came from the east. It beat the woman, "whirl, whirl, whirl," tearing her clothing to tatters.

When the whirlwind had passed, the woman returned to the village. The people in the village asked the woman, "Why do you come in this torn condition? What happened to you?"

"I thought that I would go out and get some roots for making beer," she told them. "A dizziness came upon me, so that I just circled round and round. My body was all weak, and I had no strength at all. I could not travel, but just went bumbling around in the bush until my clothes were all torn in this way." Her children were troubled about this story, and so was their father.

Another day she told her children to go to the fields by themselves, that she was going out to look for roots for making beer. But instead, she returned once more to the grave of her

[1] In the Benguela highlands, whirlwinds are a common occurrence of the dry season and are believed to be driven by some ghost.

rival. She knocked upon it, "Tap, tap, tap." Then she said, "Wake up! Let us revile each other with the words of our jealousy. As you are a woman, come out." The woman beneath the grave was silent and did not come out. And so the woman above the ground knocked once more upon the grave, "Tap, tap, tap," and said, "Wake up! Let us revile each other in the name of our jealousy."

To this second challenge, the dead woman replied, "I left the young men in the conference house to you. I left the girls in the kitchen to you. Let us bow to the decision of fate. O whirlwind mine, come and whip this woman for me." The whirlwind came again from the east, whirled with great force, and whipped the woman, "Whirl, whirl, whirl," until her clothing was torn in rags.

When she came into the village, the villagers were again astonished and asked her, "Look at you! How did this happen?"

And again she replied, "My misfortunes! My misfortunes! I went out to dig some beer roots, and while I was digging there came a great whirlwind. I did not see it coming and only knew that I was engulfed by it and that it whipped me until my clothes were all torn, as you see them."

The villagers were astounded and said, "Hear her! This is some ghost, some work of magic!"

These same events happened to her three times, and a fourth time. Still she would not give up going to her rival's grave. She told her children, "Go off to the fields without me, for today I am going to dig beer roots, even though I have seen portents[2] when I went to dig them in the past." And she went to the grave as she had done before.

Reaching the grave, she knocked upon it and implored the dead woman to come out, as she had done in the past. The woman in the grave was silent. She knocked and implored a second time. Still the woman in the grave was silent. So for a third time she knocked upon the grave, this time saying: "By your womb,[3] I call on you to wake up. Let us revile each other because of our jealousy."

When this had been spoken, the corpse emerged from the

----

[2] "Seeing portents" is a common expression, meaning to see something unusual, which is interpreted to be a divine warning, not connected with human magic.

[3] *Ngandi yove*, translated "womb," is used among women as a deadly insult. *Ngandi yene*, which means "womb-relative," has no such connotation of insult.

grave clad in its decomposing burial mats, leaped upon the back of the living woman, and cried out, "Let us two go. Let us go to the tomb in Chilenge. Let us go to the burial place of the heads, to the place where they bury the heads of kings." [4]

Then the woman said to the corpse, "Now, now dear, just stay here, for the children may become frightened."

But the corpse kept on, and said, "Let us go. Let us go to the tomb in Chilenge, to the place where they bury the heads of the kings." So thus they went, the one begging for mercy and the other unrelenting, until they came to the edge of the village.

At the edge of the village the woman stopped and said to the corpse, "Now dear, just be merciful to me and stop here. I, for my part, what shall I do? On no day shall I ever bother you in your grave again. From here on let us stop our jealousy. Oh my relative, if I shall go with you into the village, the people are going to be frightened, and then because of the fear they are going to run away."

Still the corpse kept right on saying, "Let us two go. Let us go to the tomb in Chilenge, to the place where they bury the heads of the kings."

jealous wives

Once, one of a man's two wives noticed that the husband came to her house infrequently.[5]

She brooded over this. One night she left her house and went out into the woods, saying to herself, "I am going out and kill myself." She took her child on her back and her hoe in her hand. As she walked toward the woods she came to a small stream. There were toads in the stream singing:

Go away, go away.

Go away, go away.

[4] By tradition, a select committee strangled a king who showed incompetence or old age. They then buried his body in a sacred grove, but placed his head in a box which was put away in a cave with the heads of preceding kings.

[5] Among the Ovimbundu, plural wives live in separate houses or huts, all near each other in the husband's compound. The husband is expected to sleep with each on a rotation system which keeps him with each for either four or seven consecutive nights.

They stopped singing and fell into silence when she neared the stream. She crossed the stream and walked on.

After she had walked a short distance into the woods the toads began singing again:

> Go away, go away.
>
> Go away, go away.

When she had walked still farther into the woods she noticed that the toads had again stopped singing. Fear overcame her, for she heard what she imagined were lions following her. To escape the lions, she climbed a tall, tall tree, taking her child and her hoe up with her. As she waited in the tree top, trembling, she saw that what was approaching was a caravan of people, bringing a herd of cattle with them. Carriers were holding poles from which hung live hogs, each carried by two men. They were also carrying hogs which had already been killed and scraped.

When the caravan reached the tree which the woman had climbed, the men stopped under the tree and put down their loads. As they sat beneath the tree and the woman waited up in it, her child urinated, and the water falling down upon the men surprised them. One of them asked the others, "What is that which is wetting us in this way?"

Another man said, "There must be a galago[6] up in this tree."

Next the child defecated. When the excrement fell down upon the head of one of the men he said, "Now that beast has gone and messed on my head!"

The others said, "Yes, it must be a galago all right."

After the soiled man had felt his head and smelled his fingers he said, "This excrement is human!"

But the others said, "No, no. That is from a galago. How could a person be out here in the woods in a tree top? When have you ever found anyone sleeping up in a tree?"

During the talk that followed one of the men said, "Listen to me! The flesh of the galago is a delicacy. It is most delicious. I am going to climb up the tree and catch this galago." Having

---

[6] The galago is an arboreal, nocturnal lemuroid, about the size of a rabbit, with beautiful gray fur, bushy tail, large eyes, and a piercing cry altogether out of keeping with its small size and mild appearance.

said this, the man began to climb the tree. When he reached the branches he began to grope about for the galago. The woman began to think about what she should do. Taking the hoe in both hands, she brought it down hard on the head of the galago hunter who was climbing up toward her.

Then the woman screamed from the tree top, "Now your time has come, you robbers! It is all finished for you! My friends gathering to attack the robbers, listen to me! Those of you upstream come along by the foot of the hill. Those downstream spread out through the woods. Hurry! And keep silent as you surround the robbers! I alone, here in the tree top, shall direct you. Everyone else closing in on the robbers keep silent! Steal in on the robbers silently from all sides. Hurry!" And in her loudest voice she added, "Now you robbers are finished!"

While she was making this loud noise she heard the retreating robberts shouting: "We have left! Give us just a moment! All we want is to escape. Only one of us is still there, and he is dead. Take our wealth. All we wish is to be alive to go and steal more."

The woman came down from the tree. Since none of the robbers came back, she left their loot under the tree for the night and went back to the village. She went straight to the house in which her husband was sleeping. She knocked on the door of the house and said, "Husband, wake up! Come out right now, so that I may tell you of the wealth which I have secured for you."

When the man was awake he answered her, "You! What have you gotten for me, you bitch? It is jealousy that is stirring your fat buttocks awake at this night hour! Don't argue with me, or I will come out and give you some hard blows with my staff."

Still the woman continued urging him to come out, saying, "Husband, please, do me just this one favor. Come out and call all the men of the village to follow me and see what wealth I have acquired for you."

"You bitch with your jealousy!" said her husband. "You are an animal! If I do get up and go out, and call out all the men in the village, and then it turns out that you have aroused me for nothing: then today will mark the end of your life."

"No, husband, no, you will not be disappointed," she said. "Go wake up all the men of the village."

So the man went to call out all the men of the village, saying to them, "Kinsmen, come out as a favor to me. Join me in going into the woods with this bitch I married, whom you see has waked me up at this hour. If she has nothing in the woods worth waking us up to see, then I know what I will do to her. Tonight will mark the end of her life."

All the men followed the woman as she started toward the woods. One had an ax; another a knobkerry; another a sword; and another a gun. Since it was still night, all carried such weapons as they could find. The woman went before them until they reached the place, and there she found that the fire the robbers had left was burning low. The cattle were still inside a makeshift corral, bales of cloth were lying scattered about, some pork cracklings were still sizzling in a pot, the live hogs were still tied, and the dressed and scraped hogs were still on the ground. There was much wealth, wearing apparel, and even money. Everything was scattered about, for the robbers had left in great haste, dropping everything when they fled.

When her husband grasped the extent of the booty, he began shouting loudly and blowing a whistle. The woman said, "Who is that, blowing his little whistle, 'peep, peep'? Is that you, my husband? Do you like what I have here for you?"

The man answered her, "Oh wife, our little pond will never go dry, and that is a fact. Ah-h-h hee-eee! It was I who brought you to the men's house and to our village. You are perfect. Come sit here close to me so that I can hug you. Oh my wife, my helper! Now let me go and arrange the loading for the wealth to be carried to the village. But you remain sitting here so that you will not tire yourself." The man had all the wealth arranged for transport to the village, making certain that nothing would be left behind.

They returned to the village in jubilation. When they reached the village the husband made payments to all those men who had carried loads for him.

From that time onward the man gave all his love to this woman. He slept in her house every night and did not go to the house of his other woman at all.

When the other wife suffered this treatment, she in her turn became jealous. She said to herself, as the other woman had earlier, "I shall go away and kill myself." She took her child upon her back and started for the woods. When she approached the little stream she heard the toads singing:

> Go away, go away.
>
> Go away, go away.

After she had passed the stream, the toads stopped singing. This silence frightened her, and she heard what she imagined were lions following her. She was so afraid that she was unable to climb a tree. So she found a small cave and went into it. In this cave were lion's cubs, who began to lick the baby which the woman had on her back. There really had been lions following her, and she had crawled into their den. The lions had found her scent and were following it in haste. The scent led them straight to their own den.

Since the lions did not believe that a person would enter their den, they circled further to regain the scent, but could not find any further human scent. They came back to their den, backed into it, and crouched looking out to watch for any movements of a person in the woods. While they were looking out into the woods the woman took a small bell which the child had as his plaything, and working slowly, tied it tight to the tail of one of the lions. When she had fastened the bell tightly she pulled the lion's tail. The lion whipped his tail away, making the bell ring. The sound of the bell so frightened the lions that they loped hurriedly away from their den. The one that had the bell on his tail said, "What is this that has me by the tail?" The lions were so alarmed that they even fled from each other. They ran far away into the woods.

The woman crawled out of the cave and hurried back to her own house again. Her chief desire was to escape being eaten by the lions. As for finding something which would please her husband, the lions were not it.

two sisters and the younger sister's child

Two sisters, Chilepa[7] and Chilombo,[8] had married men of
the same village.

One day Chilepa, the older sister, said to Chilombo, "Sister,
come, let us go and visit our home country. We have not been
home since we were married. That is a long time to be away
without returning home." To reach their homeland they would
need to sleep once on the journey and travel until sunset on the
second day.

When Chilombo's husband heard of this plan he said to the
sisters, "Postpone this visit, for the present. Later, we shall all
go together and shall carry gifts for your family."

After hearing this, Chilepa said to Chilombo, "No, it will
not do to postpone this visit as Brother-in-law has suggested, for
we have already stayed away too long. If you postpone the visit,
Chilombo, I will leave you behind and go alone."

Chilombo replied, "I will not stay behind. I wish to make
the visit, and since you are the older, I should not make the
visit unless we go together."

After they had decided the matter they made preparations
for the journey. Chilombo, the younger sister, had one child,
Chimuma, two years old and not yet able to talk. Chilepa was
the mother of twins who were still quite young. The sisters prepared cold mush and boiled sweet potatoes as their food for the
road.

Carrying their food on their heads and their children on
their backs, they entered the path. After they had traveled the
distance drained by two streams,[9] Chilepa said to her younger
sister, "Put down that child of yours, Chimuma, and carry one
of my children."

[7] This name means "the tall one."
[8] The most common name among the Ovimbundu.
[9] Distances are commonly described in terms of the number of streams crossed.
The distance between two streams is a rather irregular and flexible measure of
distance. Another common measure of distance employed in this story is the
number of nights one must sleep while journeying.

"If I put down my child, who will carry her?" replied Chilombo. "She is not able to walk at all."

The older sister became violently angry and said, "Put her down on the ground and leave her in the path! Then take my child on your back." Since her older sister had spoken with such anger, Chilombo lowered her child to the ground and took her older sister's child upon her back. They started away, leaving Chimuma behind on the path.

The child stood up and called after her mother, screaming "Ee-eee," screaming that she was being betrayed, and demanding in baby talk that she be taken back to her "dada" [10] or at least that her "mai" [10] wait for her.

Chilombo said, "Sister, my child is crying," and then she called back to Chimuma, "O my child, do not cry."

Chilepa said, "We are going on. Will you remain behind, saying 'My child, My child?'" They went on, leaving the child behind.

Chimuma, trying to follow, was falling down and bumping herself. Still she came along, crying all the while. Later she traveled on all fours like an ox. Then she sat down flat on the ground, hitching along by pulling herself, getting scratched and bruised. But luck was with her, for after dark she reached the place on the path where her mother had stopped to sleep. When she came to her mother, her mother wept. Chilombo said, "I am bringing my child into my bed."

But Chilepa would not allow it and said, "Leave that thing outside." Chimuma kept pulling and pulling at her mother's clothing, but Chilepa would not allow this either, so Chimuma cried and complained all night long.

In the morning they ate breakfast, but Chimuma was given only a little to eat. As they were taking up their loads Chilombo said, "Now I am going to talk with my child."

And Chilepa replied, "What do you intend to do with that thing, your child? We are leaving now, and if you don't move along and leave it behind, I shall beat you." They started away.

After they had moved away a short distance, a man traveling along the path behind them came upon the child, complaining bitterly as she dragged herself along, bruising her bottom. When the man saw the child's situation he took pity and called

[10] The children of the Ovimbundu employ these babytalk terms for father and mother.

out to the sisters, "You women, ahead there, stop!" He lifted up the child, carried her to the women, and said to the sisters, "Whose child is this?"

"She is my child," said Chilombo.

"Surely you are lying," said the man, "or why would you leave her behind in such misery?"

Then Chilombo explained to him, "My older sister, Chilepa here, is the one having things done in this way. When I protested, 'I am going to carry my child,' she would not allow it. She became angry and threatened to beat me. Just this minute, when I looked back to where my child was weeping, she scolded me. I did not leave my child behind because I did not care for her, but to avoid trouble with my older sister. What ought I to do?"

Hearing this, the man grabbed Chilepa and beat her until she thought that she would be killed. Then the man gave Chimuma to her mother so that she might nurse. When Chimuma had nursed, he took her upon his shoulders and carried her, leaving Chilombo to follow carrying her basket of food upon her head. As they were leaving, Chilombo said to Chilepa, "Now, dear, let us go on. Your bruises will be healed when we reach the village. There they will care for you."

The man and Chilombo went on together until they reached Chilombo's village. Chilombo's relatives rejoiced over her coming. Chilombo related how her older sister, Chilepa, had treated her, describing in detail the miseries she and her child had suffered. She also related how the strange man had helped her and beaten Chilepa.

Hearing all of this angered the parents, who thanked the stranger, shaking his hand repeatedly and firing off guns in his honor. Also, the parents killed a hog so fattened that it could not stand, and gave it to the man. This was the hog which had been readied for Chilepa to take back to her husband. The stranger said to Chilombo, "I shall eat this hog here along with you, for we are both guests here. It would be wrong for me to take this hog away with me, for then the hog would seem to be a payment. What I have done for you was not done for payment, but because I wished to help when I saw that you and your child were in a miserable plight with no one to help you." They ate the hog, then tried out and divided the lard. Then the man left them and resumed his journey.

After Chilepa had recovered from her beating, she raised herself up and followed the others. When she arrived, she found that Chilombo and the man had already related how badly she had treated her younger sister. Because of the way she had treated her younger sister, there was no rejoicing upon her arrival. The people were angry with her and spoke harsh words to her, which saddened her. She became even sadder when she discovered that her parents displayed no joy upon seeing her. Neither did her other relatives display any joy upon seeing her.

Everyone entertained Chilombo well, cooking fowls for her. When she left the village of her parents to return to her husband, her family killed another large hog to be carried to her husband, and they provided Chilombo with two young men to accompany her all the way to her husband's house and protect her from any further trouble on the road.

The family gave nothing to Chilepa when she departed. Not even a fowl. Only a little corn meal and some parched corn ground up with salt.[11]

woman's children and woman's beauty

Mother Leopard wished to have the blacksmith forge some hoes for her.

In getting ready for her expedition, Mother Leopard caught the children of Mother Hare. She kidnapped them and put them into a skin bag. When Mother Leopard had done this, she invited Mrs. Hare to accompany her to the blacksmith's. She said to Mother Hare, "I am going to the blacksmith's. Will you go along with me and carry a bundle for me? We shall travel together,

---

[11] The native informant who provided this story went on to give this interpretation of its motives and moral: "The reason for Chilepa's actions was this: She was jealous of her younger sister, who was more robust, had a healthier child, and had better clothing than she herself. Her children were puny. So she said to herself, 'If my younger sister goes along with her child, when we reach our village everyone will admire her and her child instead of admiring me.' For this reason she did not wish to have Chimuma arrive. Like much meanness, her plan was unintelligent and certain to be uncovered to her disadvantage. When her plan had gone wrong she arrived in disgrace and unappreciated. On the other hand, Chilombo encountered joy and welcome. Chilepa had wished to say to herself, 'I am loved especially, more than my sister Chilombo.' It did not work out that way. She planned to magnify herself, but she was belittled."

and you are not to untie the bundle on the way." Mother Hare agreed.

They started off and went along the dry bed of a stream.

Soon they met Honey Bird, who was going down the water course. Mother Hare said to Mother Leopard, "Since you are one of the top society, it would be improper for you to pass one of your set without accompanying her for at least a short distance. You will show disrespect for her if you do not do this." Mother Leopard agreed that her station required this. She said to Mother Hare, "What you say is true. I shall accompany her for a way. While I am gone, take good care of my bundle. Do not untie it." Mother Hare agreed to this.

Mother Hare felt concern for her children. With her children on her mind, her interest was aroused by the command not to untie the bundle. When Mother Leopard had left, Mother Hare untied the bundle and found her children in it. She ran back home in haste, hid her children, and put Mother Leopard's children in the bag in their place.

When Mother Leopard returned, they resumed their journey to the blacksmith's. When they arrived at the forge, Mother Leopard talked with the smith and told him that she had brought in her bundle his payment for some hoes she wished him to make for her. She told him, "Do not untie the bundle until we have left, for I do not wish Mother Hare to see what is in the bundle." Mother Leopard did not know that Mother Hare had already looked into the bundle and switched the children. The blacksmith consented.

As the blacksmith worked at the forge, the women took turns working the bellows for him. While Mother Leopard worked the bellows, she sang:

> The fee of the blacksmith
> Is Mother Hare's kits.
> The fee of the blacksmith
> Is Mother Hare's kits.

When Mother Leopard tired, Mother Hare took over the bellows, and she sang:

> Escorting the honey bird
> Was your big mistake.
> Escorting the honey bird
> Was your big mistake.

When Mother Leopard heard this song, she said, "Mother Hare, what is the meaning of that song which you sing as you work the bellows?"

Mother Hare answered, "That is the question. What does the song mean which you sing when you work the bellows?"

So as they worked the bellows, the two sang back and forth. First, Mother Leopard would sing:

> The fee of the blacksmith
> Is Mother Hare's kits.
> The fee of the blacksmith
> Is Mother Hare's kits.

Then as Mother Hare worked the bellows she would reply:

> Escorting the honey bird
> Was your big mistake.
> Escorting the honey bird
> Was your big mistake.

They sang these songs and worked the bellows until the hoes were finished. Then they exchanged farewells with the blacksmith.

After they had left, the blacksmith untied the bundle. He found the children of Mother Leopard inside. He killed them and pegged their hides outside in the sun to dry.

As soon as Mother Leopard came home, she went to look for her children, but could not find them. She hurried back to the blacksmith's forge and found their skins drying in the sun. Mother Leopard was very angry and said, "I put Mother Hare's children into this bundle. When did she take them out and put my children in their place? Some day it will happen that I shall meet Mother Hare. When I do, I will kill her." Mother Leopard watched for Mother Hare.

It happened that Mother Hare had her hair braided in a new style, and the appearance of the braids was very fine. One day after this, Mother Leopard and Mother Hare met. Mother Leopard had been waiting for this meeting to kill Mother Hare, yet now that she saw her, all that she did was say, "O dear Mother Hare! This hairdo of yours! How did you braid it to have it look so very, very well?"

Mother Hare said, "O Aunt, this is easy to do. If you like my braiding, and wish to have it, I shall be pleased to teach you how to plait these fine braids, so that you may do them yourself."

Mother Leopard was very pleased to hear this, and the grudge which she had held against Mother Hare vanished before the pleasure of being taught how to braid such beautiful braids. Mother Hare gave her instructions, saying, "Go and prepare some sharp wooden pins.[12] Make them of iron wood. You should have six pins. When you have them ready, come and tell me, and I shall go and teach you how to use them."

Mother Leopard went to work preparing the pins. Just as she had been instructed by Mother Hare, she made them straight and sharp. As soon as the pins were ready, she sent word to Mother Hare, "I have finished the pins. Come right away to help me and teach me."

When Mother Hare came, she said, "Aunt, it is true that these braids are beautiful, but you cannot have them, unless you brace up to endure what it takes. It is going to hurt a bit, but they will be ruined unless you are prepared to stand it."

Mother Leopard said, "It is all right, niece. Even if it causes me pain, go ahead and braid my hair. It will be the same thing that they did to you." Mother Hare took one of the pins and began to pound it into Mother Leopard's head. Soon Mother Leopard began to yell, "O dear, O Mother Hare, you are ruining me!"

Mother Hare said, "Didn't I tell you that you would have to

---

[12] Long and sharp pins, made of iron, or wood, are actually used in braiding hair. The hair is allowed to grow long, caked with grease, and left to set for weeks, until it is so hardened and caked that a long, sharp skewer is needed to separate it into strands which can be braided.

brace up? This is what they did to me. When I have finished putting in these pins, you will see that you will have beautiful braids." Then Mother Leopard consented, and only groaned while Mother Hare was pounding in the rest of the pins.

After Mother Hare had finished pounding in the pins, Mother Leopard's head began to swell, and it swelled up very large. Her head continued to swell throughout the night. When morning came, it was found that Mother Leopard was dead.

Mother Hare said, "You wicked old woman. You wished to do something bad to me, so I have taught you something."

10. in-laws

the man who wore a mush ladle in his belt

There was a man who went with his wife to visit her family. When they came to the village of the wife's family they were well received by the wife's people. The man was assigned to their guesthouse, and they were well provided with food. That evening they visited with the family. The next morning breakfast was prepared for them. The relish for this meal was bean butter, made from hulled fresh beans, a dish which the man was fond of.

After breakfast the woman went away to the fields with the other women. The son-in-law, since he was a man, stayed in the village to wait for their return in the middle of the day. After the women had gone away to the fields, the man went into his mother-in-law's house to look and see if any of the bean butter had been left uneaten. When he came into the house and looked into the pots, he found that some had been left over and there was a wooden mush ladle still in the pot. He took the relish out of the pot with this ladle. When he had finished eating the relish, he stuck the handle of the ladle under his belt at his back, under the absent-minded impression that it was his ax which he was putting there.

When he returned to the guesthouse, he got his gun, and since he was a hunter, he said, "I am going to the woods to hunt." He thought that, since his wife and her family would not know where he was, he should pass by their field, so they would know where he had gone and would not look for him. When he came to the fields, he called to the family, "I am away to the woods for a hunt." After he had told them this, he went on.

Some of the children in the fields looked at his back as he

left, and they said to their grandmother, "Oo granny, look at our mush ladle. Father has stuck it into his belt behind."

The grandmother said to them, "Hush! You are not telling the truth."

The children protested vigorously and still said: "It is true, and it is no lie. It is true! Won't you just look at his back? Can't you see it? The bean butter that we had this morning is sticking to it." Their grandmother was silent, for she thought that if she should look and see it and speak about it, that it would make their father ashamed.

After waiting for a time the man's wife spoke to her mother and said to her, "Mother, this is a thing which he does regularly. In the village where we live, when one sees him do that, they know that he is possessed by the hunter's spirit."

While he was out in the woods that day, he shot a roan antelope. When he came to the village to announce it, his wife said, "Now mother, don't you see how it is? Isn't that true which I told you at the fields, that in our country when he is seen going off wearing a mush ladle in his belt, it is understood that he is possessed by the hunter's spirit?"

Her mother replied, "Yes, indeed it is true. You said so. You did not lie."

In this way he escaped being shamed before his mother-in-law. From that day on, the mother-in-law believed that when a hunter went out wearing a mush ladle in his belt he was possessed by the hunter's spirit.

imprisoned in mother-in-law's granary by a pig

There was a man who went along with his wife when she visited her family.

They came to the wife's village and received the customary warm welcome. They were put up in the guesthouse, and in the afternoon the wife's family brought them many foods which had been cooked for the guests. In the evening they visited with the wife's family.

The next morning the woman went out to the fields with her mother. About noon the man, who was fond of peanuts, went to his mother-in-law's granary and opened its door,[1] for he knew that she kept peanuts in there. While the man was eating peanuts in the granary, a pig rubbed itself against the pole which held open the outer ends of the door planks. The pole fell, and the door slammed down and locked itself shut.

The man did not see how he could get out, with the door shut. He became worried. He thought that the most important thing was how he would come out of this predicament in the end. Although worried, he kept right on shelling and eating peanuts.

While he was shelling and eating peanuts to pass the time, the women returned from the fields. He heard them throw down their bundles of firewood. One of them went into the house to look for the guest, but he was not there. They did not guess that he was locked in the granary. The mother-in-law became worried and kept saying, "Where has the honored man gone? We must give him food now, for the hunger of the afternoon is real hunger." They put a skillet on the fire and sent a sister of the wife to get some peanuts to roast for the guest.

When the girl came to the granary, she lifted up the ends of the door and propped up these planks with the crotched pole. Looking into the granary, she saw her brother-in-law sitting in there shelling peanuts. They looked at each other. When she saw who was in there, she left hurriedly, went back to the house, and said to the other women, "Before I get the peanuts, I am going to the stream for water. I shall be right back. Let no one go to the granary for peanuts, in my place, for I shall get the peanuts as soon as I get back from the stream. I shall run to the stream." When she went to the stream, she did not shut the granary door, but left it wide open.

On the way back from the stream she dashed her pot of water to the ground, and as it smashed she screamed, "Help! Kidnappers[2] are here! All you in the village, come quickly, I am being kidnapped. Mercy! Come! Kidnappers are here!" When the men heard this, they all came out in haste. One carried

---

[1] The opening into the granary is covered by two or three hand-hewn heavy planks, each separately attached to the top of the doorway. The bottom ends of the planks are pulled outward from the doorway to gain entrance. All of the planks can be propped open by a single pole, and if the planks slam down they will lock into place and can be opened only from the outside.

([2] Kidnappings are conducted to procure slaves or victims for ritual murder. Young girls are valued as slaves, since it is difficult for them to run away.)

an ax, another a sword, another a spear, and another a bow and arrows. All came running out and asked the girl which way the robbers had run. The girl pointed away from the granary and said, "They ran off in that direction."

The brother-in-law came out of the granary, hurried to the guesthouse to get his gun, and then followed all the others who were running toward where the girl was still shouting. When he came with his gun to the place where the girl was standing, he said to her, "O sister-in-law, which way did the robbers run? I shall run after them and shoot one of them, for sister-in-law, they were about to rob me of yourself."

The girl replied, "Brother-in-law, they are far away by now. When I shouted and yelled for you, they ran fast and went away. I am very pleased at the speed with which you came out to save me. If you had not hurried to me, it is certain that I would now be far away with the robbers."

Everyone began to return to the village. When the women had returned to the house, the girl immediately went to the granary to get peanuts. After she had shelled them, she roasted them and took them to her brother-in-law, and he ate them.

He pondered over what he might do to reward his sister-in-law, who undoubtedly had saved him from being shamed before his mother-in-law. When he and his wife were ready to return to their village, he said to his wife, "Let us take sister-in-law back with us. She can live with us in our house and be a help to you." The wife's family agreed for the wife's younger sister to return with them, and so the girl went with them back to their village.

At the time they returned to their village, all the women of the village were pounding meal to be sent to the coast along with the king's trading caravan.[3] When the wife's younger sister heard about the caravan, she said, "I want to go too. I shall go along with my brother-in-law, who can chaperone me." Both the man and his wife agreed to let the younger sister go along, chaperoned by her brother-in-law. After this, they were all busy pounding meal for the caravan.

When it was time for the caravan to leave, the man and his sister-in-law went with it. The caravan came to Benguela. The

[3] Trading was conducted at the coast. It was the custom of kings to send local products to the coast by a caravan, which would trade at the coast and return with valuable goods for the king's treasury. Sometimes, as in this story, a member of the caravan might carry along some product belonging to himself and do some private trading at the coast.

brother-in-law sold the things he had brought with him, and used the proceeds to buy cloth. He bought sixteen yards of cloth and a head kerchief for his wife. He bought fourteen yards of cloth and a head kerchief for his wife's sister, as a reward to her for saving him from being shamed. The cloth for the sister-in-law was not from the same piece as that for the wife. It was of a better quality.

When they returned to the village, and his wife saw the cloth that her young sister had, she was angry. She said to her husband, "How is it that you bought fine cloth for my sister, and it is only a little shorter than my cloth? Perhaps this is not without a meaning. The meaning is that while you were away on this journey, my sister took the place of your wife, and you slept together." The wife was very angry over this. She talked about it on every occasion. The husband became irked that his wife repeated the accusation over and over to everyone. Finally he said to his wife, "You do not trust what I say at all. You still believe that I slept with your sister. Because of this, summon all your family to come here to our house. Then I shall come before them all and explain why I presented my sister-in-law with this piece of cloth. I know that when I have explained the case and defended myself, I am going to die. The responsibility for this will be yours." He repeated, "The blame will be yours."

His wife answered him "How my fault? You will not die at all. This is just one of your crafty tricks, and the only answer is this: Just let her stop saying this. Let her forget it. Really, it is the truth that you slept with your sister-in-law. Indeed, the only thing for me to do is to summon my family and have them come here. You can explain everything at that time. Both of us can state our cases, and then we shall see whether you will die. You are just making threats."

The woman sent for her family to come to their home. The man also sent word to his family for them to come, which they did. The man told them privately what he intended to say, so that they would know what was happening. He told them, "When we have heard this case, I shall die. Because of this woman, I can not continue to live." When his family heard his intention, they decided what they would do. They said, "If our relative actually dies today, this woman will be forfeit. Their whole family will be at an end. We shall take their whole seed, and all of them will be lost."

Later, they brought the case to trial. All the people concerned, old and young, were assembled. They were all present to hear the statement of the case and see who had the right in the case. The husband began by explaining exactly how everything happened when he went to visit his wife's family. He told how he went into the granary of his mother-in-law for peanuts, how his sister-in-law found him there, how she went to the stream, and every other incident of the day. Then he related everything else that had happened, including the trip to Benguela. When he had finished explaining this, he told of the hatred and misunderstanding his wife had developed. When he had told all, he cut his throat and died.

Then the members of his family seized the woman and bound her with rigor.[4] They said to her, "It was you who killed our relative, or he would not be a corpse." Then they tortured her, along with other members of her family. Her whole family surrendered themselves and pledged to go to the rich and raise the funds for the settlement of the case. The family paid as their fine: eight young men, eight girls, and twenty head of cattle. As a result of the wife's jealousy and accusations, her whole family was impoverished. Some of them even became slaves.[5]

the man who insulted his mother-in-law

Once, when a man went to visit his wife's family, he took a small boy along with him.

When he came to the village of his wife's family, he was given a glad welcome. They provided a house for the guest. In the evening they brought him a good meal. It was the rainy season, and the corn in the gardens had mature ears. The man yearned for some roasting ears to bite on.

When it was dark in the evening, the man told the small boy to go to a garden and fetch him a few ears of green corn. The boy refused to do it and would not go. The man decided to

[4] The custom is to "bind with rigor" in such a case, binding the elbows, and not the hands only.

[5] Suicide actually occurs among the Ovimbundu as a form of vengeance. It is believed that the ghost of a suicide will return to haunt and punish those against whom the suicide has been committed.

go and get the corn himself. As he was leaving he charged the child, "I am going out to snap off some ears of corn. While I am away, I want you to keep the fire burning brightly in the fireplace, so that the house will be lit up when I come back, and I shall know which is our house and not miss it.

The man went away to a garden. But while he was away the boy did not keep the fire going as he had been told to do. Later the mother-in-law built up the fire in her house, so that it lighted up the house. The man found plenty of good ears of green corn. He began by stripping back the husks from ears of corn and tying two ears together by the husks, so that he could hang them across his arms. But he picked so many ears that he could not carry them all in this way, so he pulled up his cloth by the front edge[6] to make a bag between his belt and his hand. Into this he put the ears of corn. This left his lower parts bare. But since it was dark, this caused him no concern.

As he came back into the village, he looked for a brightly lighted house, expecting to find the boy keeping the fire burning high in the guesthouse, as he had told the boy to do. He saw the house of his mother-in-law all lighted up and thought that it was the guesthouse in which he was staying. He pushed the door open with his foot and went in with the corn. Coming from the darkness into the lighted room, he was blinded for a moment and did not see that he had come into the house his mother-in-law. He began to speak abusively, he thought to the boy, saying, "By your dirty bottom, haven't I come back now? Haven't I brought the stuff? But shall I give you any of it? Not by your west end, for you were a disobedient young one and would not go when I wanted you to go."

The mother-in-law looked to see who it was, and she saw that it was her son-in-law, bare below the waist, for his whole cloth had been used making the bag for the corn.[7] Seeing who it was, she said, "My father, in here? Not in here!"

[6] The traditional man's dress is a five or six foot piece of cloth, hung from a raw hide belt so that each of the cloth's two folds hang down about three feet below the waist. When lying down, a man can draw the top fold up over his shoulders, leaving the bottom fold covering his legs. Here, the man used both folds, even the bottom one, in making a large carrying bag, hanging from his raw hide belt.

[7] The taboo between mother-in-law and son-in-law prohibits their looking directly at each other, talking directly together, or entering each other's houses. They may speak about each other, but only in the most honorific terms. In practise, they manage to converse together by sitting near each other, but looking away, and speaking to others words which are actually intended for each other.

Since she was at the back of the room wringing juice out of beer root,[8] he did not hear her clearly and still did not know where he was. Still wishing to be insulting, he clicked his tongue[9] and said again, "This corn is mine. Since you disobeyed me, I will not give you any."

Once again his mother-in-law spoke out, saying, "My father, in here? Not in here!"

This time he heard what it was that she said, and looking about, saw where he was. He ran out of his mother-in-law's house as fast as he could and ran away.

He was desperate with shame, and when he came to the guest house he called to the boy, "Come quickly. Let us go. We are leaving now, in the night. We are going straight back home. We shall spend the night in some field hut." [10]

When the boy understood what he was being asked to do, he answered, "I am staying here for the night. I am not going out in the dark, for fear that I stub my toes."

The man, his mind agitated, replied, "Then you will have to stay alone. It is your affair. I am already off." The man went off into the dark. He left behind the meats that had been cooked for them, not thinking of them at all.

The boy remained in the house by himself. In the morning the boy roasted the cold mush and ate what was brought for the guests in the worning. Then everyone began to ask the boy, "Now then, where is your elder?"

The boy answered and explained, saying, "The elder went to our village in the night."

Then they asked him, "What was the elder running away from, that he left in the middle of the night?"

The boy replied and said, "I have no idea. I do not know. He called me and said, 'We are going tonight.' I would not go, and so I stayed here all by myself."

When the sun was high up and shining brightly, the boy tied into a parcel all the meats which had been cooked for the

[8] A wild root is dug up, pounded in a mortar, and soaked. Then the juice is squeezed out and used to flavor a non-intoxicating family drink.

[9] The Ovimbundu click the tongue to express insult, disgust or anger.

[10] The field hut is a small house with unplastered walls, built in the fields of corn or millet when they are far from the village. It is used by the women who work in the fields as a place of refuge from heavy rains, a place to leave their children while they work in the fields, an extra place to cook, and a temporary storage house for crops.

two guests, took up this parcel, and left to return to the village from which they had come.

When he returned to their own village, his parents gave thanks for his return and then asked him, "Your elder, where is he?" The boy related all that he knew: that the elder had fled, but where he went the boy did not know, for he did not see where he went.

The elder himself, as he traveled in the darkness of night, came to a field hut. It was so dark that it was impossible to go farther, so he took refuge in this field hut. He had no idea that there was a corpse in the hut. As he sat in the dark, he noticed that drops were falling from some object up in the top of the hut. These drops had an odor. Later, in the middle of the night, he just barely heard the sound of a person coming quietly to the doorway of the hut, as though about to enter. But he had fastened the door when he came in. The person trying to get in was an old woman. Finally she spoke and said, "My child, when you go to Njembo, may you go well and there sleep well.[11] Truly, I know that I killed you, but I shall make the sacrifice for murdering you. My child, I have already arranged for your goat, which I am sacrificing for killing you. Child in there, take hold of my arm."

While the little old woman was talking thus outside the field hut, the man inside became terrified and thought, "Haka! What have I gotten into tonight?" After he had stilled his fears, he sat tight on his chair so that he would not be afraid. When he sensed that the little old woman had reached her hand through a hole in the wall, he decided to take hold of it and not let go again.

After a time, the little old woman tried to withdraw her arm. When she realized that it was held fast, she spoke and said, "My child, indeed that is right. Now it is clear to me that you will go to sleep. Now let go my hand, my child." After she had said this, she again tried to withdraw her arm. Still it was held tightly. She begged again, saying, "Now my child, just let me go, for I am your relative. Really I am able to make the sacrifice for having killed you. The goat is ready at hand. If you are not satisfied with a goat, I am able to provide a person. My child, anything that you wish, I shall do for you." Then she thought

---

[11] An ironic curse, meaning "How difficult for you to go well!"

that she would be able to withdraw her arm, but it was still held fast.

At this, she began to be afraid, for by that time the roosters were beginning to crow in the village. She began to speak again and said, "My child, your relatives that I killed, after I killed them I performed the sacrifice for killing them, and they did not bother me any more. It is you alone who this time resists me and will not let me go. Haka! Have you not heard all the things that I have named to you, that I am willing to sacrifice for you! My child, let me go, for I am your relative. Indeed I am begging this of you. Everything that I did not do for the others, your relatives, I shall do for you now, to show that the others were of less value, and that you are their superior." The man still held her arm. The little old woman had thought that after her last promise, she would be able to withdraw her arm, but it was held firmly still.

By this time it was daybreak. When it was really morning, so that the sun had power, the people began calling to each other saying that it was time for them to go and bury the dead man. All the members of the family came together and started for the place. As they approached the field hut, they saw that some person was at the door of the hut. Then they began to say to each other, "Now who is that person who came on ahead and is already at the door of the field hut? Is it the witch who killed him?" When they came near enough to the field hut they began to call: "You there, you little old woman, what are you doing there? Maybe you are the witch that killed this child?"

When the people had come quite close, they heard a voice from within the hut, saying, "All you people who came here to bury the corpse which is in the hut, listen carefully and do not be afraid, for I am not a ghost. I am a human being who eats corn, even as you do. The kind of people that you are, I am also. I came to this country to visit my wife's family, and I brought a boy along with me. When I came to the village, my wife's family welcomed me warmly, and they also provided us well with food. They cooked small pigs and fowls for us. In addition to this, I had a yearning for green corn, and since they had not yet brought us any mush, I told the boy to go and snap off some ears of green corn. The boy would not go. He was disobedient. So I went myself. When I was leaving, I told the boy this,

'While I am away, you keep up the fire in the fireplace, so that the place will be lighted up. You are to do this, for you would not go to snap off the corn. Then when I come back I shall see the place lighted up and shall not mistake the house.' But the boy acted like the son of a widow. He did not do as I had charged him. The fire in the fireplace burned down until it went out. But the house of my mother-in-law was lit up bright and red.

"When I came back from the gardens I thought that the house that was lighted up was the house in which we were lodged, and that the boy had kept up the fire as I had told him to do. When I came into the house, I did not look about at all. I became abusive and used insulting words. But it was my mother-in-law I was insulting. Then she spoke and said, 'In here? Not in here!' This caused me great shame. When I came to the guesthouse, I told the boy, 'We are going home to our village.' But this boy was a son of a widow. Again he would not go, and he said, 'I am not going in the middle of the night.' He stayed. When I thought about it, I saw that I could not stop for the night. Then I fled. I was traveling in the night, and because of the thickness of the darkness, I came to this field hut and went inside. I did not know that there was a dead person in it. When a drop of blood fell on me, it was not clear to me what it was.

"Later, in the middle of the night, a person came to the door and spoke. She said, 'Oh my child, I know that truly I am the one who killed you, but I have already gotten the goat to be sacrificed for your death. If you have really gone to Njembo and are well, then take hold of my hand which I reach into there.' As she was saying, 'I killed you,' I realized that the witch who had been murdering people was here. I tell you now that I did not miss the chance. Indeed, I held her arm until you were here. While I held her arm, she talked a lot to herself. She said, 'It is true that it was I who killed you. I shall make the same sacrifices for killing you that I made for killing your relatives.' But I would not let her go. I said to myself that I would hang onto this witch to save my fellow men, even if she should kill me for doing it. I thought, 'Let her do what she may.' "

When the people of the village outside the hut heard this, they thanked him profusely, shouted loudly, and said, "You have done very well indeed." Then they took the little old woman and bound her with bark strips. They removed the sticks which closed the doorway, and the man came out. The people said, "Let us go to the village and reward you, for you have performed a great and worthy service."

This is just what they did. He went with them. When he came to the village they made him a present of four girls and four boys, and added sixteen head of cattle. The people of the village cooked a hog for him. When he left the village, he was a wealthy man. As for the little old woman, they cut off her head, and because she was a witch they burned her body.

a piece of skin from a sister-in-law

Once a man went with his wife to visit her family. At the end of the visit, the family named a sister of the wife to go back home with them. The younger sister was to help the married sister with her household duties.

They were walking along the path to their village when the sister stubbed her toe so hard that the whole nail came off. The girl wailed and wept over the injury.

Her brother-in-law comforted her and said to her, "It is too bad. It must hurt a great deal. Oh, my dear sister-in-law, let me look at it." He took his knife and cut off a piece of loose skin. He wrapped this piece of skin up in a leaf and kept it.

As they went on with their journey, the girl thought about the piece of skin and was troubled. She turned this over in her mind and thought, "Why did brother-in-law wrap up that piece of skin and carry it with him, instead of throwing it away?" Later she asked him, "Brother-in-law, the piece of skin that you cut off my toe, aren't you going to throw it away?"

He replied and said, "Oh yes, sister-in-law, I am going to throw it away farther on."

They traveled along, but he did not throw it away. This really troubled the girl. She asked him again, "Haka, brother-in-law! The piece of skin that you cut from my toe, do you intend to throw it away at all? Do you mean to take it with you into the village?"

He told her, "No, no, sister-in-law, I mean to throw it away immediately."

The older sister now said to her, "Why do you keep

troubling your brother-in-law about a piece of skin? Won't the master throw it away at last?"

Because of this word from her older sister, the girl neither said anything more nor asked about the skin again, even though she saw clearly that her brother-in-law did not throw away the piece of skin. She did not ask again, for fear her older sister would be angry.

When they came into the village, the man went straight to the king's compound to deliver the piece of skin which he had cut from the girl's toe. He came to the king and explained the matter to him, saying, "O Lord and Grandfather, I came back to the village with two sisters. While we were on the way, the younger sister stubbed her toe and the whole nail fell off. I thought that the matter could not be left that way, and that the best thing was for me to carry this nail and piece of skin to the king, so that he might cut this up and let all the people have a taste of it."

When the king heard this, he was much pleased. He took the nail and the piece of skin, cut them up, and gave some to all the people of the head village. After he had done this, he climbed into a tree[12] and shouted a royal proclamation. He shouted: "You who hear, listen! Tomorrow, the women will hull corn. The men will carve the wooden bowls in which pepper is ground. The day after tomorrow, the meal will be pounded. The day after the day after tomorrow, we are all to stay in the village with our children. We adults shall eat our two animals that have no tails."

The whole village applauded, clapping their hands, jumping up and down, and saying, "We have heard it! We have heard it!" The women spent the next morning hulling corn. The men worked carving out dishes for the grinding of pepper.

The next day all the women pounded meal. Even the victims, the wife and her sister, hulled corn and pounded meal. Yet they pondered the meaning of the king's announcement.

A little old woman went looking for the girl and her older sister, because she thought that two good people were to be eaten, and she pitied them. She spoke to them and said, "You children, did you understand the royal announcement the king made the other day? Now I ask you, do you know what it means? These

---

[12] It is customary for the king's crier, rather than the king himself, to climb into a tall tree and shout royal proclamations. That may be intended here.

animals, what are they? Really, you are the animals to be eaten. It is not my affair, but if it is possible I shall save you."

Then she gave the sisters a special esako[13] of hers. She directed them: "Now then, while you are pounding meal, conceal this magic esako in your basket of meal. Something which you have never seen before will come out from the basket. When it has reached its full size, mount it and go wherever it takes you."

Then, as the girls pounded meal, they sang over and over this song:

> Wake up, good Esako,
>
> Come take us to our mother.
>
> We shall go with fear and trembling.
>
> Save us, rise and take us safely.
>
> The lowlanders now are singing:
>
> "Come, let's eat the Ovimbundu,
>
> While we dance and dance and shimmy."

The two girls kept singing their song, while the villagers were singing their songs.

When the people of the village saw all the meal being pounded, they were much pleased. Their minds were not troubled at all, and they were saying to each other with pleasure and hope, "If we finish the pounding today, we shall eat these fine, fat Ovimbundu tomorrow." As they pounded meal, the people of the village were happy as they had never been before.

The two sisters pounded much meal, but with heavy hearts, for they realized that they were the animals to be eaten. Even though the little old woman had given them the magic esako which was to change into something which would save them, yet they did not know how it would work. They felt great fear for themselves, for they were still in the village of man-eaters. They asked each other, "Are we going to be saved or not?" However, they went on singing their little song:

[13] The *esako* is a long iron rod or skewer, used by women in braiding their hair. The hair is allowed to grow very long and then caked with heavy grease. It is left in this condition for some time, until the grease hardens and the hair straightens, at which time the esako is used to pry apart rope-like strands of the grease-caked hair, for braiding.

> Wake up, good Esako,
> Come take us to our mother.
> We shall go with fear and trembling.
> Save us, rise and take us safely.
> The lowlanders now are singing:
> "Come, let's eat the Ovimbundu,
> While we dance and dance and shimmy."

So they continued singing as they pounded the meal.

When they had finished pounding the meal, they began to sift it and put it into baskets. After some time, their attention was drawn to the basket in which they had concealed the esako. This basket had been upset, and the esako had become a large animal, as big as an ox. They lost no time in mounting the animal. When they were safely on it, the animal rose into the air and began to fly away.

When the people of the village saw this, they let out a great wail, saying, "The Ovimbundu are getting away! Help! The Ovimbundu are escaping!" The villagers followed, running underneath them, but were not able to get at the sisters, who flew along with great pleasure, until with much joy they came to their country. When they arrived, the animal came to the earth, let the sisters off, and then flew back again. There the animal changed back into an esako once more.

The sisters related their adventures to their parents, telling them all that had happened on the path, everything which took place in the village while they were there, and how they came to be saved. When the parents heard their tale and realized the danger their daughters had been in, they were very glad to have them back alive and well. As they thought of how close their daughters had been to being eaten by cannibals, they wept.

the bride and her small brother

There was a bride who took her young brother with her when she went to her new home. Since he was a small boy, she said to him, "Your work will be to stay here in the village and cook a little relish for your brother-in-law. So that it may cook well, pour the water in a little at a time, and keep the fire burning. Whether the relish is of beans or of meat is not important. The main thing is that I wish to have the relish cooked well. Did you hear that, little brother?"

"Yes, I heard it all," he answered.

Then she told him, "That is good. Do just as I have told you, so that your brother-in-law, whom I married recently, will not have to eat poorly cooked relish. For in that case he would say to me, 'Woman, you are a slovenly wife.' "

In this same village, in which the boy was to cook the relish, keeping the fire burning and pouring in the water a little at a time, there happened to live another bride with a younger brother in her house. When the first boy had poured in the water he went out to play with the other boy. After they had played but a short while, the boy returned to look at the pot. He found the pot already dry and the relish burned.[14] This made him feel very bad. He expected that his sister would whip him when she came in from the fields.

His sister was very angry when she came in from the fields and found the relish burned. She was starting to whip her younger brother when her husband intervened and saved the boy from being whipped, by saying, "You cannot whip the child for this. Here in the village, he will learn quickly. What he has done is not serious. Then he said to the boy, "What you have done today will not be held against you, but do not do it again another day."

Another day, the woman left the boy to cook another pot of relish, saying to him, "Cook this carefully. Do not act as you did the last time, letting it burn again." He gave attention to her words and then said to her, "This time I really shall cook it well."

The other small boy expected him surely to come out and play. But the boy did not come out. After a time the other boy came to the house in which the first was cooking the relish, and said to the little cook, "Playmate, aren't you coming out to play?"

"Today I cannot go out to play," answered the boy engaged

[14] Because the Ovimbundu use unglazed pottery, pots are frequently ruined when their contents burn fast to the sides of the pot.

in cooking, "for my sister left me to watch over the cooking of a little pot of relish. I am afraid that if I go out to play the relish will burn, as it did that other time. If that happens, she will whip me. So if you wish to play with me, come in here. Then we can play, and if the pot begins drying up I shall see it." The other boy agreed to play inside, and came into the house where his friend was cooking the relish.

After the pot had been filled with water and just a small fire placed under the pot the boys then went just outside the door to play. When they had been playing but a short while the boy doing the cooking said, "I must go in and look at the little pot." He found that the little pot was dry and the relish already burned. Thinking of what his sister would do to him when she returned, the boy began to feel very upset.

When his sister returned and found the relish burned she was more angry than she had been the first time. She said to him, "You are causing me great shame before your brother-in-law. He will now call me names and say that I am worthless. Now that you are causing me to be scolded I have no further need for you here. You may go home to your mother in your village. I need not consent to feed a worthless person like you."

The husband heard his wife scold her younger brother in this way and said to her, "Now! Now! Let it go. That is not the way to deal with a child. Bawling him out so much will not work. To get along with a child one must be considerate. Otherwise he will feel that he is no more than a slave." Then the husband cooked another pot of relish, and they ate their meal.

On yet another day the sister left the boy to cook another, and final, pot of relish. This time she said to him, "The important thing today is this: do not burn the relish again. You have your last chance today. Burn the relish again and out of my house you go; out you go immediately." Thus it was that she left the boy to cook another pot of relish, as she had done previously, but did now for the last time. She admonished him a second time, saying, "My young brother, give your entire attention to this little pot of relish being cooked for your brother-in-law. See that it does not burn again. That is all."

The boy said, "Aye."

Then he tended the cooking of the relish with extreme care. He did not go out to play, nor go anywhere. The pot boiled and boiled until the relish was cooked enough and really cooked well. At this point he felt an urge to go to the bush, and debated with himself whether he should leave the pot. He decided that he could leave the pot, since the relish was already cooked. Before leaving the pot he poured water into it until it was quite full. Then he went to the bush but did not delay there long. When he returned to the house, he found the relish already burned.

The boy waited patiently to see what his sister would do.

When his sister came home she looked at the burned relish in the little pot and said to the boy, "I have already warned you that I would do more than scold you if the relish burned in the pot today. Now you get out, you leave, you go anywhere you please, but you go from here."

And so he left, to go anywhere his fancy should take him.

While he was walking along he met an old man afflicted with the itch. This old man, covered with dirt from a long past, had never bathed his body. The old man asked him, "Where are you going?"

The boy's answer was this: "I was living with my sister. My duty was to cook a little pot of relish. Though I tended the little pot well, the relish always burned. Finally, the last time that this happened, my sister became very angry. After she thought of the times I had let the relish burn, she turned me out and told me to go wherever I pleased. It was thus that I came this way, to seek someone who will give me work by which I can earn my food, and to learn how to cook relish in a way that will please my sister when I return to her house."

The old man said to him, "First lick off my body, and then I shall explain to you carefully how you should conduct your journey."

The boy agreed to this proposal. He began to lick off the man's itch scales and filth. When he was on the point of spitting these out upon the ground, the old man said to him, "Do not spit that out upon the ground. Complete your licking; swallow the stuff." At first the boy only pretended to swallow it. But the old man forced him to finish swallowing, and to continue doing this until the old man's body was licked clean, pink and shining.

When the boy had finished his work, the old man gave him medicine that caused him to vomit up all that he had swallowed. Next, the old man gave him gruel to drink, which restored the boy's strength, for he had been exhausted. When his strength had returned to him, the old man gave him solid food to eat. And when the boy had finished eating, the old man gave him three bananas. These were well ripened. The old man told him the use of the bananas: "Take these. One you will strike against a scorched and blackened stump of a tree. One you will strike against a white ant hill.[15] One you will throw into a pond."

The boy continued on his journey, so that he might do these things he had been directed to do.

Finding a scorched and blackened stump, he struck the first banana against it. When he had done this, there came from the stump a herd of sheep and a herd of goats.

Then, finding a white ant hill, struck the second banana against it. Out from the ant hill came a herd of cattle and a herd of asses.

Finally he came to a pond, into which he threw the third banana. From the pond emerged much wealth: a trading post filled with cloth and other merchandise. The trading post was complete with a staff of servants to operate it, who could also tend and care for the animals he had already acquired. By this luck the boy became a real man, a wealthy person of property.

The boy then returned to his sister's house. When she saw him with all this property she danced with joy, for she expected to share this wealth which met her eyes.

When the boy who had played with him heard of his good fortune, the former playmate was filled with envy and coveted his wealth. So this former playmate thought, "The best course for me to follow, since my sister leaves a pot of relish in my care every day, will be to let this relish burn in the pot, and then my sister will be angry with me and turn me out of her house, as my friend was turned out of his sister's house; so that I may go where my friend went, and thus become wealthy in the way that my friend has become wealthy."

When next his sister and her husband left him a pot of relish to cook, he poured water into the pot only once, built a fire hot enough to burn the relish, wandered away wherever he pleased, and did not come back until late in the afternoon. Yet when he came back he found the relish in the pot well cooked, a fine deep red, and not burned at all. He had expected to find the

---

[15] The bush country is dotted with these ant hills, cones of clay several feet high.

relish burned, and when he found it so well cooked his heart turned black with anger. But even though he had been frustrated, he still expected to burn the next day's relish.

The next day his sister and her husband gave him another pot of relish to cook, saying to him, "Cook this well, as you have done in the past." To this he replied, "Aye."

He took up the beans, put them into the pot, added just a few drops of water, and built a very hot fire. Then he went away, thinking, "Today the beans will surely burn, and my sister and her husband will turn me out of their house, after which I may go to the place where my friend has been. When I think of his fortune and of my own, my heart becomes black and rebellious." He wandered far, confident that he would find the relish burned when he returned to the house. But when he returned he actually found a pot of well cooked relish, deep red and not burned at all.

When his sister and her husband came back from the fields they praised him and said to him, "Brother, you have cooked this so well that we love you." Though they praised him, their words brought pain to his heart. When the next day they left him relish to cook he resolved, "I will put the beans in the pot without water, put the pot on the fire, and go where my friend went without saying good-by to anyone." He prepared the beans, placed them without water on the fire, and departed.

Walking on the path, he encountered the same old man whom the other boy had encountered and licked clean. On this occasion the old man was afflicted with boils and covered with dirt.

The old man asked him, "Where are you going?"

This boy answered him, "I will go wherever I please, and there I will travel about."

"Now my dear, before you go on, come over to me and lick me clean," said the old man. Before making this trial of the boy, the old man could already see the greed for his playmate's wealth in this boy's heart.

The boy glowered at the old man, spat at him in contempt, and said to him, "Old man, do not be so proud. You expect me to lick you? I would rather defecate on you. Don't stare at me, you inanimate thing, or I shall have to bathe myself. I vomit to think of doing anything for you."

To all of this the old man replied, "Say no more. Do not

spit out all that you have in your mouth. The wealth which your friend obtained, he obtained through me, and because he licked me clean."

The boy was taken aback and stammered, "That wealth, you did that for him? Will you please let me lick you now?"

Now the old man would not permit himself to be licked. He merely said to the boy, "Take these three green bananas. This one strike against a scorched stump; the second one strike against a white ant hill; and the third banana throw into a pond."

The boy went away with the bananas and did with them as he had been told. He struck the first against a scorched stump, which gave forth two sheep and two goats. The second banana he struck against a white ant hill; which produced four head of white cattle. Coming to a pond, he threw the third banana into the pond, from which there came lions who ate the sheep, the goats, the cattle and the boy. They were all of them eaten and never seen again.

katiukaila and ngeve

Once there was a country in which it was law that a man must promise, when he married, to be buried with the corpse of his mother-in-law, whenever she should die.

In that country was a girl named Ngeve,[16] who was desired by a young man named Katiukaila.[17] When he came to discuss engagement with her parents, they explained to him the ancient custom of their country that every man marrying a girl from this country must first promise that he will consent to be buried along with the girl's mother, even if he is not yet senile when his mother-in-law dies. After the young man had heard of this custom, he replied, "I love this girl Ngeve very much, so I will consent to make the promise you demand if you will consent to our engagement." The terms were agreed upon, he courted Ngeve, they became engaged, and finally they married.

After they were married, everything went along well. But

---

[16] A common name for a twin of either sex.
[17] This name means "I do not return."

after about six months, the mother-in-law became sick and died. Messengers came and informed the daughter and son-in-law of her death. Realizing that her husband would be buried along with her mother, the wife killed a fowl and cooked mush and fowl for him. Katiukaila took only small portions of the mush and fowl from the dish, saying to his wife, "My name is Katiukaila." Then he put on his best clothes and shoes, which came from Mbaka, for at that time his people had already begun trading at Mbaka.

He accompanied his wife to the village of her people, where he would be buried, and she would weep the death of her mother and the burial of her husband. When they came to the village, they found some people were hewing boards for the coffin, while others were digging the grave. He presented eight yards of cloth, the amount needed to cover the coffin of his mother-in-law.[18]

When the men of the village had finished hewing boards and nailing them together for the coffin, they went to find if the grave had been dug. The grave had been dug, and so they took the corpse of the mother-in-law, and took the son-in-law to the grave.

When they arrived at the grave, it appeared that it was not deep enough, for the son-in-law had brought with him twelve boxes of possessions and a bed to lie upon.[19] Katiukaila told them that the grave was not deep enough. The grave diggers dug and dug until the grave was very deep. Then they put in the coffin with the dead woman in it, and put in the twelve boxes and the bed belonging to the man.

The man went into the grave and reclined on his bed, which was on top of his twelve boxes of possessions. It appeared that the grave was still not deep enough, for the man reclining on his bed and boxes could not be covered up. He came out and they took out his boxes and bed so that they could dig still deeper.

At this point, Katiukaila posed a question to those gathered by the grave: "All you people gathered here know my name. Who am I?"

They said, "You are Katiukaila, meaning 'you do not return.'"

[18] The custom is to fasten a fine cloth to the coffin with valuable brass tacks. The same type brass tacks are worn by the women in their hair.

[19] The Ovimbundu often bury a man's possessions with his corpse. Twelve boxes of possessions would indicate great wealth.

Then he said to them, "That is right. You have put me into the grave, and you have taken me out again. I cannot return into the grave now, for you have already said, 'You do not return.'"

Then Katiukaila had men carry away his boxes and his bed to his village. He went there with his wife, who was much pleased. They left behind her people, filling the grave and burying the corpse.

a girl believes that her brother-in-law laughs at her

A hunter was living in a country that was not his own. He had married a woman of the country, and was living in her country. One day the hunter was voicing complaint. He said, "Here I have shot a roan antelope, and because there are none of my relatives in this country, there is no one to carry the animal for me."

While the hunter was ranting about this, he heard someone behind him say, "Do not make any more noise about this, for your protests have pained us. Just pick up your gun and walk on ahead. We shall carry your antelope for you. Furthermore, from now on you will be able to understand the talk of snakes, insects and animals. However, on the day that you reveal anything these living creatures have said, or reveal that we have promised to help you, on that day you will die."

One day his wife's younger sister came to visit them. The hunter wished to kill something with which to entertain his sister-in-law. At daybreak he took his gun and went hunting. He shot and killed a roan antelope, which he encountered in the woods. He came home to the village. Those who had promised to carry the meat for him carried the animal to the edge of the village. The hunter asked the people to come and help cut up the animal. In the evening the girl asked her brother-in-law to do her a favor. She said, "Brother-in-law, will you braid my hair tomorrow?" She asked her brother-in-law to do this, because in addition to being a hunter he was also a hairdresser.

Early the next morning the hunter called to the girl, "Sister-in-law, get up and come outside, so that I may braid your hair."

She came out of the house. While he braided her hair, the girl kept scratching an itchy spot. Finally, as a result of the scratching, a scab fell off onto the ground.

At that moment, the hunter heard an ant calling to the other ants, saying, "Come, for Kapila has found an elephant." Then the other ants came, and were giving thanks for the find. They said, "Mba, mba, mba, mba." Then they began to sing a triumphal hunting song. The ants sang:

> The zebra does not bite.
>
> The zebra does not bite.
>
> Oh hunters, will you listen?
>
> We have found a gift from heaven.
>
> The zebra does not bite.
>
> The zebra does not bite.

When the hunter heard the song of the ants, he laughed. When the girl heard the hunter laugh, she said, "You were laughing at me. Unless you tell me what you were laughing at, I shall know you were laughing at me."

The hunter said, "Now, sister-in-law, it was not you that I was laughing at."

The girl said, "If you do not tell me what you were laughing at, I will kill myself,[20] and you will have caused my death."

The hunter said, "I shall not tell you, until you have fetched your brothers." Then the girl left to go and get her brothers. When the brothers had come to the village, the hunter summoned his friends.

The next day at daybreak they all assembled. Then the hunter said, "Bring the meat that has been on the fire during the night." Then the meat was brought, he distributed it among them, and all the people ate. When they had finished eating, he addressed them, saying, "All you folks, listen while I tell my sister-in-law what I laughed at. The day that I shot my first roan antelope, I complained, saying, 'Every day I have been getting small animals, and so I have been in the habit of carrying

[20] This threat of suicide was probably not idle. Suicide is a known and practised mode of vengeance among the Ovimbundu, since the suicide's relatives must avenge the death by action against the person who caused the suicide or his group.

them in myself. But today, who is there to carry the roan antelope for me?' While I was ranting on, I heard a voice saying, 'Do not make further complaint. Your complaining has hurt us, so we shall carry your meat in for you. And from now on, you will hear and understand what the snakes, insects and animals say to each other. But on the day that you tell this to anyone you shall die.' Later, while I was braiding my sister-in-law's hair, I heard the ants singing a song of triumph. They sang:

> The zebra does not bite.
> The zebra does not bite.
> Oh hunters, will you listen?
> We have found a gift from heaven.
> The zebra does not bite.
> The zebra does not bite.

Oh my sister-in-law, it was that at which I laughed."

When the hunter had spoken those words, he died.

As a result of his death, the friends of the hunter rose up, seized the girl, and then bound her whole family. They sold the girl and her family, and they all became slaves.

monkey and spider

One day Monkey invited Spider to go with him on a visit. Monkey said, "Spider, you are a friend and my brother. Will you go with me to visit my wife's family?"

Spider readily agreed to this invitation and said, "All right, I am willing to go with you when you go to visit your wife's family." So one day they entered the path.

They went along pleasantly until they came to the village of the family of Monkey's wife. The wife's family welcomed them with pleasure, saying, "Guests have come! Guests have come! Thanks, thanks, thanks." After the family had greeted the guests, they put them up in a guesthouse.

When evening came, food was sent from the house of Monkey's mother-in-law to the guests at the guesthouse. They sent a child with the food for the guests, saying to him, "Go and carry this food to the house of the guests." When Monkey heard this he hurried away to the guesthouse. He went into the house and stretched his tail across the doorway.

When the child came through the doorway, it stepped on the tail of the Monkey. The child was frightened and cried out, "I stepped on Monkey's tail!"

Monkey immediately stood up, took the food from the hands of the child, and then gave thanks, saying, "Ah kuku, ah kuku. One does not invite the hungry to share a personal gift." Monkey ate up the food all by himself. His companion, Spider, slept with hunger.

The next day they visited from morning to evening. In the evening the mother-in-law again sent the child, telling him, "Go take the food to the guests." Monkey heard this and hurried away to block the doorway with his tail. When the child came near the house, it said, "Monkey's tail is in the way again."

When Monkey heard this, he hurriedly got up and took the food again, saying, "Ah kuku, ah kuku. A person does not invite the hungry to share a personal gift." Again Monkey ate all the food prepared for both guests, without sharing it. Once more Monkey's companion, Spider, slept with hunger. So things went that night and the next day.

In the evening the in-laws, as they had done on previous days, sent a child to carry food to the house of the guests. As he had done previously, Monkey stopped the doorway with his tail. The child, as it was passing through the doorway, stepped on Monkey's tail. The child said, "Today I am disgraced! What will happen to me for stepping on Monkey's tail?" Again Monkey took the food from the child's hands, saying, "Ah kuku, ah kuku. One does not invite the hungry to share a personal gift." Then again Monkey, all by himself, ate the food prepared for both. His companion, Spider, slept hungry.

All the time that Spider had been guest of the family of Monkey's wife, he had suffered from hunger. Every day he became more gaunt. He was drying up from lack of food. He was becoming weak from hunger. So it came about that during the days when he was suffering from hunger, Spider made a plan to save himself from dying of hunger. The plan was this:

while Monkey was asleep, Spider began to spin a web across the doorway. When they left the house in the morning, Monkey did not notice the web Spider had spun.

When it came evening, a child was sent from the house of the mother-in-law to carry food to the guest house. As the child was about to pass through the doorway, it became entangled in Spider's web. The child said, "Oh mother! I am tangled to my eyes in Spider's web." When Spider heard this, he slid down swiftly from above, took the food from the child, and said, "Naho, ah kuku, kuku. One does not invite the hungry to share a personal gift." Spider, all by himself, ate it all. In his turn Monkey slept with hunger.

First, Monkey had eaten all the food, because it was offered in his name. Now Spider had reversed this.

The next day things went the same way. The child bringing the food was held up by the web which Spider had spun. The child said, "I am stuck in a spider's web!"

When Spider heard this, he said, "Mba, mba, mba, mba. One does not invite the hungry to share a personal gift." Then Spider ate all the food. He did not give any to his companion, Monkey.

On this diet, Monkey began to grow thin, and he developed a slender waist. Spider began to develop a paunch. He became quite fat, so full that he belched. At first Monkey had not been hungry at all, for he had eaten sumptuously every day. Now that the food was received in Spider's name, feast was Spider's and famine Monkey's. So it went for the rest of the time that they were guests of the family of Monkey's wife.

When Monkey had thought the matter over, he decided that on the whole it was best that they return to the country from which they came. Monkey and Spider went back to the village from which they had set out. When they came back to the home village, Monkey had a pinched waist, while Spider looked prosperous.

From that day to this, Spider's family have not reduced, for they learned to have food in plenty. And the family of Monkey never fatten at all, no matter how much food they may have. From the time that Monkey took Spider with him to visit his wife's family, Monkey has been lean, very lean. While Spider, from the time that he went with Monkey on a visit, has not been lean, but has continued up to the present time to be fat.

the man who changed into a python

There was once a married woman who visited her parents' village, and then brought back her younger sister with her, to stay in her husband's village. In the evening, when they had come within her husband's house, she said to her husband, "It will be better to have my sister sleep somewhere else."

Her husband disagreed, saying, "That would not do at all. We shall have her sleep right here in our house, on the floor near the back of the room."

Then the older sister said, "All right. It is all the same to me."

They went to bed. In the night the man changed into a python, for he wished to eat the younger sister. Soon the little girl awoke and saw the gleaming coils of a python where her brother-in-law lay. The little girl screamed:

> Sister! Sister, awake!
> For we have a chance
> To look at a snake!
> I see it gleaming.

When the older sister was awake, she said, "Why are you making so much noise at this hour?"

"For nothing, sister," replied the little girl, for the snake had changed back into a man while the older sister was waking up. Now he said to the little girl, "You are grown up, and yet you still cry like an infant."

For many days the girl kept saying to herself, "I saw a python where there was no python." But she kept very quiet and did not mention it again to her sister and brother-in-law.

Several times more the man changed himself into a python during the night, wishing to eat the girl. But she was alert. Each time, when she saw that her brother-in-law had become a python, she sang out:

> Sister! Sister, awake!
> For we have a chance
> To look at a snake!
> I see it gleaming.

Each time her sister would then wake up and scold her.

One day the woman said to her husband, "Since my sister cries out so much in the night, we must plan to take her home to my parents' village. She must cry in the night because she is not accustomed to this place." So the woman stocked her basket with meal and other food suitable for eating during the journey.

The two sisters started out on the journey and were passing through a forest, when they encountered the husband, who had gone ahead of them and again changed into a python. The python lay across their path, stretching from one side to the other. There was no opening left through which they could pass. Then there was this conversation between the python and his wife:

Python: "Come now, pay up. Pay the toll for your passage."

Woman: "This little gourd of mine, I give it as toll for my passage."

Python: "Come now, pay up. Pay the toll for your passage."

Woman: "My basket and all that is in it, I give them as toll for my passage."

Python: "Come now, pay up. Pay the toll for your passage."

Woman: "My little sister and her garment, I give them as toll for my passage."

Python: "Come now, pay up. Pay the toll for your passage."

Woman: "Myself, the only remnant, I give you as toll for my passage."

Then the python swallowed everything, even his sister-in-law and his wife.

When the woman was down inside the python, she found many things that he had swallowed in the past, even the distant past: people, animals, and many other things. She took out her knife, and beginning at his head, slit him all the way to his tail. Then everything he had swallowed spilled out: people, bales of cloth, animals, and many other things. The people who were freed praised the woman, thanked her, and said that she should be made queen.

The woman sent her younger sister away as a messenger to their father, asking him to send carriers to remove all the wealth which she had won by slitting the python's belly.

The people of her village were highly pleased to see her again. Her parents praised their daughter, saying that she was very clever, and that they would never have seen her again if she had not been clever.

11. ownership

a hunter borrows an ax

There was a hunter who lent his ax to a brother hunter, who had asked for it, saying, "Please lend me your ax, for I wish to hew out a beehive." The owner of the ax was willing, and he lent the other hunter his ax.

The man who borrowed the ax went to the woods to make the beehive. When the hive lacked only a little of being completed, the bulb on the end of the ax handle, into which the blade of the ax is inserted, split. The hunter did not think that this would make any trouble. He said to himself, "I have had experience in shaving out ax handles, so I shall shave another handle for this ax." The hunter cut the wood for the new handle and took it with him to the village, where he proposed to complete the handle.

When the hunter came to the village, he told his wife and other people what had happened. Later, the owner of the ax heard about it. When he heard that the handle was broken, he sent one of his children to the hunter, saying to the child, "Go to the hunter and fetch our ax."

The man who had borrowed the ax said to the child, "It is true that this is the ax of our friend, your father. Go and tell your father that the ax split its handle; but please, I beg him to be kind to me, and I shall send it to him tomorrow afternoon. In the morning, I shall fashion the handle, bore it, and fix the ax in the handle. Then I shall send it to your father. I have already cut the stick for the handle."

The child went back and told his father what the hunter had said. The father became angry when he heard this. He said to the child, "Go back immediately and fetch the ax. The new handle for my ax cannot be a stick from the woods, but must be the shin bone of a person, with the knee joint still attached to serve for the seat of the ax blade. No ordinary handle will do. Do not let this man deceive himself, saying, 'Tomorrow I shall shave it. Tomorrow I shall shave it.' "

The child went back in haste to do as his father had told him. When the child came to the hunter, he repeated everything that his father had said, just as his father had told him to do. When the other man heard this, he sighed and said, "Haka! What shall I do today? Have I deserved words of accusation that require such a payment, just for borrowing an ax from a neighbor? Haka!" He began to think over what he should do.

Finally, he drank a bottle of wine so that he would not feel the pain of having a leg cut off. He directed his children, saying, "When I am drunk, cut my leg off, so that we may give it to those who wish to have it."

The children felt sorrowful when they heard this, and they said, "When we cut off your leg, will that not destroy you?"

He replied, "What else can I do?"

The children tried to think of some way out of the difficulty, but they could not. So they cut off their father's leg and sent it to the one who wished to have it.

Two years later, the man who had taken the leg of his neighbor was himself in need of a drum for a Kandundu[1] ceremony in which he wished to take part. He came to this man, because this man had drums. The man said to the owner of the drums, "Will you lend me your drums, so that they can be played at the ceremonies for Kandundu?" The owner let him have the drums. The man who had asked for the drums carried them away.

The next day, the drummers played them all day long. The following day, when they were about to conclude the ceremonies, they had played the drums but a short time when the head of a drum split all the way across. The drumhead was ruined. The drummer immediately began to lament, saying, "Havoyo-wey! Now what shall I do?"

[1] In the ceremony of the Kandundu cult, there is a procession in which two men carry a large curtained casket containing a small wooden casket, which in turn contains a sacred amulet. The priest of the cult employs a tall cross of wood when consulting the deity of the cult. Some elements of the cult's rites seem to be derived from Catholic rites, Catholicism having been introduced into the area by Portuguese missionaries several centuries ago.

The man who had borrowed the drums said, "It does not matter. Here is a fresh goat's skin. As soon as I have softened it up well, we shall put it on for a drumhead."

The owner of the drum heard about this. He was the man whose leg had been cut off, so that his shin bone should replace the ax handle which he had split. This man said, "I will not permit it. No ordinary hide shall go on my drum. Only the proper skin must be used."

The man who borrowed the drum said to the owner, "If you do not wish to have a goatskin put on your drum, shall I use the skin of a monitor lizard? I shall look for one and put it on the drum."

The owner of the drum said, "Not even the skin of a monitor lizard is what I wish. I want the skin from the belly of a person. That is the kind of skin that makes a proper drumhead, the head for this drum."

When the man who had borrowed the drum heard this, he would not agree to it. He said, "If you take the skin from my belly, I shall die." He had forgotten what he had done to the owner of the drum. The old men have a name for such forgetting: "He threw a stone." The old men say, "He threw a stone. He who threw it forgets it. He whom it hit never forgets it."

Since the two men could not agree on the skin to be used for the drum, they took the case to the king for a formal trial. After the king had heard them speak, he said to the owner of the drum, "You cannot have the belly of your neighbor skinned, for he would die. It is right for you to allow the drumhead to be replaced with skin from a goat or a monitor lizard."

When the man whose leg had been cut off heard this decision, he refused to accept it, and said to the king, "Our king, listen carefully to what I say: A whole patch of reeds cannot harm you, but a single reed sprout will hurt you." [2]

The king heard this statement and said, "Haka! What is back of this? But first explain your proverb."

Then the owner of the drum explained, "I borrowed an ax from this man. I hewed out a beehive with the ax. Just when I had almost finished the hive, the handle of the ax split. I cut a stick from which to make a new handle. I intended to shave

---

[2] The young sprout of reed has a needle-sharp point, as hard as horn, with which it pierces through the tough sod of the swamp.

and bore a good new handle, and fix the iron blade of the ax into it. But when my neighbor heard of this, he sent his child, saying to the child, 'Go fetch my ax.' "

"Then I earnestly begged my neighbor to have mercy on me, for I had cut a stick of the right kind and would the next day bore the handle to replace the handle that had been split, and set the ax blade in it. He would not accept that. He said, 'My ax is not going to be hafted with an ordinary handle, but only with the shin bone of a man, with the knee joint attached.' "

"After I had thought the matter over, I decided that since I had spoiled the ax handle of a free man, the only proper thing was to replace it as he wished. They cut off my leg, and I became a cripple, in order to replace his ax handle with my leg. Now I have lent him my drum. Is he not going to make restitution?"

When the king had heard the rights of the whole story, he said, "As was done in the first instance, let it be done in the second. Since you, the plaintiff, did not have mercy for your neighbor in the first instance, now let them take the hide off your belly."

Then the man who borrowed the drum went to his house, drank a bottle of wine, summoned his children, and they took the skin off his belly, and gave it to the owner of the drum.

When the victim sobered, he suffered much pain, and he screamed a great deal. Later he died.

the man who climbed a tree

A man had climbed a tree in the woods and left his ax on the ground.

Another man came along and saw him up in the tree. He also saw the little ax which the man had left on the ground. Then, in the manner used by people who have found a lost article, he said, "Thanks! Thanks! Thanks, for I have found a little ax."

The man up in the tree called down, "Friend, that is my ax."

The one on the ground replied, "Not so. If that were your little ax, you would have taken it with you when you climbed the tree. Since I have found it lying on the ground, this little ax is mine. I have come by it through good luck. It has been said from of old that to find a thing is not to get it by skill, but by luck."

The man in the tree climbed down. Nothing more was said about the ax, and the two men went away together. The man who claimed for himself the ax he had found went ahead, and the man who had been up the tree followed.

As they went along, they came to a stream. The man walking in front straddled the stream with one leg on the far side while one leg remained on the near side. The man who was following seized the leg still on his side of the stream and said, "I have a lucky find. I have found a leg."

The man to whom the leg was attached said, "That is my leg."

The first said, "This is not your leg, for if it were your leg you would keep it with the other leg, and not leave it behind on this side of the stream." So saying, the man who had seized the leg took out his knife to unjoint the leg, which he kept on saying was a lucky find. The man to which the leg was attached kept yelling, "Stop!"

two women and half of a beehive

One day a woman borrowed half of a beehive[3] from a neighbor, because she had none of her own.

She took it home and put gourd seeds in it to dry. She forgot them and left them in the hog trough for a long time. Instead of drying, the seeds sprouted and grew vigorous vines.

When the woman who had put the seeds in the half of a beehive to dry noticed what had happened she was much pleased. Her joy over possessing vines prevented her from pulling them

---

[3] Beehives are made by tying together two halves of hollowed out pieces of log, pieces which have many other uses, including serving as a hog trough. To make such a piece, a log one foot or more in diameter is cut into pieces about three feet long, and these are split into halves. The halves are then hollowed out until the sides are half an inch thick and the ends about an inch and a half thick. For use as a beehive, two such wooden trays are bound together, insulated on the outside with grass stems, and hung in the top of a tree.

up, so she left them to bear fruit and ripen the fruit. As time passed the vines spread out and produced large, beautiful gourds. Just when this happened the owner of the half of a beehive came and said, "I have come to get my hog trough."

The woman who had borrowed the wooden tray begged the other woman earnestly, saying, "Please do me this favor. Do not demand your half of a beehive back for a while, for my gourds are growing in it and will soon be ripe."

But the owner of the half of a beehive would not agree to this. She replied, "I will not leave it with you any longer. I must have it today."

"What shall I do about my vines?" said the borrower.

"Cut the vines off," said the other woman. "Give me my hog trough, and let me go. I will not sit around here waiting for gourds to ripen, for I have much work waiting for me at my house."

The owner of the vines cut them off, but with much clicking of the tongue, for it hurt her to cut them off. When she had finished cutting them off she handed over the hog trough. The owner took the hog trough and went home with it.

After a few days the vines had dried up. Holes appeared in the gourds, for they had not yet hardened when the vines were cut off.

Later, after a long period had passed, the owner of the half of a beehive returned to the woman whose gourd vines she had caused to be destroyed and said to her, "Please lend me your small brass bracelet for my child to wear." The woman whose gourds had died lent her the bracelet, which she took home and put on the wrist of her child.

After some months the growing child's wrist became thicker so that the bracelet fitted tight and could not be taken off. Just at this time the owner of the bracelet came and said, "Now I wish to have my bracelet back from you. Give it to me today, for I want it."

They pulled and pulled at the bracelet. Then the mother said, "You see that it will not come off, so perhaps we must cut it with a file to remove it from the child's wrist."

"That will not do," said the owner of the bracelet, "for it is my bracelet. It has no break in it. If you cut it, then it will have a break."

"What shall I do?" said the mother of the child.

Then the owner of the bracelet said, "Just cut off the child's hand in the way in which I cut off my gourd vines."

The mother of the child began to weep and said, "That cannot be done to my child. She will die."

Weeping bitterly, she cut off the child's hand and gave the bracelet back to the other woman.

the green grub

One day we went with our comrades to gather big green grubs.[4] My comrades found many grubs, but I did not find one until the end of the day, and the one I found was deformed. When the sun was about to set, we came home.

When we came to the village, I put my grub in a small pot to cook. I seasoned it well. Just then my grandmother called me, saying, "Go carry this mush to the men's clubhouse."

I said to her, "I will not go, for I am afraid that you will eat my grub."

She said to me, "Just run along and take the mush. I shall not eat it."

While I was away taking the mush to the clubhouse, my grandmother ate the big green grub. When I came back from the clubhouse, I said to my grandmother, "Where is my big green grub?"

Grandmother said, "I ate it."

Then I bawled and wept, and I said, "I hurt, I hurt, I shall break."

Grandmother then said to me, "Do not cry. Do not break. Do not break. Take these cowpeas in place of the grub. There —I have paid for the grub."

I took the cowpeas in pay for the big green grub. I went out and planted them. In time, when the vines had grown, spread and borne pods, a duyker came and ate them all clean. I found the duyker and said to him, "Duyker, you have eaten my cow-

[4] The green grub, called *engu*, is found on tall trees, where it feeds on the leaves. This worm is about the diameter of a broom handle, and some three inches in length. The skin of the grub is transparent and the whole is a translucent green. Its fat, digestive tract and diet are all observable. It is considered a delicacy.

peas, which came from my grandmother, who ate my big green grub, which came from Muyangandi, where my young sister was lost. Today I hurt, I hurt. I shall break."

"Do not break. Do not break," said Duyker. "But take this skin of mine." Then I took the skin.

When I came back to the village I found that the blacksmiths did not have skins with which to repair their bellows. I said to them, "Here, take this skin of mine and use it to blow the fire." The blacksmiths took the skin and put it on their bellows and used it.

In time my skin was completely worn out. When I saw this I said to them, "Blacksmiths, you have worn out my skin that came from Duyker. Duyker ate my cowpeas. The cowpeas came from my grandmother. Grandmother ate my big green grub. My big green grub came from Muyangandi. At Muyangandi my young sister was lost. Today I hurt, I hurt. I shall break."

"Do not break. Do not break," the blacksmiths said, "but take this hoe in payment." I took the hoe and started for home.

As I went along, after a time I came upon some farmers who were cultivating with wooden hoes. I asked them, "Why do you work with wooden hoes?" The farmers told me that they could not afford an iron hoe. Then I gave them my hoe to hoe with. They worked with it until the hoe was worn out. When I came to get my hoe I said to them, "Where is my hoe?"

The farmers said, "It is worn out."

When I heard this I said to them, "Farmers, you have gone and used up my hoe. My hoe came from the blacksmiths. The blacksmiths used up my skin. My skin came from Duyker. Duyker ate my cowpeas. My cowpeas came from grandmother. Grandmother ate my big green grub. My big green grub came from Muyangandi. At Muyangandi my little sister was lost. Today I hurt. I hurt. I shall break."

"Do not break. Do not break," the farmers said, "but in exchange take this basket of corn."

I took the basket of corn and came along with it until I saw some wattled cranes. The cranes were eating sand. When I saw this, I said to the cranes, "Why is this? Do you have no corn?"

The cranes said, "Yes, that is it. We have no corn."

As a matter of course I let the cranes have my basket of

corn. The cranes ate all the corn. Later I asked the cranes, "Where is my corn?"

The cranes replied, "We ate it all."

Once more I bawled, and I said to the cranes, "What provided you with my corn? My corn came from the farmers. The farmers wore out my hoe. My hoe came from the blacksmiths. The blacksmiths wore out my skin. My skin came from Duyker. Duyker ate my cowpeas. My cowpeas came from grandmother. Grandmother ate my big green grub. My big green grub came from Muyangandi. At Muyangandi my little sister was lost. Today I hurt, I hurt. I shall break."

"Do not break. Do not break," the cranes said to her, "but take some of our feathers." I took some of their feathers and made a feather headdress[5] with them.

That same day, as I went along, I came to a place where the toads were putting on a formal dance. The toads were wearing headdresses made from bunches of grass. When I saw this I said, "When other folks dance they wear feather headdresses. Your headdresses are only bunches of grass. Why is that? Here, take my headdress made from feathers. Wear it, and go on with the dance."

The toads took my feather headdress, and they danced and danced until my headdress of feathers came all apart. When I saw this, I bawled and said, "Toads, my headdress came from the wattled cranes. The wattled cranes ate my corn. The corn came from the farmers. The farmers wore out my hoe. The hoe came from the blacksmiths. The blacksmiths wore out my skin. My skin came from Duyker. Duyker ate my cowpeas. The cowpeas came from my grandmother. Grandmother ate my big green grub. My big green grub came from Muyangandi. At Muyangandi my little sister was lost. I hurt, I hurt. I shall break."

When the toads heard this, they all jumped into the water —"Plunk!"

[5] This headdress, called an *esaka,* is made by fastening quills to a cap-like base. The feathers stand up from the head, and wave about as the wearer dances.

12. *contests and trials*

the simpleton

A king was traveling around visiting different parts of his country when he saw a monitor lizard up in a tree. The king was pleased and said, "If I can catch that lizard, I shall kill it and have something good to eat."

The king tried to climb the tree, but could not do it, for the tree was very large. He went to a nearby village and called out all the people, including the old men. When they had assembled he said to them, "I have found a fine monitor lizard up in a tree. I will give a part of my kingdom to whoever will bring it down out of the tree for me."

When the people heard this announcement, they were excited and eager, and raced each other to the tree. First came those who thought of climbing the tree, but soon they gave up. Then came those who thought of cutting down the tree, but they also gave up, for the tree was as hard as metal and the axes could not cut into it. When an ax struck the tree there was a reverberation and a broken ax.

In the end, the whole population gave up.

In that village was a simpleton and he also had gone out to try for the lizard prize. He began by pondering over this problem: how shall I entice this lizard to come down out of the tree?

The village simpleton went away and brought back a goat and a dog. He obtained some food for them: corn meal mush for the dog and fresh grass for the goat. When he came to the tree he tied the goat to a stake, and some distance away he tied the dog to another stake. Then he placed the mush in a pan before the goat, and placed the fresh grass in half of a beehive before the dog. Neither animal ate the food placed before it, since it was not the custom of these animals to eat such food.

The lizard had been watching what the man was doing. The lizard laughed and laughed, saying, "For certain, this man is a real fool. I shall have to go down and teach the simpleton something. I shall simply change things around: giving the corn mush to the dog and the grass to the goat."

When the lizard came down to the ground, the simpleton knocked the lizard on the head with his ax handle and carried the lizard away to the king.

When the king saw that the simpleton had brought him the lizard, that it was the lizard he wanted, and that it was the lizard all the people had failed to get for him, he was delighted. The king spoke to the young man, saying, "I know that you are a simpleton, but since I have made a promise, and cannot refuse to honor my promise, I shall give you a part of my kingdom, even as I promised."

the broken dish

One day a hunter killed some hares. He placed them in a single pot and cooked them all together. In the afternoon he summoned all the children of the village to come and get some meat, saying, "Let all bring gravy dishes and get some stew. I shall put some stew in each dish." All the children of the village came with their dishes. Boys and girls and even little tots came.

While the children were eating what the hunter had given them, one of them broke a dish belonging to the hunter. No one saw who broke the dish.

"Who broke the dish?" the hunter asked them. Everyone denied doing it.

"It was not I," said one.

"It was not I," said another. So they all answered the hunter.

Then the hunter said, "All of you who were here, come, let us go over to the high rock you see over there, and we shall discover which one of you broke my dish." When they reached the rock, they were to climb up upon it, one by one, the larger boys first. As each climbed upon the high rock, he was to sing

If I am the one, if I am the one
 Who broke that little saucer,
If I am the one, if I am the one
 Who broke that little saucer,
 The little saucer of the second time,[1]
May the cock spread his tail feathers upon the water,
May I be condemned when we climb the rock of judgment.

All the children agreed to undergo this test, and all joined in singing the song. The test began with the oldest boy and proceeded down to the smaller boys. Each passed the test and was declared innocent until it was the turn of the child who had broken the dish. His name was Kasi. He climbed up the rock, singing

If I am the one, if I am the one
 Who broke that little saucer,
If I am the one, if I am the one
 Who broke that little saucer,
 The little saucer of the second time,
May the cock spread his tail feathers upon the water,
May I be condemned when we climb the rock of judgment.

As Kasi sang this song, his feet sank into the rock. Again he sang the song, and as he sang, he sank into the rock up to his knees. Yet again he sang, and now he sank into the rock to his hips as he was singing. Then his middle sank into the rock, while he sang the song once more. Continuing to sing, he sank into the rock up to his neck. Still he sang

If I am the one, if I am the one
 Who broke that little saucer,
If I am the one, if I am the one

[1] The idiom *saucer of the second time* indicates a dish so small that he who eats from it is allowed to fill it with food a second time.

> Who broke that little saucer,
> The little saucer of the second time,
> May the cock spread his tail feathers upon the water,
> May I be condemned when we climb the rock of judgment.

As he finished the song, he sank out of sight into the rock.

When this happened, all those looking on began to wonder what they should do. They called together all the animals and all the birds of the woods, that these might one by one try to get Kasi out of the rock. The birds were the first to try. One by one they pecked and pecked at the rock until they all had died, but without releasing the guilty boy from the rock. When all the birds had died, the animals came, and one by one they tried. Each animal failed and died, until all the animals as well as all the birds were dead, none of them able to release the boy from the judgment rock.

Then Tortoise came.

Tortoise said, "First, let me have a fowl belonging to a hunter." When this was given to him, he ate it. Then Tortoise split a small piece off from the rock, then another piece, and so on until the feet of the boy were visible to all. Tortoise continued chipping until the whole body of the boy was exposed. But it was clear that the boy was already dead. It was not possible for him to escape from the judgment of guilt and have his life once more. This was because so much time had been consumed in freeing him from the rock.

The children took Kasi's body away and buried it.

crane's eggs and olondongo

From a village a group of girls went out to gather olondongo.[2] On the way they crossed over a stream, on a bridge. Near the bridge was the nest of a pair of wattled cranes.[3] In the

---

[2] *Olondongo,* the plural form of *ondongo,* are the edible bulbs or corms of a sedge, each corm the size of a hazel-nut.
[3] A tall bird, about five feet high and with a sharply pointed bill some six inches long. In fighting, the bird frequently reaches for the eyes with this bill.

nest were eggs. As the girls passed, they saw that there were eggs
in the nest, but none of the girls touched the eggs. Later, when
they parted from one another to gather olondongo, one of the
girls stole away, went back to the bridge, and took the cranes'
eggs from the nest. She placed the eggs in the bottom of her
basket, and to hide them, covered them with olondongo.

When she returned to where the other girls were gathering
olondongo, she said to them, "I have olondongo enough. Haven't
you gathered enough yet? Let us go to the village."

"We have not filled our baskets yet," the other girls replied.

So the girl who had taken the eggs stood and waited for the
other girls to fill their baskets. While she was waiting, the cranes
came back from wherever they had been. They found their
eggs gone from their nest. They looked all around for their eggs,
but could not find them. Then the cranes went to the bridge to
ask all who passed that way about their eggs.

When the other girls had finally gathered all the olondongo
they wished to gather, they said, "The sun is low. Let us go to
the village." The girls took up their baskets and entered the path
toward the village.

When the girls reached the bridge and wished to cross it,
they found the cranes standing guard over the bridge. The
cranes asked the girls about the eggs. When the girls replied that
they had gathered only olondongo, the cranes asked them to cross
the bridge one by one and allow their baskets to be examined.
There were ten girls, and each of them denied having the eggs
in her basket. The cranes, so that they might find their eggs even
if hidden under olondongo, demanded as a test that each girl
shake[4] her basket before crossing the bridge.

As the first girl crossed the bridge, she shook her basket and
sang:

> Shake it. I have shaken ondongo.
>
> Shake it. I have shaken ondongo.
>
> Thus have I passed the test of Muyandi.

---

[4] The Umbundu verb translated *shake* has the meanings shake, sift, flip, and
swirl. Olondongo grains are customarily sifted by tossing or swirling the containing
basket in such a way that larger particles come to the top. About two such tosses or
shakes of the container would be sufficient to bring large eggs to the top.

To which the cranes replied in song:

Pass on, pass on.
That which eats you, you are leaving behind you.

So the first girl passed by the cranes and went on across the bridge. Then the second girl came to the bridge and was challenged by the cranes. She shook her basket as the first girl had done, and sang the same song the first girl had sung, and the cranes sang to her as they had to the first girl, allowing her to pass on. Thus it was with the first nine of the ten girls, these nine girls shaking their baskets of olondongo, singing the song sung by the first girl, and being allowed to pass when the cranes sang:

Pass on, pass on.
That which eats you, you are leaving behind you.

Last came the girl who had taken the cranes' eggs. Being afraid, she had stayed away from the bridge until the last. Then she came forward trembling. As she moved her basket very gently from side to side, hardly shaking it at all, she sang in a thin, soft voice:

Shake it. I am shaking ondongo.
Shake it. I am shaking ondongo.
Thus shall I pass the test of Muyandi.

But the cranes then spoke to her, saying, "We did not hear you well. Sing out with loudness and shake the basket with vigor."

Thus was she forced to shake the basket with more of a sifting motion, again singing with a tremor:

Shake it. I am shaking ondongo.
Shake it. I am shaking ondongo.
Thus shall I pass the test of Muyandi.

As she was singing, she shook the basket so nervously that the eggs fell out and broke upon the bridge.

The cranes picked her eyes out with their bills, and then picked her whole body to pieces. Only the bones remained, and no flesh at all.

Later, when the other girls reached the village, they would not talk at all about what had happened. They closed their mouths and would say no word about it.

The parents of the tenth girl went out to look for her, but all they found were scattered bones.

the woman who insulted a pebble

One day, as some women were walking along the path to the fields, one of them stubbed her toe on a small stone. The woman cursed the stone, saying to it, "You hurtful stone! May your insides have pain!" The women walked on to their fields.

When they were returning home, they found that the little stone had become a great mountain which stretched from one river to the next. There was no way for the women to pass by. Seeing the mountain barring their way, they sang this song:

> O mountain, dear mountain, have pity!
> You have become a terrible monster.
> Be good, I have left my child in the village.
> Can't you hear? The drum it says, "Come home."

And then the mountain was heard to say:

> Pass on.
> It is only she
> Who insulted me.

Then the mountain allowed them to pass. When other women came to the mountain, they also sang the same song the first women had sung, and to them also the mountain replied:

Pass on.

It is only she

Who insulted me.

Thus did the mountain let all of them pass, until there came the woman who had cursed the stone.

She in her turn knelt down and sang:

O mountain, dear mountain, have pity!

You have become a terrible monster.

Be good, I have left my child in the village.

Can't you hear? The drum it says, "Come home."

Then the mountain opened its mouth and swallowed her.

the fowl family tree

One rainy day Rooster said to the water running through the village, "Please greet my Great-uncle Crocodile for me, when you come to his stronghold in the river."

When Floodwater came to the stronghold of Crocodile he said, "When I came through the village, Rooster said to me, 'Please greet my Great-uncle Crocodile for me.' "

When Crocodile heard this, he was angry and said, "The impudence of that bird Rooster! He has maligned me. I am a great four-legged animal, of whom all are afraid, while he is a skinny, feathered, two-legged bird, only feared by bugs and worms. I am no kin of his. He has insulted me. I shall challenge him to the poison test for this."

At the king's village, a day was set for the poison test. All the folk of the water and of the mud came, together with Hippopotamus, their king. All the feathered folk of the air came also, with Eagle, their king. While the materials for the poison test were being prepared, Rooster made a formal statement of his case. He said, "As a preliminary, I wish to state the basis for my contention. If Grandfather Crocodile was born as other four-legged animals are, then I was wrong, and he is not of our family. In that case I shall apologize, and pay a fine for the insult. But if Grandfather Crocodile was hatched from an egg, he is of our kin, and I am not in error."

When Crocodile heard this statement, he arose and said, "Stop the test. I will not drink poison, for I was hatched from an egg."

Then all the assembly agreed and said, "We have heard the word. Rooster is not guilty."

the nighthawk cried

One day a king called together in the clubhouse the old men of the village, and said to them, "Now, fathers, I am about to leave with the young men on our annual looting raid of the dry season. The responsibility for the care of my new field I am leaving with you. As you know, all the trees have been felled, their branches lopped off, and the trunks piled along with the brush and branches. I wish to have these piles thoroughly dried out before they are burned. I do not wish to have logs lying partly burned all over my new field. It is important that you do not hurry the burning. Have you heard my words?"

Then one of the old men replied, "Oh Lord and Lion of the clan, we have heard. What will be the sign, by which we may know that the time has come for burning the piles in your new field?"

The king said to him, "Father, you ask a good question. When you hear the cry of the nighthawk in the evening, then it will be the time to fire the piles in my new field."

At this time the king's chief councilor spoke up and said, "Oh Lord and Lion, I wish to beg a favor. This year I have no heart for going to war. If it be your will I shall stay at home."

Then the king said to him, "Sir, by all means stay at home. For in our enterprise there is no place for the faint-hearted."

The chief councilor said, "Father, we thank you."

One night in the dry season, while the old men were sitting talking in the clubhouse, a nighthawk was heard to cry. One of the old men said, "There is the cry of the nighthawk." Another said, "The king said, 'When you hear the cry of the nighthawk, you are to burn the piles of logs in my new field.' "

Then all agreed with him and said, "Indeed that is true. That is what he said." The next day the old men called all the boys together, and they went out to the king's new field and fired the piles of brush and logs. The logs were not yet dry enough to burn well, so unburned logs were left all over the king's new field.

When it was time for the rains to begin, the king returned from his raiding. The next day he went to look at his new field. He found half burned logs lying all over the field. The king became angry, called the old men together, and said to them, "Before I left on my raid, did I not charge you to use care in burning the piles of brush and logs in my new field? Now I find that you burned the piles too soon, before the logs were dry. Now there are logs lying all over my new field."

One of the old men replied to this and said, "Oh Lion, that is true. But you said also, 'When you hear the cry of the nighthawk, then you are to burn my field.' We remembered this, and when we heard the cry of the nighthawk, we burned the piles. The piles did not burn well and there are logs lying all over your field. The responsibility for this rests with the nighthawk."

Then all the old men agreed with him, saying, "It is true. We all heard the cry of the nighthawk."

Then the king called Nighthawk. Nighthawk came along with his wife. The king spoke to them, saying, "When I was about to leave for my dry season raid, I charged the old men with the care of my new field. I told them that I did not wish to have the piles of brush and logs fired too soon. If fired too soon they would not burn well, and logs would be left lying all over my field. Since I knew your regular habits, and that you are not accustomed to cry at night until the end of the dry season, I said, 'When you hear the nighthawk, that will be the time to fire the piles of brush and logs in my new field.'

"When I returned from the raid, I found that they had fired the piles too soon, the piles had not burned well, and there were logs lying all over the field. I was angry with the old men. They said that they had heard you cry at night, so they burned the piles in the field. The trouble is that you cried out of season. Because of this, the old men burned the piles too soon, and there are logs all over my new field. Uncle Nighthawk, why did you cry out of season, and cause me all this damage?"

Mistress Nighthawk spoke in reply and said, "Oh King and Lion, who would not cry when all their children were destroyed in a moment? I cried in anguish, for that was a time for crying."

The king said, "I am grieved and sorry for you. How did such a calamity happen?"

Mistress Nighthawk told him, "It was Hippopotamus who came along in the night and put one of his great feet squarely on my nest."

When the king had heard this, he sent and called Hippopotamus. When Hippopotamus came, the king said to him, "When we were about to go on our dry season raid, I charged the old men with the task of burning the piles of logs and brush in my new field. I told them not to be in haste about this, lest the logs should not be dry enough to burn well. In that case I should have logs lying all over my new field. I told them that when they heard the cry of the nighthawk, that would be the time to burn the piles in the new field.

"When I came back from my raid, I found that they had burned the piles too soon. There were logs lying all over the new field. When I blamed the old men, they said that it was no fault of theirs, for they had heard the cry of the nighthawk. Then I called the nighthawks. I accused them of crying out of season, and thus leading the old men to burn the piles too soon, and thus leaving the logs lying all over my new field.

"The nighthawks said that they cried out of season because you stepped on their nest and destroyed all their eggs. Now, Elder and Father, why were you in the bush, so far away from the river that you stepped on the family of Nighthawk, and thus caused them to cry out of season, and thus caused the old men who heard it to burn the piles in my new field out of season, leaving logs lying all over it?"

Then Elder Hippopotamus replied to the king: "Oh King and Lion of the land, just let me explain, and you will see that I was in no way at fault. As you know, my eyes are for seeing in the water. You know also that the nest of Nighthawk is hard for good eyes to see even in daylight. I am exceedingly sorry for this sad accident."

The king was not satisfied with this answer and he continued, "Grandfather Hippopotamus, why were you not at home at your own house in the river, instead of walking about in the bush?"

Elder Hippopotamus replied to this and said, "Oh King and Lord, please be patient. My neighbor, Elder Crocodile, said to me, 'Tonight when you go out in the evening to feed, and you are not using your house, let me sleep there.' I agreed to this. After I had eaten my fill, I did not wish to disturb my guest, so I was just walking about to pass the time. It was while I was doing this that I stepped on the nest of Mistress Nighthawk."

When the king had heard the explanation given by Hippopotamus, the king excused him and sent for Elder Crocodile. When Crocodile came to the capital of the king, the king said to him, "Honorable Sir and Lord of the River, when I was about to leave on my dry season raid, I said to the old men that I was leaving my new field in their care. I charged them not to burn the piles of brush and logs too early, lest unburned logs should be left lying all over my new field. I told them that when they heard the cry of the nighthawk, that would be the time to burn the piles in my new field. When I returned, I found that they had hurried the burning, and there were unburned logs lying all over my new field. The old men said that they had waited until they had heard the cry of the nighthawk, even as I had said. So I called Nighthawk, who came with his wife. When I accused them of crying out of season, and thus causing logs to be left lying all over my new field, the Nighthawks said that Elder Hippopotamus had stepped on their children. Thus they had a reason for crying.

"Elder Hippopotamus, when he came, explained that he was just wandering about when this accident happened, because you were sleeping in his house, and he was not able to retire. Noble Lord, I have called you, so that you may explain why you were not sleeping at home, instead of in the house of Elder Hippopotamus, since you caused the disaster which destroyed Nighthawk's children, and thus led the old men to burn the piles in my new field out of season, leaving logs lying all over it."

Then Great Crocodile answered and said, "Oh Lord and Lion, master of the road to Njembo, it was from consideration for you nobles that I acted. Knowing that neighbor Hippopotamus feeds at night, and that consequently his house is empty, I asked permission to sleep in his house during his absence. I did this because your chief councilor wished to use my house for the night, to consummate an affair he had been carrying on with your daughter. I am quite innocent."

From this has come the saying: "That which happens under the water will become known."

13. hunting, gathering and agriculture

cricket holds a work bee

Cricket[1] used to be an obliging person. One day, when he wished to clear a new field, he invited people to come to his house for a bee.[2]

The first to come to the work party was Rooster. When Rooster came into the house, he was given a gourd of beer. As Rooster sat drinking his beer and was about to put the gourd down on the floor, he saw Wildcat coming, so he said to Cricket, "Please hide me." Cricket hid Rooster.

When Wildcat came in, he said to Cricket, "Didn't I see someone else in here?"

Cricket answered, "No, no one."

Wildcat drank his beer, and as he was putting the gourd down, he looked through the doorway and saw Dog coming, so he said to Cricket, "Please hide me." Cricket hid Wildcat.

When Dog came in, he said, "Cricket, did I see someone in here?"

[1] This is a large cricket, which digs a burrow more than a foot deep in sandy soil. At the bottom of the burrow is a room, where the cricket stores and eats food. Food is gathered during the day, and eaten during the night. This cricket is a solitary creature; when two or more are forced together, they eat each other. Like many of these stories, this one offers a description and a mythical explanation of the appearance and habits of some creature commonly encountered in the natural environment of the Ovimbundu. The Ovimbundu are very observant of animal life, plant life and terrain, and use even their stories to sharpen and fix their observations. This story, like many others, deals with the customs and morals of the Ovimbundu, even while explaining the disposition and habits of a well-known lower animal.

[2] The bee or work party is a regular feature of Umbundu life. The community gathers to assist one of its members in a difficult and major work project, and he in turn supplies food and drink to his community helpers. The scene of this story is simultaneously the deep, dark dining hole of the cricket; and the ordinary house of the Ovimbundu: a small, windowless thatched hut, furnished with a couple of low stools for guests and a supply of sour beer served in a small drinking gourd.

Cricket answered him, "No. No one yet."

Dog sat down and drank from his gourd. When he had finished, he put the gourd down, and as he put it down, he saw Hyena coming. He said to Cricket, "Please hide me." Cricket hid Dog.

When Hyena came in, he said to Cricket, "Didn't I see someone in here?"

Cricket said, "No. No one."

Then Hyena drank from his gourd of beer. When he looked through the doorway he saw a hunter coming, so Hyena said to Cricket, "Please hide me." Cricket hid Hyena.

Hunter came in and said to Cricket, "Didn't I see someone in here?"

Cricket replied, "No. No one."

Soon after this was said, a cockroach fell from the roof of the hut to the floor below. When Rooster saw the cockroach fall, he could not restrain himself and dashed out from his hiding place saying "My free plunder! A cockroach!"

Wildcat saw Rooster, and rushed out of hiding, screaming, "My free plunder! A rooster!"

When Dog saw Wildcat kill Rooster, he ran out from hiding, saying, "My free plunder! A wildcat!"

When Hyena saw Dog kill Wildcat, he rushed out from where he had been hiding, saying, "My free plunder! A dog!"

As Hyena was finishing off Dog, the hunter saw Hyena, reached for his gun, and said, "Now Hyena is a dead one." He killed Hyena.

Later, Tortoise came along and asked the bystanders what had caused all the devastation. They told him what had happened, and Tortoise said, "Go call Civet Cat." When Civet Cat came, the people had him dig a grave and bury the victims in it; then they all paid Civet Cat for his work.

Cricket had fled to his underground shelter. They dug him out and killed him. Their verdict on Cricket was: "Cricket has been too obliging."

rat hunting

One day a group of girls went out to hunt rats.[3] When they came to the fields on the bottom lands, they found a hole which had been much used, so they began digging there.

Among these girls was one named Kalesu who thought, "Too much of this! When all dig in one place they do not find enough to go around. I am going off alone and find a hole to dig all for myself." Kalesu walked away alone to look for another rat hole.

After a time she found a hole that had been much used, and there she began to dig. When she had dug down a considerable distance she found a hoe, which she took out. When she had dug farther she found a large quantity of food, which she removed. She kept digging and came to a field basket. She took the field basket out. When she had dug farther she found a sword, and she also took it out. Still farther on she excavated an ax. Next she found bows and arrows. She took these out. Then she reached through the hole with her arm to discover what might be inside. What she found was that something inside caught and held her arm.

When the sun was sinking in the west, the other girls who had been digging up rats divided the rats they had found, giving each girl her share. They said, "Look! The sun is departing. It is time for us to go home to the village."

Then they began calling to their companion, "O Kalesu, let us go!"

Kalesu answered them with this song:

Come help your comrade, whose arm is imprisoned.

I would be coming, but a beast holds Kalesu.

O woe!

[3] The field rat is considered as edible and tasty as the hare. Rat hunting is usually conducted after the dry season grass fires, by women and girls using hoes.

Her arm was drawn completely into the hole. While they went away, the other girls continued calling to her, saying, "O Kalesu, let us go!'

Once more she sang:

Come help your comrade, whose arm is imprisoned.
I would be coming, but a beast holds Kalesu.

O woe!

Now her head was drawn into the hole, as well as her arm, and still the others continued calling and calling to her, until they reached the village.

Kalesu continued answering them with her song until her whole body was drawn into the earth.

When the other girls entered the village they were asked, "Where is Kalesu?"

"We left her digging rats. She went off alone by herself. We called and called to her, and yet she did not come. Since the sun was going down, we left her there digging rats," answered the girls.

When morning came, Kalesu's parents together with her whole family compelled the other girls to go with them and show them where they had left Kalesu. The other girls pointed out to the family where Kalesu had been digging. They did not find her there, for she had disappeared into the rat hole. They dug and dug but found no trace of her.

So all the family returned to the village weeping. When they came to the village they began to make preparations for the funeral of Kalesu.

the king who called for a hunt

There was once a king who sent his servants to call all the men to come to a drive hunt.

At daybreak in the morning, all the men came to go to the drive hunt. The king told them that he wished to have a certain small animal. When the king had named the animal, all went out and hunted and hunted, but they did not find a single animal of the kind which the king wished.

Finally, the hunt came to the edge of the king's village. As they passed near the stockade of the village, a small animal of the kind which the king wished started up from behind the king's spirit house and ran swiftly into the king's kitchen. Then the hunters went around the stockade to the entrance of the village, and went in. When they came to the king, the king asked them, "Where is the small animal which I sent you out to get for me?"

The master of the hunt said to him, "We did not find one out in the bush, but just as we passed behind your spirit house, we started one up and chased it, and it went into the royal kitchen."

When the king had heard this, he said to them, "Stop the hunt. I'll kill it myself."

hunting in a fog

Once Hunter went hunting in a fog. He was hunting for animals, but he found none. He went and he went[4] until he found a little bird. He said to himself, "I am going to shoot that, so that I may have something to roast." He raised his gun and shot at it. But the bird was not killed. Instead it was changed into a fierce Great Bird, which began to sing this song:

He who went sneaking about in the fog—here he comes.

He who went sneaking about in the fog—here he comes.

Out in the fog was a giant bird—here it comes.

That which will look at the nape of your neck—here it comes.

When Hunter saw Great Bird and heard it sing, he was afraid and ran. He ran to Duyker, saying, "Duyker will stab Great Bird with his horns." When he came to Duyker, Duyker said to Hunter, "Why are you fleeing to me?"

[4] The language contains no special word for "walk," since the Ovimbundu usually move from place to place by their feet.

Hunter said, "I am running away from a bird."

Duyker said, "Hide right here. And the bird, where is it?"

Hunter said, "It is coming. Just listen carefully."

Duyker listened and heard Great Bird, heading for his house singing:

He who went sneaking about in the fog—here he comes.

He who went sneaking about in the fog—here he comes.

Out in the fog was a giant bird—here it comes.

That which will look at the nape of your neck—here it comes.

When Duyker heard this singing, he was seized with great panic and said, "Oh Hunter, go away from here, for I am not able to contend with that."

So Hunter did not stop, but went right on by, heading for the house of Reedbuck. When he came to the house of Reedbuck, Reedbuck asked Hunter, "What are you running away from?"

Hunter said, "I am running away from a big, big bird."

Reedbuck said, "Hide in here for the time being. If it comes here, I shall gore it with my horns and slash it with my hooves."

At that time Great Bird was approaching, and as he came he sang:

He who went sneaking about in the fog—here he comes.

He who went sneaking about in the fog—here he comes.

Out in the fog was a giant bird—here it comes.

That which will look at the nape of your neck—here it comes.

When Reedbuck heard this, he said, "That Great Bird? Is that it?"

Hunter said, "That is it."

When Reedbuck had heard the bird clearly, he became frightened. He said, "By my sacred grandfather, please go somewhere else. I do not want you here." [5]

After having been to the houses of all the animals, Hunter

[5] From there Hunter flees to Roan Antelope, Lion, Wart Hog, Water Buck, and as many animals as the narrator cares to name. Each animal gives some hasty excuse for turning Hunter away, after hearing the song of Great Bird.

came to the house of Tortoise. Tortoise said to him, "Hunter, what are you running away from?"

Hunter said, "I am fleeing from Great Bird. I have already been to the homes of all the animals and not one of them has been able to save me."

Tortoise said to him, "Just go into my kitchen. I shall stand in the doorway."

Soon Giant Bird could be heard, and as he came he sang:

He who went sneaking about in the fog—here he comes.
He who went sneaking about in the fog—here he comes.
Out in the fog was a giant bird—here it comes.
That which will look at the nape of your neck—here it comes.

Tortoise wiggled back and forth in time with the beat of the song. The bird kept repeating the same verse until it came to Tortoise. Then the bird thought it would just push Tortoise aside. The bird caught Tortoise by the tail. When the bird did this, Tortoise shut his shell on Great Bird's beak. Soon the bird was wailing. All the animals came to look on.

So it was that Hunter escaped with the help of Tortoise. To celebrate this, all the animals began to sing:

Tortoise he is the old, old wise one.
Chah, Chah, Chako.
Tortoise he is the old, old wise one.
That is it, that is it.
There, there, that is it.

a ghost interrupts the making of a new field

After their marriage, a young man and his bride went out to start a new field. The man cleared ground until the trees he had cut down made two large brush piles. The woman hoed enough of this cleared ground to make one large section of a field. Then they quit work and went home to the village.

The next morning they went out to work again. But at the place where they had worked, they found that the trees the man had cut down had now been put back where they had originally stood. Even the lopped branches had been put back onto the trees, and the trees were standing. The ground which the woman had hoed was now as it was before she hoed it. The place was just uncleared bush, where the trees had not been felled, nor the sod turned.

When they had seen this, the man said to his wife, "Woman, let us clear the field again. When we finish, I will not return to the village. I will stay here to watch for those who replaced the trees and sods while we were gone." When they quit work, the man stayed behind to watch.

When the sun was touching the mountains, two men came. Their bodies were not like those of ordinary men. Their heads were two colors. Also, their noses were two colored, their eyes two colored, their mouths two colored, their arms two colored, their hands two colored, and their feet two colored. They came into the field and began to put the trees back into their original places, singing as they worked:

> Plant, plant! Thus we plant the trees of Njembo.
>
> Plant, plant! Thus we plant the trees of Njembo.

The man who was hiding with his gun and watching came forth and shot at the two-colored men, but his bullets did not harm them. The two of them fled, with the man running fast after them. The two, looking back and seeing him running after them, called back to him:

> Wait, brother, wait! Wait, brother, wait!
> Please turn away. Now turn away.
> We are ghosts, not men of flesh.
> We cross over Makelengenge,
> Then we go over Matolevela.
> Who goes over a little youngster
> Will come back an aged gaffer.

When they came to the river Makelengenge, the ghosts went across, but the man did not find a place where he could cross. He looked and looked, tried and tried, but it was a large river and he could find no place to cross. Finally he found a place, crossed over, and went on following the ghosts. Again he fired his gun at them, but every time he fired he missed. The ghosts kept fleeing, still singing:

> Wait, brother, wait! Wait, brother, wait!
> Please turn away. Now turn away.
> We are ghosts, not men of flesh.
> We cross over Makelengenge,
> Then we go over Matolevela.
> Who goes over a little youngster
> Will come back an aged gaffer.

Soon they came to a second river, the Matolovela, as large as the Makelengenge. The ghosts crossed over quickly, but the man wandered up and down the banks and could find no ford. Finally he found a place to cross, and followed the ghosts until they went into a patch of tall grass. Then he could see no more of them.

After searching and searching in the tall grass, he found a small hole in the ground. He dug and dug in the small hole. Finally he came to a narrow passage, and crawled through it like a worm until he came out into a wide country that stretched away and away into the distance.

He gazed on this and saw hyenas clothed like people. Some of these hyenas were lying sunning themselves on the cliffs. He looked more closely and saw old men greeting each other, and young men scraping the hair off a hog. When the old men saw him, they greeted him, saying, "A guest has come! A guest has come!" Then all the old men came and greeted him, making formal welcoming speeches, and finally saying, "Honored sir, will you sleep here?"

He replied, "Honored elders, we shall sleep here, but we did not come here to ask anything of you. I have merely been

following those who replanted the trees I had cut down and replaced the sod my wife had dug up.

The elders considered his statement, and then said to him,
"You have tried to make a new field in a grove sacred to the
dead. Make your new field in the bush next up the stream, and
the ghosts will guard it for you." The man begged their pardon
for disturbing a grove sacred to the ghosts, and promised to move
his field. The elders were pleased with this promise, and then
told him, "When you go back to your country, you will understand the creatures when they talk with each other: what the
birds say, what the ants say, what the elephants say, what the
snakes say, what the antelopes say, and whatever the animals say
to each other. But on the day that you tell other people what the
animals say, on that day you will die." He left the place and
went back home.

One day, while a friend was combing and braiding his
hair, the man saw ants passing by. The ants were talking to each
other. Some of the ants suggested that they all go to a certain
place for the night, but other ants thought the place was too far
away. The first ants repeated, "The place is near here."

The other ants ridiculed this statement, and said in an insulting way to the first ants, "How can you argue with us! You!
Look at your waists! They seem hewed out by an amateur using
a dull adze."

The man was amused by the conversation of the ants, and
was convulsed with laughter. So the man braiding his hair said
to him, "What are you laughing at?"

The man remembered that he must not tell people what the
animals said, and so told the other man, "Oh, I was just laughing." [6]

But the friend who was braiding his hair insisted on having
an answer, saying, "Just tell me this: what were you laughing
at?"

This time the man replied, "Oh, I shall tell you about it
later."

But the friend insisted, "You must tell me what you were
laughing at."

[6] It is common to several versions of this story that a man having his hair braided
or the lice removed from his head overhears and laughs at a conversation of the
ants, whereupon the person braiding hair or removing lice fears that he has been
laughed at.

Then the man who had laughed asked his friend, "Would you press me to tell you what I was laughting at, if my telling you meant that I should be brought to the grave?"

The friend replied, "Yes, I would."

Then as the friend went on braiding his hair, the man explained, "I went to a far place, chasing those who disturbed my new field, and when I left that far place, those who bid me good-bye told me, 'When you return to your country, you will hear and understand the conversations of the creatures, but you will die on the day you tell any other person of this.' Then when I returned home I found that what I had been told was true. Now, friend, listen to what these ants nearby are saying."

The friend replied, "I do not hear anything."

The man who could hear and understand the ants told his friend what the ants had said to make him laugh. When he had finished relating what the ants had said, he died.

14. famines and adventurous journeys

hunger time

Once there was a time of such hunger that there were people who stayed alive only by trapping rats. Among those who were trapping rats there was a man who caught no rats. He tended his traps every day, yet he caught no rat. The other trappers were catching rats every day. Encouraged, they were adding to the number of their traps. They looked upon the man who caught no rats as a man destined for bad luck. Still, he did not despair, but kept on trying.

One day he examined nine traps and found nothing caught in any of them. But in the tenth trap, he found a small animal. His first thought was to crack its head by a sharp blow. When he hit the animal, instead of its head breaking, the animal exuded a quantity of corn meal mush. The second time that he hit the animal, it exuded gravy. He ate the mush and gravy and was satisfied. He did not tell the other trappers of his catch, but carried the little animal back toward the village to give it to his wife.

Recently his wife had been very cross with him, scolding him and saying, "You are worthless. Do you know how to set traps? Your friends catch rats. How is it that you catch no rats?" When he reached the village, he told his wife about the animal he had caught, enthusiastically describing how it could exude good things to eat. She accused him of lying, but added that if what he described so enthusiastically proved to be true, now they would be well off. Putting the animal down before her, the husband said, "Do not pound this little animal with a club. But first put a dish under its back end, and then tap it gently with a switch."

Though without belief, she placed a mush bowl under its rear end as directed, and then tapped the animal with a switch: and it dropped good mush. She tapped it again and it dropped gravy to go with the mush. This excited her to dancing with joy, for she was desperately hungry. From that time onward the man and woman ate well, but they did not tell the man's younger brother about their find.

For several days, the man and woman gave none of the food which came from the little animal to the man's younger brother. But finally the older brother said to him, "When the sun rises and it becomes warm, tap this little animal and it will give you some food. Your starving appearance these days makes one feel pity." Later, when the sun had risen high, and it was warm, the younger brother said to his friends, "Come with me. Let us go and eat some mush." Upon hearing him say "mush," they all came in haste with a loud clamor. All the youngsters of the village came—not one was missing.

All these boys being told by the younger brother that the little animal gave good mush when tapped, began to give the animal a relentless beating. The small animal was terrified, for it had never felt such blows or heard such noise before. Finding a hole, it escaped.

When the older brother and his wife returned home from the field, the woman placed the mush bowl down and said to her husband, "First let us tap our little friend, and then we can eat." But then she said to her husband, "I have looked where the animal should be, and it is not there."

At this, the man called to his younger brother, "That little animal, where is it?"

"It ran away," answered the younger brother.

Reaching for his gun, the older brother said, "Now I am going to shoot you."

"Brother, do not kill me so hastily. I shall go out and find the little animal," pleaded the younger brother.

"Then go and find it, but if you do not return with it, I will kill you."

The younger brother started searching along the path which had been taken by the animal. He went a long way. Finally he came upon an old woman afflicted with boils. She was also decrepit and filthy. "Where are you going?" she asked of him.

"I am looking for a small animal which belongs to my brother, but has run away," he answered her.

She said to him, "First, suck out the pus from my boils and spit it on the ground, also taking care to cleanse my whole body, for it is very filthy. Then I shall help you." These things the younger brother did, sucking all her boils and cleansing her body until it was everywhere red.

When he had finished, the old woman gave him two small horns, saying to him, "The names of these two horns are 'Yawova' and 'Yemana.' Wherever you may go, if any difficulty exceeds your powers, first ask advice from Yawova and afterward from Yemana."

Taking the two horns, the young man traveled until he reached a large river, as large as the Keve. Seeing no way to cross the river, he first asked Yawova, "As there is no bridge, how shall I cross the river?"

"Why do you ask me?" answered Yawova. "Do you not know to cross at the ford?"

Then the young man, as he had been instructed, asked Yemana, saying, "Father, where is a bridge across this river?"

"Very near here, up stream," answered Yemana.

The young man crossed over on the bridge and continued his journey. After some journeying he came to a village surrounded by a stockade. He could find no gate in the stockade, so he asked advice of Yawova, saying, "Father Yawova, where is the gate?"

"Just climb over the fence," answered Yawova.

Yemana was also asked about the location of the gate, and answered, "The gate is there, a short distance to one side of you."

The youth entered through the gate, and soon reached the men's clubhouse of the village. He could see people inside the club, but since he could see no entrance into the club, he asked Yawova, "Where is the entrance to the clubhouse?"

Yawova answered with irritation, "Are you again asking me about an entrance? Just pull some sticks from the side wall and enter through the gap."

Once more the youth turned from Yawova to Yemana, asking, "Father, where is the entrance?" Once more Yemana revealed an entrance, and the youth entered the clubhouse. Those inside greeted him and inquired what he was seeking to find.

"A small animal belonging to my brother escaped, and I

come searching for it," he explained to them. The men told him that he had come to the right place, but that the matter must be saved for the morrow. They gave the youth a sleeping place in the ancestral guesthouse.

After sunset the people of the village brought him mush to eat, and for relish to season it the flesh of a cock. He remembered that when he had left the old woman, she had given him eight crabs and told him that he must eat these as relish with the next mush he should be given. So the youth asked Yawova, "Shall I eat the cock's meat and the mush?" Yawova replied, "How old are you now, that you still ask how and what you are to eat? Will you not eat the mush with the flesh of fowl the people cooked to be eaten with it? In addition, you will crack the fowl's bones to get out the marrow. Is not that the way everyone eats? Will you continue on and on asking me childish questions again and again?"

Hearing this reply, the youth turned to Yemana and asked him, "Father, how shall I eat?"

"The meat, do not eat that, and do not even touch the bones of the cock." Such was the advice of Yemana.

Following Yemana's advice, the youth began to munch on the crabs the old woman had given him. The villager who had brought the mush and fowl's flesh had waited secretly outside the door to know when the young man had begun eating the food brought to him. When this stealthy villager heard the crunching of the crab shells he returned to the other villagers and reported to them, "I left the guest already eating and cracking the cock's bones."

Very late in the night, when it was almost dawn, the youth was awake and heard outside the voice of the village's town crier. The village crier delivered a message on behalf of all the people, crying with a loud voice: "Perhaps when we needed eggs of fowl you laid them for us. If not, let the cock, which we cooked for you, now crow."

When this pronouncement had been made, the meat which the youth had left untouched changed into a living cock again and crowed loudly.

Soon, the village crier spoke again: "Perhaps you cultivated our corn for us. If you did not cultivate our corn for us, let the corn mush be changed back into whole kernels of corn." When this pronouncement had been made, the still uneaten corn mush which had been brought to the youth turned back into whole kernels of corn.

When dawn had come and it was quite light out, the people showed him many small animals, saying to him, "Now select the animal which belongs to your brother. If you select the correct one, you may have it to take with you, but if you make a mistake in the selection, you may not have any of the animals."

Since his own powers seemed inadequate to make the selection, the youth consulted Yawova, asking him, "Since these animals all look alike, how am I to know the right animal?"

"Are you troubling me again?" Yawova answered. "Just say that any little animal is the right one. Then keep it close to you and do not let it get away from you again. You have yourself pointed out the main thing: they are all alike."

Then the youth said to the other of the two horns, "Father Yemana, how am I to choose the correct animal?"

"A small fly will come and alight upon your nose," Yemana said. "The animal that fly settles upon, after it leaves your nose, that will be the right animal."

Then the youth felt a fly alight on his nose, and when it flew off again he noted which animal it lit upon, and pointed out that animal to the villagers, saying, "That is the one." They gave the animal to him, and he was so pleased he danced with joy.

Next the youth noticed a tree with figs hanging from its branches. He wished to have some of the fruit, and the people consented that he take some. To free himself for climbing, he removed the traveling bag he had been wearing and handed it to a nearby man to hold for him. He fastened the belt of the bag around this man's waist. Then he asked the people to boost him up, so that he could climb out onto the branches and gather fruit. While he was up in the tree gathering figs, the owners of the tree said, "O tree of ours, perhaps this person now in your branches was present when you were planted. If he was not there, pray carry him to the sky for us." The tree plucked itself up by the roots and flew skyward.

Then the youth spoke and said, "When I bought you, O traveling case of mine, perchance the owner of the tree was there, and if not, O traveling case of mine, cut him into two pieces for me."

As he spoke those words, the belt of the traveling case began to tighten around the waist of the man to whom the youth had tied it. The fig tree continued to fly skyward and the belt continued to tighten, until the man wearing the belt was howling in anguish and very close to coming apart at the middle. Then the owners of the tree shouted, "O tree of ours, return him, return him. O tree of ours, return him." At this, the tree stopped ascending and began to return to earth. It lowered itself until its roots were in the ground again. The youth now said, "O traveling case of mine, do not release the man you bind until I have come down out of this tree to the ground again." Then the young man picked the fruits he wanted, came down to the ground, and took back his traveling case.

The fruit he had gathered was delicious.

Then the youth, taking with him the small animal he had selected and the fruit he had gathered, left the villagers and returned toward his own village. When he reached his own village he gave the small animal to his older brother. His brother said, "That which you have followed, you have returned."

Then the younger brother left the fruit which he had brought back with him in his brother's house to be kept there for him. When the younger brother had left the house the elder brother looked at the fruit and then tasted one of the figs. The fruit had such a delicious taste that the older brother kept eating until he had eaten all of the figs.

When the younger brother returned to the house he wished to eat some of his figs and went to get them from the place where he had left them. They were not there, so he said to his brother, "Where is my fruit, which I left stored here?"

His brother said, "Brother, I ate the fruit."

Hearing this, the younger brother took up his weapon and said, "Truly, I will kill you unless you give me back my figs."

"O brother, please let me live, and I shall go and bring other figs to take their place," pleaded the elder brother.

When agreement was reached between them, the older brother left upon his journey. As he was going along, the older brother came to the same decrepit old woman afflicted with boils. The old woman said to the older brother, "Lick me off."

The brother stopped walking, looked sternly at the old woman, and said to her, "You inanimate thing, you animal, what are you attempting?"

"Friend, just go along past," the woman said. "Do not destroy me with your mouth."

He passed on by her, and kept going until he came to the village which he sought. When he went into the men's club-house, they asked him, after they had greeted him, why he had come there.

"I have come to gather some figs for my brother," he told them.

"You have found the place. Tomorrow you may pick them," said the people to him.

After taking him to the guesthouse, the people cooked mush for him, and a fowl to be eaten with the mush and flavor it.

In the early morning the village crier cried: "Perhaps the guest raised that fowl and fed it. If he did not, let the cock crow." Since the fowl had been eaten by the guest, it did not crow. The crier continued: "When we planted the corn, perhaps the guest hoed it. If he did not, let the cooked mush become grains again." The mush did not become grains again, for the older brother had eaten it.

When it had become day, the people of the village came for their guest and took him to the fig tree. They told him that they would now see how well he could gather figs. When he had climbed up into the tree the owner of the tree said, "Perhaps, when we planted the tree, you were present, but if you were not present, then we say, 'O tree of ours, loose him from the earth.' " At that, the tree pulled up by its roots and flew aloft. The people shouted, "O tree of ours, carry him away."

As the tree flew higher, the brother was frightened and fell out of the tree. When he came to earth his body burst upon the ground. He never returned the figs to his brother.

the land of joy

There was once a young man, the only child of his parents. As he thought over his future, he decided that his best course would be to seek out a friend to be his companion. He went about this search, and found just such a person.

One day this friend came to him to bid him good-by, saying, "My friend, I am leaving to visit the villages of my kinsmen. To reach those villages, one must sleep five times on the journey, and will reach them on the sixth day." The only child agreed to his friend's desires and said good-by to his friend.

When the friend had returned, the young man asked him, "What is the name of the villages which you have just visited?"

"Their name is the Land of Joy," replied the friend, naming the villages to the young man.

The young man said to this, "In none of the countries which I have ever visited have I heard of a place called the Land of Joy. Can I go there if I wish?"

The friend told him that he could go there, and would neither miss the way nor get lost. Hearing this, the young man asked, "Which path does one take to that country?"

His friend thought about this matter, and after a pause said, "Simply follow the main path which is the caravan route[1] until you reach a village beside the path."

It was some time after this conversation that the young man announced: "I am going to travel and visit the Land of Joy, for I have never seen such a place."

The youth prepared food for a journey of five days, said good-by to his friend, and entered upon his journey along the path. After he had traveled for five days he began inquiring if he were near the Land of Joy. The people whom he asked would question him in return, "How many days have you been traveling?"

"Four days and today is the fifth," he answered them.

"Then tomorrow, on the sixth day, you will arrive there," they told him.

The next morning he started out with pleasant anticipation, believing that surely he would come to the end of journey now. In the afternoon, as he looked ahead, he saw that the main path was becoming overgrown and difficult to follow, only a faint trail continuing any farther. Even this faint trail came to an end under a large tree. He then said to himself, "I shall go back and take a look around."

But when he turned around and looked back, there was no path at all where he had just passed. There was only grass, and no sign of a path. He had the feeling of a person who has just

[1] The region of Portuguese West Africa inhabited by the Ovimbundu has been crossed by traders, slavers and militarists for centuries. The broader paths used by such region-wide travelers are customarily called "caravan routes" or "main paths" to distinguish them from the almost innumerable narrow paths through the bush and jungle.

become lost. He became disturbed and talked to himself. He said, "What am I going to do today? In a little while the sun will go down. The stream is far away, and I have no fire." He sat down upon the ground under the great tree, leaning his back against its trunk.

Soon Great Bird flew close and alighted in the tree, for the bird was accustomed to eat in this tree. When the youth peered up into the tree, trying to get a look at the bird, the bird defecated and the dropping hit the youth squarely between the eyes. Then Great Bird spoke and asked him, "Are you a human being?"

"Yes, I am a man. The reason for my being here is that I am lost," replied the young man.

Then Great Bird said to him, "Some day you will obey the words of a woman."

The young man answered this by saying, "I will not obey the words of a woman."

Great Bird flew away, leaving him alone.

The next morning Great Bird flew back, and again said to him, "Some day you will obey the words of a woman."

"I shall not yield to their wiles," said the man.

For five days Great Bird flew back every day, and each day said that the young man would yield to the voice of a woman. Each day the young man denied this, saying that he would never yield to a woman. After he had made his denial on the fifth day, Great Bird said to him: 'Go and set a trap by that big white ant hill." The man found the materials for a trap and set a trap by the big ant hill, as the bird had told him to do.

As he was preparing to go and examine the trap the next morning, Great Bird came and asked him, "Have you visited your trap this morning?" The youth replied that he had forgotten to visit the trap.

He went to look at the trap, and arriving, found a girl caught in the trap. When he raised the trap, the girl stood up and came out from the trap. She was living and had brass rings on her ankles. This girl was a relative of Great Bird. They had a common soul, so that everything the girl said was already known to Great Bird and everything Great Bird said was already known to the girl, as soon as either spoke.

When the girl appeared before the young man, he said,

"Now my eyes are opened. As I look around me everything is changed. The trees which appeared to me as ordinary trees of the bush are in reality eucalyptus trees." Looking farther, he saw many dwellings. They were fine houses, equipped with everything one could need. His name was written upon the houses, as well as upon their furnishings. They belonged to him to do with as he pleased. There was a large herd of cattle complete with herders. The cattle numbered at least a thousand. There were sheep, goats, and all other animals which man makes tame. He had suddenly become a person of importance. The ordinary bush country had been transformed, and now he was a rich man among rich men.

Later he was overcome by the joy of possession and thought, "What shall I do for Great Bird?" He thought this matter over. When he had considered it, he said, "The proper course is for me to kill two oxen and eat them along with Great Bird, for he caused me to have all this prosperity. Not only that, but he gave me this excellent and beautiful girl whom I have married."

This speech had been heard by the listening girl, who now gave her opinion, saying, "What! That contemptible bird? Will you go and kill two oxen for that? How shall it eat all that meat? A better course would be for you to kill that bird and give it to me to eat." All these words of the woman were heard by Great Bird. Great Bird took off his feathers and made them into a figure resembling a bird with its head under its wing. Then he hid himself. Great Bird listened carefully to hear how the young man would reply to the woman.

The young man answered the girl's words, saying, "Isn't what you say true? All right. I shall kill Great Bird so that you may have it to eat." The youth had forgotten completely that Great Bird had repeatedly said that he would yield to the words of a woman, and that he himself had repeatedly denied this.

The youth reached the place where Great Bird had been hiding, and there he saw the feathered effigy, which he thought was really the bird. He fired his gun into it, and the feathers blew away—pfff! Then Great Bird spoke to him, saying, "Did I not say to you, 'Some day you will yield to the voice of a woman?' And did you not answer, 'I shall never do that, nor will I yield to a woman's wiles?' "

The girl vanished. Great Bird vanished. The young man

looked around and said, "Now that I look at them closely, I see that those are not eucalyptus trees, but ordinary trees of the bush, and there are no dwelling houses in sight." He found himself still sitting under the big tree, lost in the bush, as he had been before.

the bee hunter's family and their slave

I

There was a bee hunter who got a splinter in his eye, while he was hewing out a beehive. No one was present to blow into his eye.[2] His small son was with him, but he was too small to do the blowing. The father said to the child, "Go to the village and tell your mother to come here and blow into my eye."

When the child came to his mother in the village, he said to his mother, "Father sent me, saying, 'When you come to your mother in the village, tell her to kill the big fat fowl, cook it, and send it to me by the child.'" The mother did as directed.

When the child came to his father, he said, "Father, here is the fowl."

The father was angry about this, and he said to the child, "Go back again, and when you come to your mother, tell her to come here and blow into my eye."

The child went back again to his mother. He said to her, "Father said, 'That pig of ours, have your mother go and kill it, and then you bring me the liver.'"

The mother was astonished and said, "Haka! What is your father going to do?"

The child said, "That is not my affair, but that which I said is really what he wishes."

They killed the hog, and sent the liver by the boy. When the boy returned to his father, his father asked "Where is your mother? Where is she?"

The child said, "She sent the liver of the hog. Here it is."

Since the father was in great agony with his eye, he became

[2] To remove a foreign particle from the eye, another Ovimbundu holds open the lids of the patient's eye with fingers, and then blows quite forcibly against the eyeball.

very angry about the sending of liver. He spoke to the child, and said to him, "My child, Haka! Do you not understand what I have been saying to you?"

The child said, "O father, indeed I do understand it."

Then the father said to the child, "Run back as fast as you can, for I am near death. When you come to your mother, tell her to come here and blow into my eye."

When the boy came to his mother he said to her, "My father said, 'Go to your mother and have her send and kill the big ox, so that I may eat the liver.'"

Then the mother asked the child, "Haka! What is your father doing? Does he wish to destroy all our animals?"

The child said, "That is not for me to know. My duty is to keep telling you what he sends me for."

The mother caused the ox to be killed, saying, "The will of the husband must be followed. The ox will be cut up, as he planned." Then she sent the liver.

The child returned and found his father so near death that his life was about to leave him. The man had so little life left that what he spoke could just be heard. When the father saw the child had once more brought liver, he said nothing and only let his tears fall. Speaking very faintly, he sent the child back once more, and spoke to him the same words that he had used before, "When you go to your mother, ask her to come here and blow into my eye."

The child went again to his mother, and this time he said, "My father said, 'When you go to your mother, tell her to come here and blow into my eye.'"

Then the mother rose hastily, with much fear, and went as fast as she could, for many days had passed. She found her husband's life about to leave him. When she realized this, she threw herself on the ground and said, "O my husband, how good it would have been if I had given you a little sick care."

II

This same bee hunter and his wife also had a daughter, who had married down country and borne her children there. This daughter had been away from the parents for so long, not even visiting them, that she had never seen some of her younger brothers and sisters. She had been away so long that she did not remember even the younger child which she had seen.

While the mother was mourning for her husband, she bade her children farewell, saying to them, "I too am about to die, from grief for your father. If I die, when I am dead you are to go down country to your older sister Njamba, in the village where she lives."

After their mother's death, the children began the journey down country, taking with them a slave which had belonged to their father. There were two daughters, and the older daughter had a baby of her own.[3] The older daughter wore good clothes and brass leg-rings, as she led her younger sister and carried her own baby on the journey.

While they journeyed, the older sister, a free woman, became thirsty and said, "I am going to drink at this stream."

The slave woman would not let her do this, saying to her, "The child of a free person does not drink ordinary water." The slave girl went to the stream and drank, and the other walked on discomforted by thirst. After the slave had drunk at the stream, she said to the other, "When we come to the place where the children of free people drink, I shall show it to you."

Near their journey's end, they came to a very steep, high rock, and there was fine, pure water up on the side of the rock. The slave took the hunter's ladder which was nearby, placed it against the rock, and said, "Now you may climb up here and drink, for this is where the free people are accustomed to drink. But you should not climb up wearing your good clothes and brass anklets. Take them off, and for the climbing, put on this small cloth of mine." Then the free girl, having removed her own clothing and having put on the slave's cloth, climbed up to drink.

While she was up on the ledge, the slave took away the hunter's ladder, threw it down on the ground, took the older sister's baby upon her back, and called to the little sister, "We are going now."

They left the rock and walked on until they came to the village. When they came to the home of the older sister, Njamba, she rejoiced and rejoiced to see them. The slave girl presented herself as the older of the younger sisters and related how the father had died and how the mother later died of grief.

The slave deceived Njamba by saying, "I am your younger sister, next to you in age." The slave spoke the village language

---

[3] Babies are carried on the backs of adults until they are about four years old.

poorly, but Njamba had been away so long that she did not notice this. The baby which the slave carried drew away from her, and would stay only with her younger mother.[4] Still Njamba was deceived, being told that her youngest sister, whom the baby drew near, was a slave. This child could not deny that she was a slave or explain the situation, for the slave had spoken to her and said, "If you explain things and say that we left your older sister on the rock, and if you tell that I am a slave, then I shall kill you some day when we go to the bush for fire wood." Due to the fears of children, the child obeyed the slave and did not tell, even though she had to endure the hardships of a slave.

But even though the child was afraid to explain things to Njamba, still she said to herself, "I am not a slave. The slave is the one that you see there. My older sister is up on the rock." And this is what the child did: when she was given mush or sweet potatoes, she saved a portion of the food, slipped away secretly, and carried the food to her sister who remained on the rock. Because of the height of the rock, she rolled the mush into a ball and threw it up so that her sister could catch it and eat it. She did the same with other food. When she came back, Njamba always said to her, "You did not eat all your food. Where have you been?" And her answer was always, "Nowhere."

In this way the sister up on the rock was getting the food that her little sister carried to her. She had plenty of good water which flowed from the rock. Her real hardship was the cold of the night, for she had neither covering enough[5] nor a fire. She did not even have room to move about. Yet she did not die, for she had food and water.

Njamba had a field of sorghum. This field was next to that of a little old woman. Since this little old woman did not have a husband, she did not have to prepare food. So she stayed at the field and kept the birds away from both fields of sorghum. After a time, the little old woman became tired of watching both fields. She knew that Njamba had a young slave, so she went to Njamba and said, "Let me have your slave, so that she and I may go and watch the sorghum fields together." When they came to the fields to keep the birds away from the sorghum, the little old woman cried out:

[4] The Ovimbundu call all of the mother's sisters "mother."

[5] She lacked the usual garment of the Ovimbundu, a folded cloth hanging from the waist, which can be pulled up over the head when sleeping.

Do not go and eat,
Do not go and eat,
Our sorghum.

The child replied, singing:

Ah, Ngungu. Ah, Ngungu.
Do not eat Njamba's sorghum, chah-a-a-ah.
There is a slave, who once was free, chah-a-a-ah.
I am the slave who once was free, chah-a-a-ah.

When the little old woman heard the child sing this, she
again shouted:

Do not go and eat,
Do not go and eat,
Our sorghum.

And again the child sang:

Ah, Ngungu. Ah, Ngungu.
Do not eat Njamba's sorghum, chah-a-a-ah.
There is a slave, who once was free, chah-a-a-ah.
I am the slave who once was free, chah-a-a-ah.

When the sun was low, they went to the village. Njamba
gave them food, saying to the little old woman, "Eat this along
with your young helper." They divided the food. Again the
child slipped away and took food to her sister up on the rock.
This was repeated for several days. They watched the birds
in the morning and the afternoon, and the child carried the food
to her sister in the evening.
One day the little old woman went to her brother-in-law
and other people of the village and said, "What is going on?
Just come out to the field and hear what my neighbor's slave
child keeps singing." In the morning the little old woman went

to the fields again, and as usual, she called the little girl to go with her. All the people followed along behind. When they came to the fields, the little old woman began to call:

> Do not go and eat,
> Do not go and eat,
> Our sorghum.

The child sang in reply:

> Ah, Ngungu. Ah, Ngungu.
> Do not eat Njamba's sorghum, chah-a-a-ah.
> There is a slave, who once was free, chah-a-a-ah.
> I am the slave who once was free, chah-a-a-ah.

Then all the people who had followed to the fields came to the platform from which the little girl was keeping the birds away, and they said to her, "Come down from your platform and go with us." The people took her to the village and questioned her about her song. Then she told them the story about her sister and the rock. They said to her, "Guide us to the rock where your sister is."

When they came to the rock, they raised up the climbing pole and said to the girl, "Come on down."

The girl on the rock replied, "I will not come down, and for this reason: here I have endured excessive hardship. Upon this mountain I have not had anything with which to cover myself, so I cannot walk along the path over which free people walk." Then they promised to pay her a fine of an ox. She consented to come down, and went with them to the village.

When they reached the gateway to the village and wished to have her enter, she said, "Since I am a slave, I cannot go in through the entry where free people pass." Then they paid her a fine of a hog.

When they came to the house and wished to have her go in, she would not, saying, "I cannot go into the house of free people. I will not enter there as a slave."

When they had paid her a fine of a goat, she went into the house, but when they wished to have her take a chair, she said,

"I shall sit on the ground. That is a chair on which free people sit. I cannot sit on it, for I am a slave." The people gave her a goat, and then she consented to sit on the chair.

Later, when they brought her some food and told her to eat it, she said, "I cannot eat the food which free people eat, for I am still a slave." To settle this they gave her a hog. When she had been given this, she ate the food.

While the people of the village were making amends to Njamba's sister, Njamba herself had been pondering on everything that had happened, and did nothing but sit and weep. She thought, "How wrong! I go and take in an ordinary slave as my sister, on her word, and give her good food and lodging, while my real sister is enduring misery out on a bare rock. This ordinary thing has slept in a house upon a bed, while my sister has slept naked out on a bare rock." She wept and wept over this, and there was nothing that she could do to put things right.

All the old men of the village met and they said, "What are we going to do with this slave who has done a thing as bad as this?" They decided, "The correct thing to do is to throw her into a fire." They gathered hardwood logs to make a fire.

In the evening the town crier made an announcement, shouting: "Let everyone listen carefully! Tomorrow, let us all gather, children and adults, and go out to eat our little animal that has no tail."

Then all the people echoed: "That is the right thing. That is the right thing."

Then the person concerned, the slave, said, "Good! Tomorrow we shall go and eat our little animal which has no tail."

Then the crier made an announcement to the women. He cried to them: "Tomorrow, when you go to the feast, you are not to wear your good clothes, and your leg ornaments are to be taken off. When you gather around the fire, you are to stand apart from each other. Let no one stand in front of another." All the women consented to these commands. The next day they were glad to stand apart from each other, for all of their hearts were filled with hatred, thinking, "Today we shall burn that Ochingangela[6] who caused the child of a free person to undergo such torture."

---

[6] An *Ochingangela* is a person from any tribe to the east of the Ovimbundu. The Ovimbundu regard these as inferior races, and get most of their slaves from the region.

When the women gathered around the fire, they stood apart from one another, all facing toward the fire. Two men crept up silently behind the slave, seized her, and hurled her into the fire, where she perished with no chance of escape. They did this to her because she had done a monstrous thing.

the little white horn[7]

One day Hare said to Galago,[8] "Let's play a game." Galago agreed. Their game was to see which of them could resist the most fire. One of them was to hide somewhere, and then the other set fire to the hiding place.

Hare found a patch of dry grass, around which the ground had been burned. He went into this patch of grass and hid in a burrow. When Hare had hidden, Galago set fire to the grass on all sides. When the grass had burned, Hare came out of the burrow and said, "Galago, don't you see that we hares do not burn?"

Galago answered, "That seems to be true. Now, let me hide in another patch of grass, and you can fire it to find whether we galagos burn." Hare agreed.

[7] This long story is probably the most synthetic in this collection. The episodes hang together loosely, and some of them are as complete as other and shorter stories. In spite of the many deaths and injuries, the dominant mood of the story seems to be one of festival gaiety, and indeed it ends with a festival to end all festivals. The rollicking spirit perhaps accounts for the freedom with which disconnected narrative sequences are patched together. Some of the other stories have a much tighter narrative and a moral and psychological organization, even when they display as many surface incongruities, accidents and sudden shifts as we see used in this story. A few of the long stories are very tightly organized, being little more than expanding repetitions of a very short story, e.g., *Mupuiyakalangi*. Yet other long stories progress systematically, developing new themes, new aspects of character, and new actions throughout, e.g., *Kalitangi*. The present long story is different from either of those types. Its development appears to be neither repetitious nor progressive. Most of its characters and episodes appear in almost identical form in other stories, long and short. It is improbable that even the same native informant would tell this story exactly the same way twice. The story-telling informant probably did what Kipling thought Homer had done: "Wat 'e thought 'e might require, 'e went and took."

[8] An arboreal, nocturnal animal about the size of a rabbit. It has large, soulful eyes, a beautiful gray coat, and a voice like a banshee, which belies its small size and chills sleeping travelers into wakefulness.

Galago chose a patch of dry grass, went into it, climbed up a tree, and concealed himself among the leaves. Hare took a firebrand and set fire to every side of the patch of dry grass. A strong wind came and caused the grass to burn fast and blaze up high. Flames licked up into the tree and burned up the leaves in which Galago had hidden. Galago was cooked in an instant, fell to the ground, and popped.

When Hare saw this happening, he shouted: "Let my little white horn stay, and the black horn go away."

When Hare examined the corpse of Galago, he found a little white horn. When he blew upon the horn, it gave a musical note: "Pey!" Hare sang a funeral song for Galago:

Dear Galago is but ashes—pey, pey, peyko.

To the woods we went together—pey, pey, peyko.

To the stream we went together—pey, pey, peyko.

To the fields we went together—pey, pey, peyko.

Dear Galago is but ashes—pey, pey, peyko.

Woe is me that you are ashes—pey, pey, peyko.

On a later day, Duyker came to Hare and said, "O Hare, let us exchange horns. Trade me your little horn for this small horn of mine you see here. It is a good one."

Hare said, "Your horns are very poor, Duyker, and I will not touch them. I do not want to trade."

Then Duyker said, "If you feel that way, I see that you will not trade. But please, just let me look at your horn."

Hare said, "All right."

When Duyker examined the white horn, he saw that it was very fine, so he started running away with it. But Hare threw his bolas,[9] and they wrapped around Duyker's legs so that he could not run. Then Duyker cried out, "O Hare, come and release me from your bolas."

Hare said, "First give me back my little white horn, and then I shall release you." Duyker gave up the horn and was released from the bolas.

Once again Hare blew his horn, "Pey!" All the animals of

[9] *Bolas,* heavy balls on the ends of cords which are tied together at the center, are not in use in the part of Angola occupied by the Ovimbundu, but they are known, can be named, and occur in this story.

the bush came to Hare, and one by one they tried to exchange something for the little white horn, as Duyker had tried to do. And like Duyker, each of them tried running away with the horn, when he could not get it by trading. But each time, Hare brought down the running animal with his bolas before the horn was lost.[10]

Crocodile came last of all and said, "Let us make an exchange, Hare. I will give you a basket of fish for your horn." When Hare would not trade, Crocodile said, "If you will not trade, then let me just look at it."

Hare let Crocodile take the horn to look at it.[11] When Crocodile saw how beautiful the horn was, he started to make off with it. Hare threw his bolas at Crocodile, but the bolas did not stop him, and Crocodile went into the water with the horn.

Hare pondered what to do. Hare had a beehive in a tree that stood near Crocodile's river, upstream from Crocodile. Hare sat down by this bee tree and waited.

[10] A summary statement of repeated episodes, such as this statement, is rare in these stories. Enumeration and repetition are more commonly employed than summary. The storyteller could doubtless provide a whole evening's entertainment with this one story, by relating how each of the animals known to the Ovimbundu ran off with Hare's horn and was caught in Hare's bolas: eland, roan antelope, steinbuck, klipspringer, bushbuck, dikdik, kudu, waterbuck, reedbuck, gnu, oribi, hartebeest, sable, oryx, springbuck, etc. The basic story is usually known to the audience, so that the storyteller establishes his skill through his variations and his manner.

[11] This, even after every other animal has already tried to steal the horn when allowed to hold it and look at it! The personae in these Umbundu stories do not seem to gain knowledge or modify their behavior on the basis of experience, even after repeated failures. Actions seem to flow from necessities of character, situation or plot, more often than from knowledge. But is this an unrealistic view of human behavior? Where knowledge and wiles appear in the stories, they are usually an original rather than an acquired trait, e.g., the wiles of little Tortoise throughout the *Tortoise Saga*.

In the present story, Hare has already shown resourcefulness and intelligence in his fire contest with Galago, and will show further quick thinking in later episodes of the story. Therefore, we may be allowed to wonder whether he really wants to keep his little whistle, at this point in the story. Not only does the plot require that the whistle be lost, but Hare himself may desire to lose it, either permanently or long enough to throw his bolas at the fleeing thief. The pleasures of revenge, apprehension, and repossession may outweigh the pleasure of simple possession in the mind of this rollicking story's wily hero. A major theme of the story, and of the culture of the Ovimbundu, is the pleasure and satisfaction which injured parties take in exacting their "fine" from the wrongdoer. These stories are told and heard rather than written and read, and the teller indicates subtle feelings and ambiguities of feeling by his voice and manner. The native listener is conscious of complex motives and moods, especially multiple levels of motive. This note is intended to remind the reader that native listeners "hear" subtle complexities of motive in these stories, rather than to impose on the reader any speculative guide as to exactly what the native listener's interpretations are.

Later, Crocodile sent his children out to gather firewood. While gathering wood, the children saw the hive and saw that bees were in it. They said to each other, "That hive is ready to be eaten. When we go home, we must tell father about it." When the children came to their father, they told him about the hive.

Crocodile said, "If that hive is upstream, it belongs to Hare and is private property. When you go out for wood tomorrow, go downstream, and if you should find another hive of that sort there, we shall eat it."

While Crocodile was talking, Hare was listening to what he was saying. He went away and moved the hive from its tree to another tree downstream from Crocodile.

The next morning, Crocodile said to his children, as he sent them for firewood, "Go and get firewood, but look for it downstream today."

The children went downstream looking for firewood and saw the beehive with bees in it. When they came back home, they told their father, "Today we found another beehive that is ready to be eaten."

Their father said, "Let us go and eat it."

When they came to the hive, the father climbed up the tree to the hive and lowered the hive to the ground. He began to break the bark bands which held the hive together. Then Hare jumped out from his hiding place and sank his teeth into Crocodile's arm. Crocodile yelled. Hare said, "Bring me my little horn and then I shall let you go."

Then Crocodile said to one of his children, "Go fetch the horn! You know it, the little white one." Since his father was crying out with pain, the child went in great haste, picked up a duyker horn, and came running back with it.

When Hare saw the duyker horn, he braced himself and began to bite harder, and Crocodile began to yell louder. Then Crocodile sent the child back once more to fetch the little white horn. This time the child came with the horn of a roan antelope. When Hare saw this, he began to bite harder.

This went on and on until the child had brought the horns from all sorts of horned animals. Finally, when there was no other horn left, the child brought the right horn and gave it to Hare. In the meantime, Hare had bitten and bitten, until he had cut Crocodile's arm completely off with his teeth.

Crocodile, maimed, considered what he could do to even matters with Hare. He said to himself, "I shall arrange a party with dancing and eating and ask all the people to come. Hare will not come to the party because he has cut my arm off, but if he does come I shall grab him."

When the people[12] met for the party, Leopard was the drummer. When the dancers gathered on the dance floor, the song they sang was this:

> Where is Uncle Hare? He doesn't dare
> To the dancing come, at the music of the drum,
> For he chewed off the arm of Grandfather Crock.

One who listened well could hear Hare, who was hidden in the drum, singing this song:

> Hare is here, Hare is here,
> In the belly of the drum.
> Hare did no wrong.
> Uncle Hare, sir, he is right.

While the others were dancing and singing, Crocodile heard what the drum was saying and was annoyed by it. Crocodile took up his razor and threw it into the maw of the drum. Hare caught the razor and put it aside, and the razor did not cut him. Then the dancers sang again:

> Where is Uncle Hare? He doesn't dare
> To the dancing come, at the music of the drum,
> For he chewed off the arm of Grandfather Crock.

And to anyone who listened, the drum was saying:

> Hare is here, Hare is here,
> In the belly of the drum.

[12] The informant stated that the characters themselves would resent being called "animals," and must be called "people."

Hare did no wrong.
Uncle Hare, sir, he is right.

As Crocodile listened, he became so annoyed that he got some hot water and poured it into the drum. This brought Hare out of the drum fast. When the drummer, Leopard, saw Hare jump out, he chased after him, for he was afraid that Crocodile would be angry and say that he had plotted with Hare.

Hare went into a burrow and hid himself underground. When he was down in the burrow, he shaved off all his hair with Crocodile's razor. In the meantime, Leopard was digging and digging. When Hare had shaved off all his hair, he shaped it into a mock-up of himself, and placed within it the razor which Crocodile had thrown at him.

When Hare had done all this, he spoke to Leopard and said, "Ancestral noble, please let me pass. We are the smooth hares. We have no fellowship with the hairy hares."

When Leopard saw Hare all red and bare, he thought, "This is not the hare that I chased," so he asked, "Is the hare with the hair in there?"

Hare replied, "He is still in there."

So Leopard let Hare pass by and then continued his digging. As he was digging, Leopard caught sight of the mock-up. He looked at it hard and thought that it was that very Hare he had been chasing. He said to it, "Hare, now I have caught you!" Then he thrust forward his paws with their claws extended, saying, "Now is the time that I kill you!" Leopard grabbed the bunch of hair—Pooma! All his fingers were slashed by the razor hidden inside. Then Leopard yelled, "O you Hare, someday I'll catch you. You just wait!"

On a later day, Leopard found Hare taking down a beehive, and Leopard said, "Hare, remember what I said that day when I did not catch you?"

Hare said, "All right, Uncle, today you will eat me, but before you eat me, just taste a little of this honey, the kind I'm in the habit of eating." Then Hare took up a piece of comb with honey in it and said to Leopard, "Please, just take a bite of it."

Leopard ate the piece of honey and found it very tasty. He liked it so much that he asked Hare, "Is this the sort of food that you eat right along?"

Hare replied, "Yes, and if you would like more of it, just send me two empty gourds, so that when I come to your house, I may bring you a lot of it. Then you, Uncle, and my aunt, may have a feast. So that folks shall not peek in at you and see what you have to eat, go now and plaster up every hole in your house, so that there will be no peepholes."

Leopard promised to do this. He went home, and they shut up every hole in their house, just as Hare had directed. Leopard sent two large empty gourds to Hare. When Hare got the gourds, he filled them nearly full with bees. He covered the bees over with grass, and put some honey on top of the grass.

When Hare carried the gourds to the leopards, he told them, "Eat none until I have gone out the door. When I have shut the door, each one of you take a gourd, and then dash the gourds onto the floor. After that, you may eat as freely as you wish. I tell you to do this, lest the other people see me here, and come to beg honey from me."

Hare went outside, locked the door with the key, and then called, "Now smash the gourds!" At the word, the two leopards smashed the gourds, and the bees swarmed out from the gourds and stung the leopards until the children died and also the wife. Leopard himself made a hole in the roof. He climbed through it and shouted, "Hare, where is the key?"

Hare answered, "There it is on the top of the pig's hut." Leopard unlocked the house, and the bees flew out and went away. Leopard was left weeping for his wife and children.

As Hare went away, he pondered over his feud with Leopard. He thought, "Now, what shall I do next?" Hare decided to go to Lion.[13]

When he came to Lion, he said to her, "I have come to get work."

Lion said to him, "You can have work. Your work will be to care for my children."

The next day Lion went out into the bush to hunt animals, leaving her children in the care of Hare. After Lion had gone, Leopard came along, and when he found Hare there, he said,

---

[13] "Lion" has been used instead of "lioness" in the translation, since Umbundu does not classify or inflect nouns according to gender, and since the personified animals in these stories often seem to represent all of their species of both sexes. Pronouns have no gender in Umbundu, but here "her" has been used as preferable to "it."

"Now Hare! Haven't I found you? Today you will not escape me again, for I am going to eat you!"

Hare said, "Uncle, do not eat me right here. Give me time and I shall repay my debt to you." Then Hare gave Leopard one of the children of Lion. Leopard ate the lion cub and then went away.

When the sun was about to set, Lion came back from hunting and said, "Hare, bring the children out,[14] so they can suck." Hare obeyed, but he brought out only one at a time. He brought one of them out twice, for there were only two of the three left.

Lion said, "That is the whole lot. Indeed, you have cared for them well."

The next day Lion went away again to hunt in the woods. Later in the day, Leopard came along and said, "Hare! Haven't I found you again?"

Hare said, "Uncle, do not eat me now. Give me time, and I shall repay my debt." Hare gave Leopard another lion child, and Leopard ate it.

Later that afternoon, Lion came back and said to Hare, "Bring the children to suck." Hare brought out the one remaining cub and said, "Do not let them eat too much at once, lest they mess up the cave." As the cubs all looked alike, Lion did not notice that the same one had been brought out three times. Lion said to Hare, "You have been caring for them very well."

Lion went hunting again the next morning. Soon after she left, Leopard came again and said, "Hare! Haven't I found you again?"

Hare said, "Uncle, do not eat me right here. Give me time, and I shall repay my debt to you." Hare brought out the last of the lion children and gave it to Leopard.

After this, Hare began to think about what he had done, and he said,[15] "What am I going to do when Lion comes home?" Finally, he smeared some gum over his eyes so that they could not

[14] The idea is that the cubs are brought out from a shallow cave some distance onto the grass, where their mother nurses them. In the region inhabited by the Ovimbundu, caves are rarely very deep; they are usually shallow recesses under ledges.

[15] Umbundu has many verbs meaning "to think" and has reflexive forms for expressing "to say to oneself," but these stories most frequently employ a verb expressing a positive, declaratory act of pronouncement, close in meaning to the English "to say," even in situations in which the speaker obviously can "say" things only to himself. Similarly, Umbundu has verb forms meaning "to reply," "to ask," etc., but these stories usually employ a more formal and positive verb, similar to the English "to say" or "to state," in the dialogue of the stories.

be opened. Then he flopped himself down at the door of the cave.

When Lion came home she cried out, "What is this? Hare! What has happened?"

Hare told her, "Leopard came and found me playing with the children. He destroyed my eyes and left me thus. Then he caught the children and ate them. That is why I am weeping." Lion passed one of her claws under the gum on one of Hare's eyes, the gum came off, and Hare could see with one eye. She did the same for his other eye. Then Hare could see again.

Hare and Lion discussed the future. As they talked, Lioness said to Hare, "Let us go and build a big circular corral. I shall stay inside this corral, lying on the ground and playing that I am dead. Then you will go and invite all the animals to come, saying, 'Let us all go weep for Lion, who is lying dead on the cold, cold ground.'" Then they went and prepared the corral, in the way that they had planned it.

Then Hare summoned all the animals[16] to come, saying, "Let all come together to weep for Lion, who is now lying dead on the cold, cold ground." All the animals, both large and small, were glad to hear this word, so they all came. When they had gathered inside the corral, they all did their weeping, and as they wept they sang:

Oh! Oh! Oh! Old Lion is lying dead
On the cold, cold ground. Be it her final bed.

While they were singing, Hare and Tortoise[17] went outside the corral and shut the gate. They said that they did not wish to weep too much. When the gate had been shut, Hare shouted: "O Lion, wake up and eat!" At the word, Lion rose up and

[16] The stories seem to employ the word for "animals" instead of the words for "people" or "folk" when a variety of particular animals is meant: lion, tiger, gnu, duyker, hare, etc.

[17] It is interesting that Tortoise suddenly appears with Hare at this late point in the story, since throughout the story Hare has displayed a craftiness often assigned to Tortoise in these stories. Each of these two animals is usually depicted as intelligent, but Hare's reputation is that of a malicious trickster, while Tortoise has a reputation for performing communally useful feats. The almost standardized plot in which Tortoise appears is one in which all the larger and more pretentious animals first try to accomplish some community task but fail, after which "little Tortoise" surprises all by trying and succeeding. The Ovimbundu feel strong sympathy for the underdog and for the little man.

began to kill animals. Hare shouted to her: "Now, I have paid you my debt!"

kalitangi[18] *who talks back to god*

Once all the animals who wished to live together peacefully arranged a dinner to be followed by dancing.

The goats went in costume, and they had agreed among themselves that none of them would admit being a goat, and none of them would say "Mba." They danced excellently, but would not give their names. This annoyed the leopards, who wished to have some goat meat.

While the dancing was going on, a young goat came who had not heard of the agreements. She skipped onto the dancing floor, shouting: "Mba-a-a, we are the goats."

Then a leopard started to chase this young goat, saying, "Indeed, I am going to eat this one." The goat fled, jumping and jumping. She jumped upon and climbed a high rock, where Leopard could not follow. Leopard lay in wait at the foot of the rock. Goat would not come down. Then Leopard spoke to Goat and asked her to come down. Goat replied, "I will not come down, for I am afraid that you will eat me."

Then Leopard begged her to reconsider her resolve, and said to her, "Just come on down. I shall do nothing to you, but you

---

[18] This name is related to the verb *tanga,* which means "to mix up, confuse, weave, knit or conflict." By coincidence, it has both the sound and meaning of the English verb "to tangle." This word is the root of many other words in Umbundu; *onanga* is cloth, produced by tangling, weaving or confusing threads. Applied to people, the verb means "to confuse, to think in a confused way, to confound, to talk back," etc. However, since the introduction of written script *tanga* has assumed the new meaning "to read," and has thereby acquired the alternate meaning "to untangle." The reflexive form is *litanga,* which applied to persons means "He tangles himself up," and from this form derives the name *Kalitangi.* Applied to more than one person, this reflective form of the verb seems to mean "They tangled, they fought, they confused and confounded one another," as often happens between Kalitangi and his opponents.

Kalitangi is a well-known mythical character, who appears in this and other stories of the Umbundu. He sometimes appears to be confused himself, but at other times he confounds great people or even deity. The character is sometimes called "Kalitangi of God." The character and his actions in this story suggest the ancient introduction to the Book of Job, in which Satan attempts to confound the Lord. But this story is Umbundu: its god is less omnipotent than the god of the Book of Job, and Kalitangi is a bit ahead of Satan as a confuser of god.

will be my friend, and we shall live together in peace and love."
Finally Goat came down from the rock. They became friends.
Leopard did nothing to her.

Later Leopard made a proposal to Goat. She said, "Goat,
we are both pregnant, and since there is great hunger at this
time, let us make a pact: that we shall eat the child of the one
who first gives birth. We shall share in this, and later we shall
eat the child of the other, when it is born." Goat agreed to this
pact.

Shortly afterward, Leopard gave birth, and following the
agreement, they ate the child.

It was now the turn for Goat to perform her part, but
time went on and on and she did not bring forth anything.
After waiting a considerable time, Leopard said to Goat, "Come
on now, are you not going to bring forth something?"

Goat replied, "Yes, surely, in good time I shall give birth."

When Leopard heard this, she was angry at Goat and said
to her, "Now you understand this: if you do not bring forth
something, I shall eat you yourself."

To this Goat said, "Now, do not eat me on the spot. Truly,
in a little time I am going to give birth." Once more Leopard
put off the day of reckoning.

A short time later, Goat began to have birth pains. When
Leopard saw that Goat was in distress, she asked her, "Are you
going to give birth to something today?"

Goat said, "Yes indeed, I am about to give birth. Watch
me." Leopard sat down to watch. Goat cried out, and a spear
came forth.

Leopard said, "What is this that you are producing? Others
bring forth some living thing, but you produce metal articles."

Goat said, "This is the way I gave birth. This is just preliminary."

Later, when Goat cried out again, she brought forth arrows
and a bow. Leopard, who was still observing, said, "Now, you
there! What are you doing anyway?"

Goat said, "That is all right. You must keep watching.
Soon we shall get down to business, and then we shall have
something alive."

Goat cried out again, and this time she brought forth a
sword. Leopard said of this, "Now, you tell me the truth, or I

shall eat you. I am not going to sit around here just to observe the production of weapons."

Goat said to her, "These are only pre-births. This is the way it always begins with me. In a little while you are going to have something to eat."

When Goat cried out again, she brought forth a gun and a cartridge box. When this happened, Leopard came forward and said, "Perhaps you need me to hold you so that you may give birth as you should."

Goat told her, "You just let go of me, and I shall attend to this all right, if you will only sit down and watch." Leopard sat down to watch.

Again Goat cried out, and this time she gave birth to a child. Immediately, as soon as he was born, he took up his weapons and said, "I am out. I am Kalitangi. I talk back to Suku."

Kalitangi's taking up his weapons frightened Leopard, who had expected something to be born that she could eat. Leopard said to Goat, "I said that you would give birth to nothing I can eat, so that I shall have to eat you. Now don't you see it?"

Goat answered her: "Haka! This doesn't mean anything! Some day you will eat him. Are you afraid of your own child? [19] When I send him somewhere, you can go there and catch him. I am going to send him to the field now, to fetch me some bean vine straw. You go and hide yourself in the straw so that when he comes to the field you can jump out and catch him. Leopard agreed to this plan, went out to the field, and hid in the straw pile.

Goat called her son and said to him, "My son, go to the field and bring me some bean vine straw."

Kalitangi said, "Sure enough."

As he went, he took his weapons with him, saying, "A man does not go anywhere empty handed." He went to the field and found the pile of straw. Then he spoke in a loud voice and said,

---

[19] In the usage of the Umbundu, sisters call each others' children "my child," and the children call their maternal aunts "mother." Women who are quite friendly also call each other "sister." Hence, Goat's child is called Leopard's child.

The kinship terminology of the Umbundu separates one's mother's relatives from one's father's relatives, but otherwise takes rather little account of gender, grouping under single kinship terms relatives of both sexes, such as "mother's grandparents" and "father's descendants." The language itself does not classify or inflect nouns according to gender; hence, the general forms "goat" and "leopard" have been used in the translation, as closest to the spirit of the original.

"Before I pick up this straw, I am going to shoot my gun into it."
He cocked his gun in order to shoot.

Leopard jumped out of the pile of vines and said, "Grandfather, this is I. Please do not shoot me." Leopard went back to Goat and began to revile her. She said, "Look at this, Goat! This is just what I said would happen. Kalitangi was about to shoot me."

Goat replied, "Oh, just let that pass. When I send him somewhere else, you will be able to hide more carefully. When he comes there you will catch him."

Just at this time, Kalitangi, who had returned quickly, came in and said, "What is this about? Why are you making a row with my mother?" Leopard fled from the house.

Later Goat said to Leopard that she was sending her son to the river for water, and that near the river there was a thick clump of grass and weeds in which Leopard could hide. Leopard went and hid in the clump. Goat sent Kalitangi, saying to him, "My child, now go and get me some water from the river."

Kalitangi obeyed, but he carried his weapons with him. He said, "By my father! A man should not go anywhere without some weapon in his hand, lest he run into something which can harm him, when he has no defence. When he came near the stream he said, "When one finds a bunch of grass like this, he should fire his gun into it, for there might be something in it." He fired his gun into the clump of grass.

When he did this, Leopard came rushing out, and she said to him, "My child, you might have shot me, your mother. What were you trying to do?"

Kalitangi said to her, "Let us two try to get on well together. How does it happen that you have the habit of going to hide in places where I am about to go? We two may come to get on well together some day, but I don't see how we shall before you are dead."

Leopard hurried back to Goat and said to her, "It has come to the point that you should let me eat you, yourself, for this child is too crafty. He is impossible."

Goat said, "Ridiculous! Just calm down. Our agreement was to eat each other's children, not to eat each other.

Then Leopard said, "Just let me gnaw your hooves, which I can see there. All that I want is to taste them." Just then

Kalitangi came in and found Leopard talking to his mother. When he saw Leopard, he jumped aside and went quickly to the back of the room and hid under the corn hanging there. Later, when Leopard had left, Kalitangi said to his mother, "Mother, how does it happen that every time I come along, I find Leopard making a row with you?"

Then she told him, "In the past, in a time of great hunger, we made a mutual pledge. When Leopard had a child, we ate it together. In the same way, she waited for me to have a child. When I bore you she wished to eat you in payment for her child which we had already eaten."

When Kalitangi heard this he said, "Oh! So that is it! If Leopard thinks that she is going to eat me, she fools herself."

Then Goat sent Kalitangi to the corn crib to get some corn, saying, "My son, go to the corn crib and get some corn." Kalitangi replied, "Ee-ee! I am taking my spear. A man does not go anywhere unarmed."

When he came to the corn crib, he stabbed his spear into the corn. When he did this, he pierced Leopard right through her middle, and the spear came out through her far side. As a consequence of this Leopard died.

After the death of Leopard, Suku heard that Goat had given birth to Kalitangi of Suku. When Suku had heard of the birth of Kalitangi, Suku said, "Let Goat come here." Accordingly, Goat went. Kalitangi thought that she would return soon. When he noted that a long time had elapsed, he said, "I shall follow her to that place." Since he did not know where that village was, he had a quantity of meal pounded, and after that a supply of mush cooked for the road.

Kalitangi set out on the road, carrying this food. As he was going along he met Hog. Hog said to Kalitangi, "Where are you going?"

Kalitangi told him, "I am going to seek my mother."

Hog said, "I shall go along with you." When Kalitangi heard this, he broke off some of the mush, and adding some bean relish he gave it to Hog.

The two went along together until they met Spider, who said, "Where are you going?"

Kalitangi told Spider, "I am going to seek my mother."

Spider said, "I am going along with you." As he had done before for Hog, Kalitangi broke off some of the relish and some of the mush and gave them to Spider, and then she followed him.

As they went along they met Aardvark, who asked, "Where are you going?"

Kalitangi told him, "We are going to seek my mother."

Aardvark said, "I will go along also." Kalitangi broke off food for him, both mush and relish. As they went on again, Spider built a bridge for them, so that the whole company passed over.

From the river the whole party passed on until they came to a mountain of dung. At this barrier, Hog came forward and ate up the whole mountain of dung. When this had been done, they passed on.

They went on and on until they came to a mountain so high that they could not climb over it, and so broad that there was no way around it. Now Aardvark came forward and said, "Rest for a minute. Just let me do this job all by myself." Aardvark dug a tunnel right through the mountain. They all passed through the tunnel.

After they left the mountain they came to a village, the village which they were looking for. This village was large, very large. They entered it and came to the place of Suku, but Suku had changed himself into a deep pool. Kalitangi was searching for Suku, and when he came to this deep pool of water, he said, "Oh Suku, here is where you have hidden yourself, right here." Then Suku and Kalitangi laughed together.

Then, in turn, Kalitangi hid himself. He turned into a strychnine tree with yellow fruits on it. Suku searched and searched for Kalitangi, but could not see him. After a time, he came to the tree with yellow fruits, and he picked one off. Kalitangi said, "Are you still picking on me?" Then they laughed and laughed together.

After they finished laughing, Suku in his turn went away to hide. He changed himself into a big rock. Kalitangi looked and looked. Finally he came to the big rock, and here he said, "This is the place where you are hiding." Once more they laughed together.

After they had laughed, Kalitangi went once more to hide himself. He changed himself into a threshing floor. Suku searched until he was tired. When he came to the threshing floor, which was clean and fine, he said, "I shall sit here and rest." Suku sat down on the threshing floor, and then Kalitangi said,

"Are you sitting on me again?" At this they both laughed and laughed.

Shortly after this, Suku summoned Kalitangi and said to him, "Go and conceal my mother." Kalitangi took her away, and when he had changed her into a trading post, concealed her by a lake. Suku went out looking for her. He looked and looked, but could not discover her. In due time Suku came to the trading post, which was stocked with all sorts of fine merchandise: full of big things and little things, and no one to guard the goods. Suku went into the place and looked about, then he started to take things out, whole bolts of cloth, and hide them in the grass, so that he could come back later and go away with them. Kalitangi spoke to him and said, "Would you be guilty of plundering your own mother?" They laughed and laughed together.

Shortly after this Suku called Kalitangi and said, "Climb that tree." Kalitangi agreed to this, but said, "My belt will hinder me as I climb, so take it and hold it for me. In order that it will not be mislaid, please fasten it around your waist. Suku did this, and then Kalitangi climbed into the tree.

Suku spoke to the tree and said, "Oh tree of mine, take him aloft."

The tree began to mount into the sky, so Kalitangi said, "Oh belt of mine, squeeze him for me."

Soon Kalitangi and the tree were very high up, but as Kalitangi went up, Suku began to realize that he was about to come apart at the waist. He shouted: "Oh tree of mine, do bring him back."

Up in the sky Kalitangi said, "Oh little belt—belt of mine— loosen a bit." Suku's waistline did not return to normal, until the tree came to earth again.

This performance was repeated four times, and then Suku said, "Let's quit it." Then Kalitangi came down out of the tree.

Later Suku had a conference with Kalitangi, in which Suku said to Kalitangi, "Tomorrow we shall have one more test. If you pass this one, you shall have your mother back again."

In the morning, when it was light, a great number of boxes were assembled, a number of boxes equal to the number of houses found in a large village. Among these boxes there was one in which Kalitangi's mother was hidden. On the evening before the test, Fly came to Kalitangi and said to him, "Have no concern tomorrow morning, for when you go out, I shall be sitting on your nose. I shall go and alight on a box, and that will be the box in which your mother is hidden."

When it was light in the morning, all the people went out with Kalitangi, who was to point out the box that contained his mother, Goat. When they came to the collection of boxes, the people went around and around with Kalitangi among the boxes. Kalitangi noticed that the fly sitting on the bridge of his nose went and lit on a certain box. Then Kalitangi pointed it out and said, "There is my mother."

Then all the people laughed and laughed together. They opened the box, and Goat came out. Then they gave her to Kalitangi and said, "Now, son, take your mother."

Kalitangi took his mother, and they went away together.

15. wilderness, solitude and ogres

an ogre visits a hunter's wife

Once there was a hunter who lived in the woods with his wife.[1] It happened that the hunter went away to a hunting camp, leaving his wife alone at their permanent lodge.

After the hunter had gone away to his camp, an ogre[2] came to the house in the evening, stopped outside the fence, and called to the woman: "Come out and open the gate for me."

The woman replied by singing:

> Temo lia Mungenga,[3]
> Temo lia Mungenga.
> O my lord, I open promptly.
> Temo lia Mungenga.

Then the woman opened the gate, and the two of them went into the house. When they were in the house, the ogre said to the woman, "Make the bed, and do it well. She replied by again singing:

---

[1] The Ovimbundu have many hunting lodges in the woods, and hunters often live together in the woods during long hunts, but among the Ovimbundu it would be very rare for a man and his wife to live in the woods, away from the village.

[2] *Ekisikisi*, the word which has been translated as "ogre" throughout these stories, always indicates some powerful and frightening being. The ogre may be human, superhuman or animal, and usually some of all three. In this story there are words suggesting that this particular ogre has the appearance of an anthropoid ape.

[3] *Temo lia* means literally "the hoe of," and *Mungenga* is the name of a neighboring tribe, in Eastern Angola. The significance of "the hoe of the Mungenga tribe" has eluded both the translator and the informant who supplied the story.

> Temo lia Mungenga,
> Temo lia Mungenga.
> O my lord, I make it promptly.
> Temo lia Mungenga.

Then they lay in the bed until daylight, since the husband had gone so far away that the wife did not expect him back yet. When it was day, the ogre went away.

The next evening the ogre came again to the gate and called, "Open the gate for me! You delighted me last night. I liked it." And again the woman sang in reply:

> Temo lia Mungenga,
> Temo lia Mungenga.
> O my lord, I open promptly.
> Temo lia Mungenga.

The woman opened the gate, they went into the house, and then the ogre said to the woman, "Hurry and make up the bed as you did last evening." As on the previous evening, she sang in reply that she would make the bed promptly, and when she had made the bed, the ogre said to her, "Now come, let us lie in it." And she sang in reply:

> Temo lia Mungenga,
> Temo lia Mungenga.
> O my lord, let us go promptly.
> Temo lia Mungenga.

Then they lay in the bed together until day, when the ogre went away.

The ogre came to the house and slept with the woman every night, just as though the house were his own.

One day the hunter returned from the camp where he had been. When he entered the house, he found it filthy, filthy. When he looked at the bed, he found it full of animal hair and with an animal odor. When the woman came in, he saw that there were animal hairs mixed with her hair. The man asked, "How has it happened that the house is so filthy? And how did there come to be animal hair in the bed, and even upon your head?"

The woman confessed to him, saying, "An animal, one that makes fear, has been coming into the house."

Then the man asked, "After it comes in, what does it do?"

She said, "It lies with me. I have had to plead for my life, for the animal said, 'If you do not consent, I shall eat you.' After that threat, I consented, for there was no man here to fight for me. Even if a man had been here, he would have fled at the sight of this animal. Even to look at it with the eye makes great fear."

On hearing these words, the man became very angry that his wife had been having relations with an animal. He said to her, "You are a worthless bitch. You consented to this. If you had not consented, he would not have lain with you."

The woman replied, "What more can I say than I have already said?"

Then the man said, "You keep quiet and make no further noise. If you say anything more, I shall beat you. Can you claim to be human when you have slept with an animal? How can I trust you at all?" The woman kept her finger in her mouth, so that she should obey him and not answer. She had made him very angry.

The man got his gun and loaded it.

Later, when it was evening, the woman heard a voice at the gate, saying, "Open the gate there for me." The woman replied, singing:

> Temo lia Mungenga,
> Temo lia Mungenga.
> O my lord, I open promptly.
> Temo lia Mungenga.

Then the woman opened the gate for the ogre, for he had threatened, "If you do not open the gate for me, I will leap over it."

Then the woman and the ogre came toward the house together. The man had lain down in the bed to lie in wait for the ogre, when he heard the ogre at the gate. Now that the man saw the ogre coming toward the house, he became desperately afraid. When the ogre and the woman had entered the house, the ogre said, "Hurry now. Make up the bed." And the woman replied again by singing:

> Temo lia Mungenga,
> Temo lia Mungenga.
> O my lord, I make it promptly.
> Temo lia Mungenga.

When the ogre thought that the woman had made the bed, he went to the bed. Thinking that the man in the bed was the woman, the ogre turned him over in the bed, and the man fell off behind the bed. The man realized the situation, his bowels acted, and then he fainted.

As the man was coming out of his faint, he gurgled and coughed. The ogre heard these sounds and believed that they came from a man outside the house, so he got up from the bed and hastily fled from the house.

The man and his wife gathered up their gear and went to the village.

a maiden alone in the wild

Once there was a country being terrorized by an ogre[4] who ate so many people that the region was losing its population.

A girl in this country was clever. She fenced her house around with four stockades made from wood of the gardenia.[5]

---

[4] Ogres may be inhuman creatures, depraved humans or even feared animals, in the Umbundu usage. They are most frequently inhuman in their cannibalistic habits and their strength, but human in their familistic, occupational and village habits. This story alternates between calling its villain "ogre" and "lion."

[5] The dried wood of the gardenia is branched at sharp angles into spikes, and is bone hard. Hunters tie these around the trunk of a tree which they are using as a platform from which to shoot lions. They believe that a lion will not attempt to pass the gardenia spikes, and perhaps they believe that gardenia spikes possess a magical power against lions.

When the ogre came to her house he went around it but could not find any point at which he could break through. Then he called to her, "Open up for me here!"

When the ogre demanded that she open up, the maiden sang this song:

> Everywhere, everywhere,
> Every hole is shut tight.
> You cannot break in,
> In spite of your might.
> I built it, I built it,
> I built it myself.
> It is built of gardenia.
> Can a lion break through?

The lion went away to his den.

Since the ogre had a bellowing voice, the girl could recognize by his voice whom she had to contend with. Another day the ogre came again and commanded her to open up. Again she refused by singing the same song. The ogre came day after day for five days, and each day the girl answered his demand by singing:

> Everywhere, everywhere,
> Every hole is shut tight.
> You cannot break in,
> In spite of your might.
> I built it, I built it,
> I built it myself.
> It is built of gardenia.
> Can a lion break through?

The ogre came on yet another day, after he had been thinking of what he might do to get the girl and eat her. In the past he had been speaking to her in a deep gruff voice. Now he changed his voice to sound like the voice of a girl. When the ogre came again and asked to get in, using his changed voice, the maiden inside was deceived and much pleased. She said to herself, "There is another girl like myself, a fellow refugee. I had thought that I alone was left in this country. Now the two of us can live here together."

She went to the gate and opened it. When she did this the ogre rushed in, caught her, and ate her.

nightshade berries

In a time of famine some girls from a village said, "Let us go gather nightshade berries." To go where the berries grew, they had to sleep three nights on the road; on the fourth they would find the berries.

When they reached the place of the nightshade berries, one of the girls carried her cloth in her hand, and the other girls wrapped their cloths around their waists. She who carried her cloth in her hand put it on the ground while she picked berries. She intended to pick it up again when she left. But it happened that as she went from place to place, picking berries, she left her cloth on the ground and forgot about it.

Finally the other girls said, "We have berries enough. Let us go to the village." Since the girl who had put down her cloth had enough berries too, she was willing to go. Still she did not remember her cloth, nor think of whether she had brought it with her or not.

When they reached the place for spending the night, the girl without a cloth said, "I shall wrap myself up in my cloth for the night." But the cloth was not to be found. She asked the other girls to go back again to the place of the nightshade berries with her, but they refused to go back with her. So she begged the other girls to wait for her there, and then she went alone to search for her lost cloth. But the others had not promised to wait for her, and while she was gone they said among themselves, "How long will it take her to go to the place of the nightshade berries and return here? Are we going to spend another day and another night at this place?" They decided not to wait for her any longer.

They picked up their baskets and left. Later, the girl returned and found that the other girls had already gone. She did not know which path they had taken, nor which one she should take. She thought that it was impossible for her to walk on alone, for surely she would become lost.

Then she saw a little old woman nearby, and so she asked this little woman, "Did you see which way the other girls went?"

The little old woman replied, "I did not see which way the other girls went."

Then the girl complained, "Oh, Oh! Today is my unlucky day. Now I am lost. I shall not see our village again."

The old woman heard this and pitied the girl. She summoned the girl and said to her, "If you will come to me and clean up my sores, then I shall tell you how to escape your troubles. When you have cleaned my sores, I shall help you to find your father and mother again."

The girl agreed to this and cleansed the sores of the little old woman. When she had finished, the woman gave her some squash seeds and said to her, "Go plant these." The girl went and planted the seeds.

Soon the seeds sprouted, and then vines had spread from them. When the vines began to have fruits, the girl climbed onto the vines, singing this song to the vines:

> Vine, O vine, have pity.
>
> Take me home to my village.
>
> Sail on well, O shade of darkness,
>
> So that coming to Chinjamba,
>
> I, his sister Lusinga—way, O way—
>
> May come again from the region of darkness.
>
>   Way-y, O way-y-y-y.

She flew on the vines, singing, until she came to her country.

When she neared her village, the people heard her song. The king called for silence and commanded: "For the present, let no one make a loud sound. He who has an ox that bellows: kill it. She who has a child that cries: let her nurse it. Thus we may listen carefully to the one who is singing. I think and I say, 'This is Lusinga, the girl for whom we have already mourned.'" After the king had spoken, the villagers fell silent.

Lusinga kept singing until she came down to the ground. She found all the people standing and waiting for her. The people were happy and rejoiced to see her again. They were all outside the village to welcome her.

Then the people invited Lusinga to come into the village. But she would not come into the village, saying, "People of standing and importance go into this village. I cannot go in, for I am a person of no value and standing." When they heard her say this, they gave her an ox. Then she went into the village. When she refused to enter the house, they gave her a hog. Then she was given a goat before she would sit down. After she had been given a fowl, she ate food. All of the people were pleased over her return, for the lost had returned.

16. *the world of the animals*

choko bird advises man

Once there was a man who was a setter of snares. Some days when he went to examine his snares he would find nothing. One day it happened that he found Choko in one of his snares. When Man saw Choko, he gave thanks, saying, "Mba, mba, mba, mba."

Choko spoke to Man and said, "Handle me carefully and do not kill me, for if you deal gently with me, I am destined to tell you three wise sayings that will be useful to you thoughout your whole life."

Man said to this, "What can you, an ordinary bird, tell me that will be of use to me throughout my life? That is, something I do not already know?"

Choko said to him, "First, do not covet that which belongs to your neighbor. Second, do not long for that which has already passed. Third, do not make plans for doing that which is impossible."

To reward Choko for this advice, Man released Choko. Choko flew off only a short way and alighted. Once more he spoke to Man and said, "Have you forgotten the things that I told you?"

Man replied to him, "I have not forgotten them. They are: First, do not covet that which belongs to your neighbor. Second, do not long for that which has already passed. Third, do not make plans for doing that which is impossible."

Choko flew farther away. Then, from a distance, he shouted to Man, "If, when you caught me, you had killed me, then when you opened my crop you would have found a pearl so valuable that your whole family would have become wealthy."

Man began to take counsel with himself, planning how to deal with Choko, in order to get his hands on him, and thus acquire the pearl. Finally, he called to Choko, "Look here! I have a whole crib full of corn. In the corn crib there is a window through which you may go in and out, passing any time you wish. The corn is of good quality. No one else has such corn. The corn is yours, for you are worthy of it. Indeed you are a bird of intelligence."

Choko replied, "You are doing what I have already warned you against: coveting what is not yours, longing for that which has already passed, and planning to do that which is impossible."

how dog became the friend of man

One day Dog was much depressed. As she wandered about in the bush she met Leopard. Leopard greeted Dog, and then she said to her, "Dog, you are looking very seedy. What is the matter with you?"

Dog replied, "Lately, I have been hunting but have caught nothing. I have become so weak that if I should find something, I could not catch it."

Leopard said to her, "How would you like a job?"

To this Dog said, "If there is anything to eat in it, I would just love it."

Leopard said, "I have no difficulty in getting food. If you will stay at my den and guard my children while I am out hunting, I shall feed you well."

Dog said to this, "Then I have a job. I am your servant. Let us begin." Then Leopard took Dog to her den, gave her some meat to eat, and showed her the four children.

The next day Leopard went hunting. As she left, she charged Dog to care for the cubs, to keep them in the cave, and to protect them from wandering animals. She also said that when she returned from the hunt, she would nurse the children.

Not long after Leopard left, Tortoise came by, and when he found Dog at the den of the leopard, he said, "Dog, what are you doing around here?"

Dog said, "I have a job here caring for Leopard's children. I became very hard up and almost starved to death. Leopard feeds me well just for looking after her children."

When Tortoise heard this, he said, "I have never seen a young leopard. May I have a look at them?" Dog agreed and took Tortoise into the cave. When Tortoise saw the cubs he marveled and said, "They are beauties. Look at them, aren't they fat? I'll wager that one of those would be good eating."

Dog said, "Now! Now! Do not say anything like that around here. It makes me afraid."

Tortoise said, "Now, now, Dog, do not get excited, but they do look delicious." After much chatting, Tortoise persuaded Dog not to be alarmed over the suggestion. Tortoise told Dog that he could arrange matters so that Leopard would know nothing about it. In the end they ate one of the young leopards. After they had wiped their mouths, Tortoise started to leave.

Dog called to him, "Are you going away without telling me what to do when Leopard returns?" Tortoise stopped, turned around, and then said, "Oh, that? When Leopard comes back from hunting, she is going to be tired. Then she will ask you to bring the children out of the cave so that they may nurse. Bring out one of the cubs. Let it suck. Take it back and bring out another. The fourth time you can bring out the first one again."

When Leopard came back from hunting she brought prey with her. She lay down to rest. Later she told Dog to bring the children out to nurse.[1] Dog gave a favorable account of their behavior, and then brought them out one by one. When she brought the first one out the second time, Leopard commented on how much some of the children resembled each other.

The next day Leopard went to hunt early in the morning. Later Tortoise came along and asked how the scheme had worked. Dog told him that there had been no difficulty, although she had been much afraid. What she feared was that Leopard would wish to visit the cave. Tortoise said, "Do not worry about that, for she is glad to have you do the dirty work. Let us take another

[1] The leopard is understood to lie down some distance from her cave, to nurse her young. The distance from the cave later becomes important to the story. "Leopard" and "Dog" have been employed in translation, though both creatures are female, since genders are perfectly clear in the context, and either "Mrs. Leopard" or "Leopardess" would introduce connotations foreign to the sense of the Umbundu, which seems to personify the entire species.

look at the youngsters." After he had admired their plumpness, he said, "Come now, let us eat another one."

To this Dog said, "I did not sleep well from thinking about one of the cubs being missing, but to have two missing is too much. No!" But in the end Dog yielded and the two of them ate a second one.

When Leopard came back from hunting she asked, "How were the children?"

Dog replied, "Very good indeed." Leopard nursed them, as they were brought out, one by one again.

The next day, Leopard went off in the morning to hunt in the woods. She charged Dog to keep the children in the cave. Tortoise came again that day, and over many objections from Dog, in the end they ate the third one of the four cubs. Dog had pondered a great deal over the fierce temper of Leopard, and she was afraid, a feeling not shared by Tortoise.

That evening when the one remaining cub made his last appearance, he showed little enthusiasm. Leopard asked if he had been well. Dog said, "These children have been fed too much. You can see how plump he is. You are producing so much milk that they are sated."

Leopard said, "Having a good nurse, like yourself, has made me lazy. Soon I am going to have them all out at once and romp with them."

The next morning Leopard went off again to hunt. After a time Tortoise came along once more and said, "Dog, why this gloom? Let us eat the other young leopard."

Dog wailed, "Oh, not that! I am distraught from thinking about what will happen. Last night Leopard said that she wished to have them all out at once and play with them."

Tortoise said, "Dog, calm yourself, for what Leopard said last night makes it certain that you have gone too far to balk over this one. To have only one is as bad as to have none. Besides, I shall tell you what to do, so that you will come out of it all right."

In the end they ate the last of the young leopards. Then after they had talked a while, Tortoise started away home. Dog saw that he was leaving, so she said, "My friend, tell me, what is it that I am to do when Leopard comes back from hunting?"

Tortoise stopped, scratched his ear, and then said, "Yes, yes. When Leopard comes back from the woods and asks about her children, you are to say this: 'Since you have not seen all your children at once for several days, perhaps you ought to go look into the cave and see them.' When she starts to go to the cave, you start for Man's village, and go as fast as you can. When you come near the village, warn the men that Leopard is coming. It will be true." Then Tortoise went away to their village.

When Leopard came from hunting, carrying meat, she asked Dog, "Nurse, how are the children?"

Dog answered, "Fine, fine, none better. Now, since you have not seen them all for some days, just go to the cave yourself."

Leopard said, "I shall do just that."

As soon as Leopard started for the cave, Dog ran for Man's village. When she came near, she dug her nails into the ground and fairly flew. As she ran, she shouted, "Help me! Help me! Leopard is coming! Leopard is coming!"

All the men came running out of their village with bows and spears and knobkerries and drove Leopard off. Leopard, furiously angry, came charging right behind Dog. With great difficulty, the men drove Leopard off. When the excitement was past, the people of the village said, "Wasn't that fine on the part of Dog to come and warn us? Otherwise we should have been taken unawares."

They all agreed to invite Dog to stay and give them warning of further attacks. When Dog had heard this offer, she accepted it, saying, "Leopards are an untrustworthy and savage folk. I have intimate knowledge of leopards."

Ever since that day, dogs have lived with men.[2] Since that time, no leopard has ever missed a chance to get a dog.

the king of the crocodiles

The king of the crocodiles was sick. The crocodiles went to consult the witch doctor about his case. When the witch

[2] Dogs are considered by the Ovimbundu to be very valuable animals. A good dog is valued equally with a slave; in the old times, a slave, an ox, a large hog and a good dog were considered interchangeable. There is a story in Umbundu, told as history, of an ancient king who ended his kingly succession by disinheriting his sons for eating his trained and faithful dogs. There are many jackal-like dogs and some large hunting dogs.

doctor had consulted the spirits, he said, "Go and kill a monkey. Take out its heart and bring it to me. Only when this is done will the king recover."

One of the crocodiles had made friends with a monkey. This crocodile went from their island to the bank of the river. He went to the place where he could see his monkey friend. The crocodile called to his friend, saying, "Good, good my friend! Is that you there?"

The monkey said, "Here I am, well and sound."

The crocodile said to the monkey, "You there, will you come with me to our village?"

The monkey said, "I am not able to go to your village."

The crocodile said to him, "I will carry you on my back." The monkey agreed to this, and the two of them started on their way to the island, and to the village of the monkey's friend, the crocodile.

When they reached the island and were approaching the village, the crocodile said to the monkey, "You are my friend, and I did not just invite you for nothing. The reason for it is: Our king is sick and he does not get well. We sent for the witch doctor. The witch doctor said, 'Go get the heart of a monkey. Only through the use of that charm, will the king recover.' "

When the monkey heard this, he said, "My friend, that makes sense. I understand it. It would have been much better if you had told me that in the first place, for then I would not have left my heart up in the tree where you found me. Now can't we go back so that I may fetch it?"

The crocodile said, "You are right."

So the crocodile took the monkey on his back and swam to the bank of the river. When they came there, the monkey jumped from the back of the crocodile and said to him, "What a fool you are! When did you ever see anyone leave his heart somewhere else, and not die?"

The crocodile went back to the island, and found that their king had died.

leopard and hare plant umbafu

One year Leopard and Hare went to trade in the country of the Ngangelas.

When they came back, they brought the seed of a tree which they found in that country. The tree was called umbafu. They found this tree in the country of the Ngangelas. The tree bore a fruit which was ripe at the time they were in that country. They ate this fruit and found it delicious. They were so pleased with this fruit that they carried some of the seed home with them.

When they came back to their village, Hare ate his seeds. On the other hand, Leopard planted his. The seeds germinated, and the plants grew and finally developed into trees which bore fruit.

When the fruits began to ripen, Hare kept coming over to Leopard's garden to steal the ambafu[3] from Leopard's trees. Leopard was angered to see the fruits disappear from the trees as fast as they ripened.

Leopard began to turn this matter over in his mind, and he pondered on how he could catch the thief who was taking away his fruit. He decided, "I shall go to some witch doctor who has a charm against theft. Then I shall be able to rest easier."

He left and went looking for a witch doctor with a charm against theft. He found that kind of witch doctor, who agreed to furnish him with that kind of charm. The witch doctor gave him these instructions: that he was to go back home and carve out the image of a person, and then to spread upon that image the medicine[4] which was given him for that purpose.

Leopard left the witch doctor and went back home to his trees. As directed by the witch doctor, he made an image and

[3] In Umbundu, the names of trees usually have a prefix of *u-* in the singular. The word for the fruit of the umbafu tree has the same stem, but the singular prefix *e-* and the plural prefix *a-*. The fruits of the *umbafu* tree are *ambafu*. Similarly, an orange tree is *ulalanja*, an orange is *elalanja*, and oranges are *alalanja*.

[4] The same word for "medicine" indicates preparations taken internally or externally to cure diseases, and preparations used in various kinds of magic and sorcery. The medicine here was probably birdlime made from the juice of a wild fig tree, a very sticky substance.

spread the charm upon it. He stood this image up beside one of the trees and went back to his house.

After Leopard had set up the image, Hare came to the tree. It was night. Hare saw the image, and thought that it was a person, so he began to talk to it and to ask it questions. He asked it, "Shall I eat from here? Or shall I eat from here?"

As the image remained silent and made no answer, Hare became annoyed. He hit the image a blow with his fist. When he struck the image, his hand stuck fast to it. This frightened Hare and he hit the image with his other hand, and that hand stuck fast also. Then Hare tried kicking the image. When he did that, his leg stuck to the image. He kicked the image with his other foot. This stuck fast also. Just then the image toppled over and fell to the ground. Hare was now completely attached to the image, and he went rolling over and over with it on the ground.

Hare saw Bushbuck passing near, so he called to him, "You, boy! Bushbuck! Come here and take this load off me, for it is too heavy for me." Bushbuck answered the call and came to relieve Hare.

Now the way the charm worked was this: if someone had been caught by it, and then a second person should take hold of the image, the first one would be released, and the second one would be stuck to the image. So it happened that Bushbuck, in having compassion on Hare, and in trying to relieve him of his load, was stuck to the image.

As soon as he was freed, Hare left and ran as fast as he could go. He went to Leopard and said, "I have caught the thief who was eating your ambafu. Come and look at him, for he is stuck to some sort of a thing that looks like a person." The two of them set out to go to the trees.

When they came to the umbafu trees, they found Bushbuck and the image rolling over and over on the ground. Leopard began to question Bushbuck, and Bushbuck began to reply. Hare broke in and said, "Honorable sir, do not let him explain any more, for he is the one we found here, and it is he who has been eating your ambafu. If you will not thrash him, give me your stick and I will thrash him for you."

Then Hare took the stick and began to beat Bushbuck, who had tried to do him a kindness.

ant and gadfly

Ant is first among the insects in intelligence and tact.

One day Ant was going about. He came at last to a man who had a sore to which there was attached a scab. Ant wished to get the scab off. Ant thought that if he acted with care he could get the scab off, without the man noticing it. Ant cut away the scab so carefully and tactfully that the man did not notice it at all. When Ant had the scab off, he dragged it away.

Dragging the scab away, Ant met Gadfly. Gadfly said to him, "Brother, who are you? What is your name?"

Ant replied to Gadfly, "I am little Ant. I live off Man. By my skill and tact I live and eat off him."

Gadfly then said, "This meat you carry, where did you get it?"

Ant replied, "Off a man."

Then Gadfly asked, "If I should go to Man, could I also get some meat?"

Ant said to him, "Man is a big animal, but you can try it."

Gadfly went away and flew until he found Man. He lit on him and began to bite. Gadfly thought that now he would get meat to eat.

The bite hurt the man, and he slapped Gadfly, and Gadfly fell to the ground dead.

From that time until now, Gadfly has gone on biting men, and through this practise has found death.

This is why Ant says, "I am little Ant, who through tact and skill lives off Man."

fruit bat and sun

When the child of Sun was sick, Sun went to the house of Elder Fruit Bat, and said to him, "Save my child for me." Fruit Bat went and cured the child of Sun. He actually cured the child, and Sun's child got well.

Later the child of Fruit Bat was taken sick. Fruit Bat went to his neighbor, Sun, and said to him, "O Sun, will you come to my house, and in your turn save my child for me?"

Sun said to Fruit Bat, "Come tomorrow, early in the morning. If you are late, you will be out of luck, for I never turn back."

Early the next morning, Fruit Bat went again to the house of Sun and said, "Now will you come?"

In reply Sun said, "Is it not the case that I said, 'If I have come out, I never turn back again? Come tomorrow morning while the ground is all black. Be here at that time."

Fruit Bat went home, and in the morning he went once more to Sun's house. Sun said to him, "You are late."

Fruit Bat went back to his house. When he came there, he found that this time his child was dead. He was very sad. He swore an oath, saying, "Never in a day nor in a year will I look upon Sun again, even if he should pass near by."

So it came to pass that from that day to this Fruit Bat will not look upon the Sun, for he says, "He did me a wrong."

bushbuck and leopard

Bushbuck and Leopard lived in the same kloof. Leopard wished to eat Bushbuck, but could not eat him, for whenever Bushbuck left the bank of the stream he hopped and jumped from side to side just like a Klipspringer. On his return, when Bushbuck came to the end of his bypath, he would again go hopping and jumping. He kept this up until he came to his bed.

Leopard thought the matter over and said to himself, "In this age, people can no longer wander about idly and find food. I shall go and scout for it."

Leopard smelled the odor of Bushbuck and went sniffing and sniffing as he followed Bushbuck's spoor, but he lost the scent when he came to the kloof. Leopard thought this over. He decided that Bushbuck had gone back into the woods. He went back over his steps, sniffing and sniffing, but did not find Bushbuck. For when Leopard went scouting, Bushbuck had already fed and then gone away to hide.

For years Leopard kept looking for Bushbuck, but never found him.

Finally, Bushbuck died of old age.

The elders say, "Bushbuck does not kill Leopard with his horns; he uses his craft to go on living."

nighthawk and viper

One day there was a fire in the woods.

Nighthawk was preparing to fly out of the woods, to escape the fire. Viper spoke to Nighthawk and said to him, "Brother Nighthawk, take pity on me and fly with me to ground that has already been burned over. When you reach such ground you may put me down." Viper pleaded and pleaded until Nighthawk consented to carry Viper out of the burning woods.

Nighthawk flew until they came to ground that had already been burned over. Nighthawk came down to the ground and alighted. He said to Viper, "Get off here, for I wish to fly on farther."

Hearing this, Viper became troublesome and said, "If you put me down here, at this time of day, when the sun has gone down, what shall I eat?"

Then Viper licked Nighthawk, beginning with his wings, until Viper had him slick and wet all over. Then Viper swallowed Nighthawk.

This is why the old men say, "When a gift has become a right, it swallows you."

17. *the tortoise saga*

a community cornfield over an abandoned village

Once all the animals of the woods joined together to cultivate a large community field of corn, on the site of an abandoned village.[1]

When ears of corn had fully developed on the stalks in the community field, all the animals began to eat corn from this field, but in a way that was not good. A woman would go to the field and pick enough ears to fill her basket. Then another woman would go with her basket and do the same. With all the animals picking the corn, it soon began to vanish from the field. The problem was how to pick the corn without using up all of it immediately. While the animals of the woods considered this problem, Corn Borer secretly went out into the field and entered a cornstalk, so that he would be able to frighten those who came to carry corn away from the old village site.

While Corn Borer was hiding himself in a cornstalk, the village elders met and decided upon a resolution: "Since there is danger that the corn will be used up immediately, we order that no one is to go into the community field and snap off corn. If any one needs corn to gnaw, he with others shall send one person to fetch corn from the field. When he comes back, he will apportion the corn equally. For the present, whenever we wish to gnaw roasting ears, we are sending only young Hare to bring corn from the field."

When they sent Hare, he went until he came to the edge of the field on the old village site. There he could hear a faint con-

[1] Village sites become richly fertilized, due to the sanitation customs of the Ovimbundu. Villages are sometimes moved, to make available for agriculture the fertile site of the former village. Whether the village is moved for that or some other reason, there is always competition for shares in the fertile area of the abandoned village.

versation going on in the field. Hare, being cautious, shouted:
"Who are you? Who is talking in this old village site?"

From the field there came a solemn voice saying, "I am
Earthshaker. We stab the elephant. We take the hide off the
roan antelope. Behind, we wear the hide of little duyker. I am
Earthshaker. Get going!"

When Hare heard this, he said to himself, "This is no place
for a little hare! I'm leaving!" When Hare returned to where
the others were, he said, "It is too bad, people, but that field cannot be entered, for there is something there that makes fear."

When they heard this, all the animals groaned in disgust.
They said, "Hare was never any good. Let us send someone of
importance. Duyker, you go."

Duyker consented, and when he came to the field, he
shouted: "Who are you? Who are you out there in the field?"

From the field there came a voice, saying, "I am Earthshaker. We stab the elephant. We take the hide off the roan
antelope. We wear the hide of the little duyker. Get going!"

Duyker left at top speed, saying, "Out of my way!" When
Duyker came to the assembly, he said, "Listen, people! That
youngster Hare told no lie. You can't get into that field, for
it is just too frightening."

Once more all the people groaned with disgust, and they
said, "You too are a liar. You! You are another Hare. You
never amounted to anything anyway. Now folks, let's send a real
man. Reedbuck, how about you?" Reedbuck accepted, saying,
"All right. I am the real man you want."

Reedbuck went out to the field, and when he came there he
called, "Who are you? Who are you, out there in the field?"

In reply, a voice from the field was heard saying, "I am
Earthshaker. We stab the elephant. We take the hide off the
roan antelope. We wear the hide of the duyker. I am Earthshaker. Get going!"

Then Reedbuck left at top speed, and as he left he said, "Out
of my way there!" When he came to the assembly, Reedbuck
said to them, "Brethren, you cannot call it a lie, for it is impossible to get any corn."

When they heard the report of Reedbuck, all the people
groaned with disgust. They said, "Oh Reedbuck, we did not expect that this would happen to you also. Now, let us send a
grown man this time. Roan Antelope, how about you?"

Roan Antelope consented and went out to the field. When he came there, he asked, "Who are you? Who are you out there in the field?"

Again the voice was heard from the field, and it said, "I am Earthshaker. We stab elephants. We take the hide off the roan antelope. We wear the little hide of the duyker. I am Earthshaker. Get going!"

When Roan Antelope heard this, he ran away crying, "Out of the way there!" When he came to the assembly he said, "This year is a hard one. Make no mistake about it."

Then all the people groaned in disgust and said, "Oh-h-h! Roan Antelope, we put our faith in you, and you turn out to be no good. Let us send a man who is really strong, one so bold that he won't run away from whatever is in the field. Leopard, how about you?" Leopard consented to their request and went.

When Leopard came to the edge of the field, he asked, "Who are you? Who are you out there in the field?" There was complete silence, so Leopard asked again, "Who are you? Who are you out there in the field?"

Then the voice answered once more: "I am Earthshaker. We stab elephants. We take the hide off the roan antelope. We wear the hide of the little duyker behind. I am Earthshaker. Get going!"

When Leopard heard this, he cried, "Look out!" and left the place as fast as he could. When he came back to the assembly, he said, "Sorry, so sorry, friends. Those who went before me did not lie. That is a place that cannot be entered. That is the truth."

Then they all groaned in disgust and said, "Brave one! Now you also turn out to be fearful. We had put our faith in you. We have reached the point at which we shall have to call upon our elder hero, the Honorable Master Lion, since all those whom we have trusted with this job, expecting them to go and fetch some corn, have just proven themselves useless."

Then Lion said, "I am really amazed that I should be called upon to gather roasting ears. I am the elder one. Have all the others failed in this?"

Then Lion went out to the field. When he came there he coughed, "Who are you? Who are you out in the field?"

The voice replied: "I am Earthshaker. We stab the elephants. We take the hide off the roan antelope. We wear the small hide of the duyker behind. I am Earthshaker. Get going!"

When Lion heard this, he backed off a distance and then asked again, "Who are you? Who are you out there in the field?"

Once more the voice replied, "I am Earthshaker. We stab the elephants. We take the hide off the roan antelope. We wear the small hide of the duyker behind. I am Earthshaker. Get going!"

When Lion heard this the second time, he left at top speed, roaring, "Out of my way. Out, out, out!" When Lion came to the assembly, he said, "Brethren, we just cultivated that corn for the weariness that we got out of it. We shall not eat any of it. At that place is something so fierce that although we spend all day at it, yet no one will get a single ear of corn."

All the animals gathered around him, but no one had courage to ridicule Lion or dispute his words.

At this point, Tortoise said to them, "Now all you folks, let me go and try what I can do. All the rest of you have been there. Am I alone to be left out? Are such things reserved for the rest of you?"

They all groaned in disgust and said, "Oh! Now Tortoise, you are just fooling yourself. Haven't all the principal people been there and given it up? You weak little thing, what can you do about it?" When Lion heard the proposal of Tortoise, he became angry and said, "Kill that little thing. He would play with the sun. We real men have already been there and have given it up. Now, miserable Tortoise, have you the gall to stand up and say, 'I too shall go there?' Kill him!"

Then the company stoned Tortoise, but he said, "We Tortoises are cousins of the Land Turtles. We shut up of our own will and open up of our own will."

The animals all tired of this dispute and said, "Let him go along. If he fails, it will serve him right."

Tortoise, carrying his sack, set out for the field. When he came there, he called, "Who are you? Who are you out there in the field?"

Out in the field a voice said, "I am Earthshaker. We stab the elephants. We take the hide off the roan antelope. We wear the little skin of the duyker behind. I am Earthshaker. Get going!"

Then Tortoise went into the field, snapped off ears of corn, and put them into his sack. Corn Borer said to himself, "This will frighten him," and shouted louder, "I am Earthshaker! We stab the elephants! We take the hide off the roan antelope! We wear the little skin of the duyker behind. I am Earthshaker! Get going!"

Tortoise would not frighten, but went on gathering ears of corn into his sack. Finally he broke off the stalk of corn in which Corn Borer was hidden and carried off that stalk along with the ears of corn.

When Tortoise came back, all the people came together. When they saw the corn that he carried, they all rejoiced. Tortoise called the elders and all the other people to come together. When they came, he said to them all, "Come here and see what you ran away from." Then he said to the cornstalk he had brought from the field: "Who are you? Who are you out there in the field?"

Then a voice was heard coming from the cornstalk saying, "I am Earthshaker. We stab the elephants. We take the hide off the roan antelope. We wear the little hide of the duyker behind. I am Earthshaker. Get going!"

Then Tortoise split open the corn stalk, and out came Corn Borer. When they saw this, all the people praised Tortoise and said, "Tortoise is a grown up. Chah, chah, chako! Tortoise is a grown up. Chah, chah, chako!"

naming foods in a time of famine

Once the people of a country were so hungry during a famine that they did not know how they were going to keep themselves alive.

Just at this time they heard of another country with food to spare. The name of this food, a root something like a yam, was *olungundonde*. This food had one peculiarity, that its name must first be pronounced by whoever would eat it.

When the animals heard of this food, they decided to send for some. They said, "Hare is a young man and can travel swiftly. Let us send him to this land to bring us some food before we all die of hunger." And so they sent Hare.

When Hare came to that country, the people there asked him, "Why did you come here?"

Hare replied to them, "Our elders sent me here to say to you, 'Please sell us some food, for we are dying of hunger.' The elders said to me, 'Ask our brothers to have mercy upon us.'"

After talking over Hare's plea among themselves, the people said, "First cook this stranger some of the food, and then let him eat it." They boiled some of the root for Hare. When it was cooked, they served it to him on a reed tray. As they gave him the food they pronounced its name, saying that it was Olungundonde. When he heard the name, Hare thought, "I must not let the name of this food escape me." Hare went away with the food for his people, and to remember the name of the food, he went along singing:

> Food! Oh joy! Olungundonde, doesn't it taste good?
> Food! Oh joy! Olungundonde, doesn't it taste good?

Hare went along singing until he came to a ravine, in which he saw a beautiful small animal. He stopped singing to watch the animal. He continued watching the small animal until it went into its hole in the side of the ravine.

The sun was about to set, so Hare started on his journey again, thinking, "Now I must sing my song as I travel." He found that he had forgotten the name of the food, and so he had to use another name and went along singing:

> Food! Oh joy! Old sweet potato, doesn't it taste good?
> Food! Oh joy! Old sweet potato, doesn't it taste good?

When Hare returned to the village, the elders received the food and asked Hare, "What is the name of this food, which we must name before eating?"

Hare replied, "It has escaped me."

The animals became angry at Hare and said to him, "We trusted you to handle this matter like a real man, and now you have gone and forgotten the name." Then the elders decided that since Duyker could travel swiftly he should go to the other country in the morning, to fetch more of the food and to learn its name.

In the morning Duyker started out and arrived soon at the other country. The elders there asked him, "Have you come here for something?"

Duyker said to them, "Dear sirs, it is shameful to relate, but the boy who came here for food yesterday forgot its name. He returned to our village with the food, but forgot its name, and for that reason it could not be eaten. May we have more? For we are starving."

"Let us cook some of this same food for him," said the elders of the place, "so that he may eat it." They boiled some of the roots. When the roots were cooked, they put some of them on a reed tray and brought them to Duyker. As they gave him the food, they pronounced the name: "Olungundonde." Duyker liked the food and thought, "I must not let the name of this food escape me." And so Duyker left with the food, remembering the name by singing this song as he went on his way:

Food! Oh joy! Olungundonde, doesn't it taste good?
Food! Oh joy! Olungundonde, doesn't it taste good?

As Duyker went on his way singing this song, he came to a ravine, in which he saw a small animal. He stopped singing to watch the animal. When it went into its hole, he had forgotten the name of the food, so he went on to their village singing:

Food! Oh joy! Old sweet potato, doesn't it taste good?
Food! Oh joy! Old sweet potato, doesn't it taste good?

When Duyker came back, the elders then asked him: "What is the name of this food?"

Then Duyker said, "Really, as a matter of fact, I have forgotten the name."

The elders said to him, "We sent you because of your speed, and thought that you were responsible. Now what are we going to do?"

Roan Antelope came forward and said, "The first thing tomorrow, I myself shall go there. These Duykers go eating along the way, as though all they had to care about was their own necks. The proper thing is for me, Roan Antelope, to go and attend to this. If someone does not bring back the name, how are we going to eat?"

The first light in the morning found Roan Antelope on the road, carrying a hamper and a sack. When he came to the country in which there was food, the people greeted him, and he replied to their greeting. Then they asked, "For what did you come here?"

Roan Antelope replied, "The elders of our village sent me. They said, 'Go to the place where they have food and buy some for us.' For those young men who already have been here came back with the food all right, but forgot the name of the food. Youths are forgetful. So the elders have sent me, an adult."

The elders of the village said, "Yes indeed, youth is forgetful. First, let us cook some of the food for Roan Antelope, so that he may taste it. Then when he has eaten, he will have strength to carry the food back home." When they had cooked some of the food, they put it into a basket for Roan Antelope. As they gave him the food, they said, "Father, before you go, take some of this food and eat it. The others who came were youngsters and naturally forgot the name of the food. So now we are telling it to you. The name of this food is Olungundonde."

While accepting the food, Roan Antelope said, "Really, aren't the young absent-minded? The name will not be forgotten again." Roan Antelope accepted the food they had cooked, ate it, and when he had finished, gave profuse thanks for it. Then he said, "Lest this name escape me, I shall sing it in a song." So Roan Antelope set out on the homeward path singing this:

Food! Oh joy! Olungundonde, doesn't it taste good?
Food! Oh joy! Olungundonde, doesn't it taste good?

Thus Roan Antelope went along singing his song.

After a while he came to the ravine. There he saw a beautiful small animal which was gleaming bright as it danced. Roan Antelope was entranced, and he continued watching, until it went into its burrow. When it went, he crossed the ravine, and went on down hill. By this time he had forgotten the song he had been singing. The best he could do was sing something similar:

Food! Oh joy! Old sweet potato, doesn't it taste good?

Food! Oh joy! Old sweet potato, doesn't it taste good?

Roan Antelope went along singing this other song until he came to the village.

When he came into the village, the elders asked him, "What is the name of this food?"

Roan Antelope replied, "That name has escaped me."

When the people heard this, they were angry and said, "What is the matter with all of you who are sent to fetch food? What are you doing on the way? As it is now, we are about to die from hunger while food is right here before us, in plain sight."

Then Leopard spoke to the assembly and said, "All these whom you have sent before, even Roan Antelope, only pretend to be adults. They are not men at all. What is so troublesome about that name? Before things become worse, let me go and attend to this myself. When I came back, I shall know what the name is."

Then all the elders said, "Good! That is the way to talk. Elder Leopard, please go. Surely you are a real man."

The next morning Leopard went. When he came to the country of the food, the elders there greeted him and said, "Grandfather, Elder Leopard, what has caused you to appear here?"

Leopard replied, "Honorable sirs, we[2] appear here on behalf of our elders, to seek a little food, for the folk are near death from hunger. All the food which you sent is stored there, really a heap of it. Even the elder, Roan Antelope himself, was bemused by youth so that he forgot the name of the food he carried. Consequently the elders sent us, the Leopards, true people, who can commit things to memory so that they stick."

Then the elders said to Leopard, "Yes, you are the one to remember. The name of the food is Olungundonde."

When Leopard heard the name he said, "Some individuals

---

[2] As among European royalty, among the Ovimbundu the first person plural is used by very important persons.

are just naturally worthless and forgetful. 'Olungundonde,' could anyone really forget that?"

Then they boiled some of the food for Leopard to eat. When he had eaten it, they gave him more to take with him. He thanked them profusely for the food a number of times.

As Leopard went home along the path he sang this song over and over:

Food! Oh joy! Olungundonde, doesn't it taste good?
Food! Oh joy! Olungundonde, doesn't it taste good?

Leopard sang until he came to the ravine. There he saw a beautiful little animal. It was plump and fat, and it danced. Leopard stood watching it until the sun went down. When the little animal went into its hole, Leopard crossed over the ravine and went on down the hill. As he went along he thought, "Oh yes, I was singing a song." He could not think, at the moment, of the name of the food, so until he should remember it he sang:

Food! Oh joy! Old sweet potato, doesn't it taste good?
Food! Oh joy! Old sweet potato, doesn't it taste good?

When Leopard came to where the elders were gathered, they asked him, "What is the name of the food?"

Leopard said, "Oh dear me. Now what is it? This name! It is a puzzler. It has escaped me."

All the people were very, very angry at this. They said, "Why are you acting like this? Can no one here remember a name so that he can come back and tell it to us?" After everyone had heard this complaint, Lion spoke up and said, "Now we have seen that the Leopards are not real men. They are children. I see that it is up to me to go myself. In a crisis like this, sending children is not enough. Now brothers, and you seniors, the Elephants, arrange to send me tomorrow, before the adults are enfeebled and the children die."

When it became light in the morning, Lion went carrying a bag and a hamper. When he came to the other country, the elders there said, "He who never runs away, the elder statesman, Sir Lion, why has he thus appeared to us?"

In reply to their greeting, Lion made this speech: "Oh

Grandfathers, the truth is that those youngsters, those sons of widows,[3] these whom we have sent previously, cannot be blamed for not bringing back food—they brought it. But when they were asked the name of the food which they brought, they said, 'It has escaped us.' It stirs pity in us to observe our elders, the Elephants, who have been weakened until now they just stand and drowse. When I saw such conditions I said, 'This is too pitiful! It is best for me to go myself, so that the elders may eat and the children live.' "

The elders of the country replied and said, "By our ancestors! Those hard words of yours are deserved. The trouble is with the adolescents, and with the adults who act like adolescents. Now then, Father, the name of this food is Olungundonde."

When Lion heard the name of the food, he said to them, "Listen to it. How can an easy name like that escape one's memory?"

They ordered that some of the food be gotten ready for Sir Lion to eat before he left. The roots were boiled and put into a basket for Lion. He ate it and perceived that it was good, with an excellent flavor. When Lion had eaten, he took up his load, the elders wished him a good journey, and he left singing:

Food! Oh joy! Olungundonde, doesn't it taste good?
Food! Oh joy! Olungundonde, doesn't it taste good?

When Lion came to the ravine, he saw the beautiful small animal. As he looked, the animal began to dance. Lion stopped to watch the animal and he stopped singing while he watched. He did not sing for fear that he would frighten the little animal into running away.

When the sun went down, the little animal went away into its hole. Lion crossed the ravine and descended the slope. As he went along, he tried to recall the song that he had been singing. He thought hard, but the name of the food was gone, so in its place he sang:

Food! Oh joy! Old sweet potato, doesn't it taste good?
Food! Oh joy! Old sweet potato, doesn't it taste good?

[3] Umbundu euphemism for bastards.

Lion sang this until he came to the place where the elders were waiting to receive him. They asked him, "What is the name of the food?"

Lion said, "Oh! Yes! Now. That name is a tough one. They cannot give us the name any longer. Now they cannot pronounce it. We all may perish from hunger."

When they heard this, everyone became very angry and said, "How did all of you get this way? You are all fools!" Then they took the food that Lion had brought and placed it on top of the heap of food which they could not eat, not knowing its name.

After they waited a while, Tortoise came forward and said, "I too am going to go there."

Everyone ridiculed Tortoise and objected to his going. They said, "No! Not Mister Tortoise! Real men have gone already, and all of them failed. How can you, little Tortoise, hope to do better?"

Then they picked up Tortoise and threw him into the fire. He came waddling out, still talking and saying, "We Tortoises, when they put us into a fire, it only makes the fire burn harder. We are the cousins of the Land Turtles." When he said this, they pelted him with stones until he was all mushy. Still he went on talking, saying, "We Tortoises are those who shut up of themselves and open up of themselves."

Since he still refused to back down, some of the people said, "Well, let him go. Let him go there."

When Tortoise was ready to leave, he said, "Please furnish me with a hamper." They gave him a hamper, and off he went.

When he arrived, the people of the other country said, "Well! Are even such as you seeking us out also?"

Tortoise replied, "Grandfathers, we little people said, 'This that the big folk failed to do must be difficult. Even though we are small and insignificant, we can go and take a look, for it is said, 'Things can look at each other.' "

The elders asked him, "Wasn't the food named by Sir Lion? Did he forget it also?"

Tortoise replied, "Sirs, he forgot it. It was for that reason that we took to the road, so that we, the worthless people, might also have a look."

Then the elders said to Tortoise, "Really, all the difficulty is due to those others. In the first place, the name is not difficult at all. It is Olungundonde. Who can forget a name like that? It should not bother anyone in the least."

Tortoise said, "If it is possible we shall memorize it."

When the elders heard this, they said, "You are one of us, but before we go further, let some of this food be cooked, so that you may eat it and thus be able to travel well as you go home." They boiled some of the food, and when it was cooked, they gave it to him on a small dish, and he ate it. When he had eaten, he took up his load and bade them farewell.

When he got out on the path, he began to sing a song so that he could recall the name of the roots when he should come to the village. He sang:

> Food! Oh joy! Olungundonde, doesn't it taste good?
> Food! Oh joy! Olungundonde, doesn't it taste good?

He sang this song along the way, until he came to the ravine. There he found a little animal, a beautiful one. It danced and ran to and fro, skipping up and down. Tortoise saw it, but was not interested, and just kept walking up stream, all the while singing:

> Food! Oh joy! Olungundonde, doesn't it taste good?
> Food! Oh joy! Olungundonde, doesn't it taste good?

Tortoise sang all the way to the village.

When Tortoise reached the village, he headed toward the people and the elders, still singing:

> Food! Oh joy! Olungundonde, doesn't it taste good?
> Food! Oh joy! Olungundonde, doesn't it taste good?

Everyone became excited and said: "At last! This is really the name. It is 'Olungundonde.'" Then they came running to Tortoise to take his load from him. They put him into a hammock, and as they carried him along in it they shouted: "Tortoise, he is the old one. Chah, chah, chako! Tortoise, he is the old one. Chah, chah, chako!"

As the people called the food by its name, they broke off

pieces of root and ate them. They ate until there was no more
hunger.

tortoise and an old woman hunt animals

One day Tortoise said to himself, "I am fond of eating
meat, but I am unable to catch animals." When he had worked
out a plan for catching animals, he went to the house of a little
old woman. Her house was beside a game path used by many
animals in going through the woods.

When he had come to the house, he spoke with the little
old woman, and said to her, "Grandmother, I am a hunter."

"Are you able to kill animals?" asked the little old woman.

Tortoise said, "I shall drive animals up to your house, and
you will kill them with your hoe. Tomorrow at daybreak, I shall
tell you how you are to kill the animals that I bring in."

Early in the morning, at daybreak, Tortoise said to the little
old woman, "Grandmother, sharpen your hoe, then hide yourself
in the bushes while I go out to wait by the path. When I have led
an animal into the house, then you are to stand outside the doorway and scratch on the door. The animal will throw me out
through the doorway. Next, when the animal puts out its head,
you are to cut it off with your hoe. And let us be sure, grandmother, that you have in your house many foods which animals
like. Did you plant such foods?"

The woman replied, "Every kind of food is in the house."

Then Tortoise went out beside the path and waited for
animals to use the path. When he saw a duyker coming, he
called to him, "Duyker, O Sir, where are you going?"

Duyker replied, "I am going to the fields."

Tortoise asked him, "Do you eat cowpeas?"

Duyker said, "I eat cowpeas. But where are any cowpeas?"

Tortoise said, "Come over here."

Then Duyker followed Tortoise into the house of the little
old woman. When they were inside the house, Tortoise got some
cowpeas and gave them to Duyker. Then Tortoise said to Duyker, "Duyker, if while you are eating cowpeas you hear a scraping

sound on the outside of the door, then pick me up and throw me outside. As you throw me out, say, 'I am throwing out a bone.' Shortly after you have thrown me out, you may come out also." Soon there was a scraping sound, "Cholo, cholo," outside the door, so Duyker picked up Tortoise and threw him through the doorway, saying, "I am throwing out a bone." Then Duyker stuck out his head and the little old woman, who had come out from the bushes and had made the scratching sound on the doorway, struck Duyker on the neck with her hoe. Duyker died.

Tortoise had hurried away into the bushes after Duyker had thrown him out of the house. But when he heard the little old woman strike the duyker, he came hurrying back to help the old woman skin the duyker. Later they cooked the flesh.

On another day, when they had finished eating the flesh of the duyker, Tortoise went out again to lie in wait. Soon, he saw a bushbuck coming toward him. When the bushbuck came near, Tortoise called to him, "Sir and Grandfather, where are you going?"

Bushbuck replied, "Do not shout at me." [4]

Tortoise said, "I just called to ask if you eat the leaves of the sweet potato."

Bushbuck answered, "Yes, I eat them."

Tortoise said, "Then come with me."

They went together into the house of the old woman. Tortoise got some sweet potato leaves and gave them to Bushbuck. Then Tortoise said, "Bushbuck, if while you are eating you should hear something scrape on the outside of the door, you must pick me up and throw me outside. As you throw me out, you are to say, 'I am throwing out a bone.' After a short time, you may come outside also." Soon there was the sound of scraping on the door. Bushbuck picked up Tortoise and threw him out, saying, "I am throwing out a bone." Soon, as Bushbuck was coming out through the doorway, the little old woman chopped him with her hoe, and he died. Then Tortoise hurried to help the little old woman skin the bushbuck. When they had finished the skinning, they ate the flesh of the bushbuck.

After a time, Tortoise went out again to lie in wait. This time he saw a wart hog coming toward him. Tortoise called out: "Sir Grandfather, where are you going?"

---

[4] The Ovimbundu consider it impolite for the young to call loudly to older people, or for those of lower status to call to those of higher status.

Wart Hog said, "I am going to the fields, where I shall eat some corn."

Tortoise told him: "But there is corn in here."

When Wart Hog had heard this, he followed Tortoise into the house of the little old woman. In the house, Tortoise gave him some corn. While he was eating the corn, Tortoise told him, "If you hear a scraping noise on the outside of the door, pick me up and throw me outside, saying, 'I am throwing out a bone.' Later you may come out."

As had happened before, there was a scraping sound on the door. So Wart Hog picked Tortoise up and threw him out, shouting, "I am throwing out a bone." Soon Wart Hog decided to go out, and as he was coming through the doorway the little old woman struck him with her hoe, killing him. Then Tortoise hurried to help the little old woman scrape the Wart Hog. When they had finished, they ate the meat.

Another day, when Tortoise went out to wait by the path, he saw Roan Antelope coming his way. Tortoise called to him, "O Honorable Grandfather, where are you going?"

Roan Antelope said, "I go to the fields."

Then Tortoise asked him, "Do you eat corn?"

Roan Antelope replied, "I eat corn regularly."

Then Tortoise said to him, "Come with me and get some."

Roan Antelope went with Tortoise into the house. When Roan Antelope had begun to eat corn, Tortoise said to him, "If you hear a scratching sound on the door, pick me up and throw me outside, saying, 'I am throwing out a bone.' Later, you may come out, if you wish." Soon Roan Antelope heard a scratching. He picked up Tortoise and threw him out through the doorway, saying "I am throwing out a bone." When Roan Antelope came out, the little old woman cut off his head with her hoe, and he died. Tortoise came in a hurry to help the little old woman skin the roan antelope. Then they ate the meat. It took them some days to eat the roan antelope.

When the roan antelope had been eaten, Tortoise went out once more to lie in wait beside the path. He saw Waterbuck coming, and called to him, "O Honorable Grandfather, where are you going?"

Waterbuck told Tortoise, "I go to the fields, and there I shall eat the vines of the sweet potato."

Tortoise said, "There are vines of the sweet potato right here."

Hearing this, Waterbuck went along with Tortoise into the house of the old woman. When Waterbuck had been given his sweet potato vines, Tortoise said to him, "If you hear a scratching sound on the door, pick me up and throw me out through the door, saying, 'I am throwing out a bone.' Later you may come out." Waterbuck had started to sample the vines when he heard scratching on the door. He picked up Tortoise and threw him through the doorway, saying, "I am throwing out a bone." Waterbuck continued eating, and when he had eaten enough he came out. As he came out, the little woman hit him with her hoe, and he died. Tortoise helped the old woman skin Waterbuck, and it took them some time to eat all this meat, but finally there was an end to the eating.

When all the meat was gone, Tortoise went out to lie in wait by the path again. This time he saw a gnu coming along, and he called out, "O Honorable Grandfather, where are you going?"

Gnu replied, "I am on my way to get a drink of water."

Tortoise said, "There is water here."

Then Gnu followed Tortoise. They went into the house of the little old woman. After Tortoise had given Gnu some water, he said to him, "Should you hear a sound of scratching outside the door, you are to pick me up, throw me outside, and as you are throwing me say, 'I am throwing out a bone.' Later come outside yourself." Soon Gnu heard the scratching sound, picked up Tortoise, and threw him out, shouting, "I am throwing out a bone." When he had had his drink of water Gnu thought that it was time to leave. As he put his head outside the door, the little old woman struck him with her hoe, and he died. Tortoise hurried to help the woman skin the gnu, after which they cooked the flesh and ate it.

When they had need of more meat, Tortoise went out to sit beside the path. Soon he saw an eland coming along the path. He called to Eland, "O Honorable Grandfather, where are you going?"

Eland replied, "I am on my way to the fields to look for something to eat."

Tortoise informed him, "In our house there are many sorts of things to eat, and you may eat all you wish of any foods you find there." When he heard this, Eland went along with Tortoise into the house. Inside the house, Tortoise said to Eland, "While you are choosing what you will have, if you hear a noise of scratching outside the door, pick me up and throw me out. As you throw me out, say, 'I am throwing out a bone.' Later you may come out." As Eland was looking around at the foods, he heard a scratching at the door, so he picked up Tortoise and threw him outside, saying, "I am throwing out a bone." Then after sampling the foods, Eland decided to go outside. When he put his head out, the little woman chopped it off with her hoe, and he died. Tortoise came hurrying to help the woman skin the eland.

After a long time, when they had finished eating the flesh of this great animal, Tortoise went out again to sit by the path. This time, as he sat watching, he saw an elephant approaching. When the elephant came near, Tortoise called to him, "O Honorable Grandfather, where do you go?"

Elephant said to Tortoise, "I am on my way to the fields to get some gourds to eat."

Tortoise said to Elephant, "There are many gourds here in the house."

Then Elephant followed Tortoise. When they came into the house, Tortoise said to Elephant, "Now, while you are swallowing the gourds, if you should hear a scratching sound outside the door, pick me up and throw me outside. As you are throwing me out, say, 'I am throwing out a bone.' Later, when you have had gourds enough, you may come out also." When Elephant heard this scratching sound, he picked Tortoise up, and threw him out, saying as he did so, "I am throwing out a bone." Elephant, when he started to come out of the house, was hit in the neck by the little old woman, and he died. Tortoise came running to help the little woman skin the elephant. They ate the elephant. This meat lasted for many days.

When they had finished eating the meat of the elephant, Tortoise went out to sit by the path. Tortoise saw a hippopotamus coming slowly along. Tortoise called to him, "O Honorable Grandfather, where are you going?"

Hippopotamus told him, "I am going to the fields, where I hope to get some squashes to eat."

Tortoise said to him, "There is a squash right here in the house."

When they came into the house, Tortoise got a squash and

gave it to Hippopotamus. As he gave it to him, Tortoise said, "If while you are eating the squash, you should happen to hear a scratching noise outside the door, speak in a loud voice and say, 'I am throwing out a bone.' Then pick me up and throw me out." Hippopotamus heard a scratchy noise at the door. Then he picked Tortoise up, and said, "I am throwing out a bone." Then he threw him out. After Hippopotamus had finished eating the squash, he came out, and the little old woman smote him in the neck with her hoe, and he died. Tortoise rushed out to help the little old woman skin the hippopotamus.

Finally, after they had eaten the last of the hippopotamus meat, Tortoise went out to wait by the path. As he sat there looking, he saw the king of the monkeys coming. Tortoise said to the king of the monkeys, "O Honorable Grandfather, where are you going?"

The King of the Monkeys said, "I go hunting mountain cucumbers."

Tortoise said to him, "Mountain cucumbers? We have some here."

While the King of the Monkeys was talking with Tortoise, the monkey children had climbed into the trees to listen to what Tortoise was saying to the king. When they saw the king going into the house along with Tortoise, they swung through the tree-tops, in order to come near to the house into which the king had gone. While Tortoise was talking with the king in the house, the little old woman came out from hiding, but before she could reach the house, the children of the king shouted to him, "Run! Run! Run right now!"

When the king heard this, he ran out so quickly that the little old woman missed him. Then the followers of the king began shouting noisily, "Haka! Haka! Haka! Haka! Haka!"

As the king fled hastily from the house, he passed by the place where they had thrown the bones of all the animals that had been eaten. When he had told his children about these bones, he said to them, "Let us go and warn all the animals which go about on the ground, saying to them, 'No one is to pass along this path any more, for all sorts of animals of the wood have perished at this place.' "

tortoise hunts the undolo bird

One day those who hunt with bow and arrow went out into the wild to have a drive hunt.[5]

The hunters found a tree with a hole, where an undolo bird [6] had made its nest and laid its eggs. Since the tree was a tall one and the undolo's hole high up on the trunk, the man who had first seen the bird took up his ax so that he could fell the tree and thus get to the nest. But he had only tapped on the tree once with his ax when Undolo heard the first blow and came out of its hole screaming:

> Who is it that thumps and thumps
> On the nest tree of Undolo?
> From plain and from mountain
> The earthquake will come on,
> Rumbling, flashing, crashing—boom!

The man fell to the ground in a faint, for he had heard the thunder of Undolo's wings and seen the light of Undolo's breast, like a bright flash of lightning. Then Undolo flew away among the trees to seek food for her children.

Later one of the hunters said, "Our brother here is of weak heart, for he fainted at the sound of the thunder of Undolo's wings. But I shall chop down the tree. I cannot be frightened by a commonplace little bird." Then this hunter took up his ax, intending to test the tree with a blow. He struck it, "Thump." Undolo heard this blow and flew at the hunter screaming:

> Who is it that thumps and thumps
> On the nest tree of Undolo?
> From plain and from mountain

[5] The drive hunt is a community affair, in which many men and boys form a wide circle and then converge inward, driving the game before them.

[6] The undolo is a small bird whose white breast suggests the flash of lightning, and whirring wings suggest thunder.

> The earthquake will come on,
> Rumbling, flashing, crashing—boom!

The man fell to the ground in a faint.

Then all the men in the company tried one by one to cut down the tree, but none of them could withstand the undolo's flashing and thundering. They all fell to the ground, one after another.

Last of all, little Tortoise came forward to try his strength on the tree. He stepped up with his little ax and started to chop the tree down. He chopped, "Thump, thump." Undolo heard this and came to save her children. As before, she screamed:

> Who is it that thumps and thumps
> On the nest tree of Undolo?
> From plain and from mountain
> The earthquake will come on,
> Rumbling, flashing, crashing—boom!

Little Tortoise did not fall to the ground. He just kept on chopping.

Undolo came again with the noise of thunder, flashing the light of her breast, trying to frighten Tortoise and strike him to the ground, as she had struck the other hunters to the ground with fright. She did this to save her children. But in spite of all she could do, little Tortoise did not fall down. He kept chopping until the tree fell down. Then he took out the nestlings.

All the men who had fallen down in fright before Undolo began to praise Tortoise, saying, "Tortoise, he is an old timer. Chah, chah, chako! Little Tortoise, he is an old timer. Chah, chah, chako!"

tortoise wins a wife

One day a woman went visiting another village. She took her daughter with her. This daughter was very beautiful.

Just before sundown the young men of the village called on the guests. The young men looked at the girl and saw that she was beautiful, very beautiful. One said, "I want her." Then another said, "I want her." Soon all were saying that they wanted her.

The mother heard the young men and said to them, "Only he who can give her secret name may eat[7] her." When the young men heard this, they went away to their houses to think of all the names for women they had ever heard.

While the others were thinking about names for women, Tortoise went to the house of the guests. He poked his staff through a hole in the back of the house. His staff poked the girl and frightened her. She cried out, "I, Etosiliachipemba Elendeliambela Lambundu, say, 'This is too much.'" When Tortoise heard this, he left in a hurry. He had heard the girl's secret name and was pleased with himself. He went away and joined the other hopefuls.

The young men planned to meet in the guest's kitchen the next evening. When the time came, they all met in the kitchen. The young men, one by one, began to say many names of women, but none of these names was the right one.

When they all had tried, then Tortoise said, "Please, let me also name a name."

They all laughed at him and said, "The real people have all given up. Now will you name the right name?" But they agreed to let Tortoise try and said to him, "All right, go ahead and name her name for her."

Then Tortoise spoke to the girl and said, "You are Etosiliachipemba Elendeliambela Lambundu."

When the mother of the girl heard Tortoise, she praised him, saying: "Tortoise, you have spoken to the point. You may marry my daughter. But the meat for the wedding feast of my daughter must be a live duyker, and the oil for annointing the bridesmaids the fat of python."

Before Tortoise did anything, he thought things over. Then he took a hamper and went off into the woods to hunt. As he was going along, he met Duyker, and they were pleased to meet each other. Tortoise said to Duyker, "Elder Brother, are you able to carry me?"

[7] The Umbundu verb "to eat" is used figuratively to mean "have," "possess," "marry," etc.

Duyker replied, "You are a lightweight. Why should I not be able to carry you?" Duyker put Tortoise into the hamper, and carried him for some distance.

Then Tortoise got out and said to Duyker, "Please let me carry you now." Duyker agreed to let him try. Tortoise tried to arrange Duyker in the hamper, but could not work it. Finally Tortoise said to Duyker, "Big brother, because you are so smooth and slippery, I wish you to put your legs through the holes in the bottom of the hamper so that you will not fall out." Duyker consented to do this.

Tortoise went along until they came near the village, and then Duyker said, "Tortoise, put me down, for there are people over there."

Tortoise refused to do this and said, "Big brother, do not be alarmed. We go to my house. No one will harm you." Tortoise shut Duyker in the goat hut.

Then Tortoise started out to search for python fat. When he had gone into the wood, he found a python. He greeted Python thus: "Hello uncle, how are you?" Then Tortoise began to tell Python about a new charm, saying, "Uncle, I have a wonderful charm against fire. Even if I am in the middle of a burning patch of dry grass, I am not burned at all. Come along with me and let us try it out. I shall go into this patch of dry grass, and then you will set it afire."

Tortoise went into the patch of dry grass. He found a hole where an eland had stepped and got down into it. Python came and set the grass on fire. The fire passed over Tortoise, not even scorching him. Tortoise came out and said to Python, "Look me over. I am not burned at all. If you wish, I shall make you a present of this charm which will protect you from fire."

Python agreed to receive the charm. Then Tortoise chewed up a leaf, squirted the spittle into Python's mouth, and said, "There, that is all there is to it. Now go into this other patch of dry grass. When I have fired it, you will see how it works."

Python went into the patch of dry grass. Tortoise ringed it with fire. Python was burned to death. After the fire had burned down, Tortoise went carefully to Python, opened his abdomen, extracted the fat, and went with it to the village to celebrate his marriage.

Later he married the girl.

One day after they were married, the wife brewed beer

and then went away to the fields for food. Before she left, she put the big pot of beer up on the food shelf.

Tortoise came into the house wishing for a drink of beer, but could not reach the pot. So he placed one stool on top of another, until he would be able to reach the shelf from the top one. Tortoise climbed up the stack of stools. As he reached the top one, the stools slipped and fell. Tortoise fell into the pot of beer and died.

hare, hornbill and tortoise

One day Hare said to Hornbill, "Come along with me and let us visit my wife's family." Hornbill agreed.

After they had walked along the path for some time, Hare said that he needed to retire to the bush. As Hare was coming back to the path, he picked up a round stone about the size of a ball of mush and put it into his food wallet.

Then when they came to a river, Hare said to Hornbill, "My mother warned me that to cross a bridge with a ball of mush in your wallet is unlucky. She said you must throw it into the stream." When Hare had said this, he took the stone out of his wallet and threw it into the river. Hornbill took from his wallet the ball of mush he carried to eat on the road, and threw it into the stream.

Farther on they came to a tree bearing an edible fruit. They sat down under the tree to rest. As they sat resting, Hare opened his wallet, took out his ball of mush, and began to eat it. Hornbill saw this. He spoke up and said, "What is this! You said, 'Let us throw our balls of mush into the river!'"

Hare said, "Yes, that is so. But since then this ball of mush just cooked itself inside my wallet."

When Hare had finished eating, he called Hornbill's attention to the wild fruit and said, "Let us gather some of these wild plums. But in gathering them, let us gather only the green ones. My mother warned me not to gather red ones, for they bring bad luck." Then they began to gather some of the fruit. Hare moved around to the back of the tree, where he picked the ripe, red plums. Hornbill, as he had been advised by Hare, gathered

only green fruit. When they had filled their wallets, they went
on once more.

As they drew near the village of Hare's wife's family, they
sat down under a tree to rest. Hare noticed that there were chips
and shavings at the place where they sat down. Some one had
hewn out a board at the spot, leaving long shavings. They
started to eat some of their fruit. Hornbill saw Hare eating ripe,
red plums and said to him, "Didn't you tell me that we should
not pick red ones?"

"Oh yes," said Hare, "I did say that, but these plums ripened
in my wallet."

After they had eaten their fruit, Hare said to Hornbill: "At
the village ahead, where we are going, they do not have any
spoons. When you see them bringing us food, you must come
back here to get some of these chips, so that we can eat with
them. You will do this instead of my doing it, since we shall
need the chips quickly and you have wings which enable you to
travel faster than I."

Hornbill agreed to this and said, "That is all right."

When they came into the village the people rejoiced to see
them and received them in fine style. They were taken to the
men's clubhouse, given chairs, and beer was brought for them
to drink. Next they were greeted with a formal speech of welcome. Later in the day they were taken to the guesthouse. Near
sundown, the hosts were seen bringing them mush and fried
chicken.

When Hare saw the food coming, he spoke to Hornbill and
said, "Hornbill, remember what I spoke to you about. Now go
and get them." While Hornbill was away, Hare ate the mush
and the fried fowl that was served with it. When Hornbill
returned, Hare gave him some mush served with beans, which
had been brought along with the other, saying, "Brother, take
this and eat it. I, for my part, shall eat nothing more in this
village, for it is an insult to be served food of this sort, of such
low quality. I had thought that the mush would be served
with meat, but it is not so." Hornbill took the food and ate it,
for he was painfully hungry.

Hare went out in the night, stole a goat, and ate it. He
cut a hole in the stomach of the goat, and slipped it over the
head of Hornbill. The contents of the stomach were warm and
brought a deep sleep over Hornbill. In the morning the owners

of the goat came looking for it. They found Hornbill sleeping with the stomach of the goat over his head. They said, "We are looking for a goat. What have you guests to say?"

Hare replied to them: "The old men have said, 'The bull of the herd does not gore his own, for he is their guardian.'" Then the owners of the goat took Hornbill away and killed him.

Hare returned to their village alone. He stayed there for some time.

Then one day, he spoke to Tortoise and said to him, "Come and go with me to visit my wife's folks." Tortoise agreed to this.

They started out, and as they were going out to the main path, Tortoise said, "I am going to the bush." Out in the bush he picked up a stone similar to a ball of mush and dropped it into his wallet.

After they were back on the main path and walking along, Hare said, "I have to step aside." Hare picked up another stone of the same kind and put it into his wallet.

When they came to the bridge over the river Hare said, "Let us throw our balls of mush into the river, for my mother said, 'If you are crossing a bridge, do not carry mush balls.'" Tortoise took the stone out of his wallet and threw it into the river. Hare did the same.

When they came to the wild plum tree, they sat down to rest. As he had done previously, Hare got out his ball of mush and began to eat it. As Hare ate, Tortoise said to him, "Now, how does this happen?"

Hare said to him in reply: "My ball of mush just cooked itself inside my wallet."

Then Tortoise took his ball of mush out of his wallet, and he also began to eat. Then Hare said to him, "How does this happen? Didn't I say to you that we should throw our balls of mush into the river?"

Tortoise replied: "I did so. This ball cooked itself inside my wallet." When Hare heard this explanation, he did not like it.

Later, when they had finished eating, Hare said to Tortoise, "Let us gather some of these wild plums, but not the red ones." Tortoise was agreeable to this suggestion. Again Hare went around to the back of the tree and gathered the ripe, red ones. Tortoise stayed on his side and also picked red ones.

They went on again, until they came to the tree with

shavings under it. Here they sat down to rest. When Hare took some red plums from his wallet and began to eat them, Tortoise said to him: "How does this happen?"

Hare said, "These ripened inside my wallet."

Tortoise then began to eat his own red plums. When Hare saw them, he said to Tortoise, "Didn't I tell you that we should pick only green plums?"

Tortoise answered, "Oh, these? They just ripened of themselves inside my wallet." Once more Hare did not like Tortoise's reply.

Hare waited for a time, and then he spoke to Tortoise, saying, "Where we are going this afternoon, if you should see them bringing food for us, you must hurry back here and fetch a chip with which to eat the food, for at that place they have no spoons."

When they stood up to go on, Tortoise said, "I have to step aside." While Tortoise was doing this, he picked up a chip and put it in his wallet.

They went into the village, were greeted, and were assigned to a house.

When food was brought in the afternoon, Hare said, "Tortoise, go and fetch a chip." All that Tortoise did was to reach into his wallet and take out the chip, which he had placed there. He gave the chip to Hare. Tortoise took the food from the child, thanking him several times for it. Together, the two of them ate the mush and the meat which came with it. Hare ate in anger.

While Tortoise appeared to be asleep that night, Hare went out once more, as he had done on the previous occasion, and stole a goat. While Hare was away, Tortoise took two cowry shells from his wallet and put them over his eyes. When Hare came in with the stomach of the goat, intending to put it on the head of Tortoise, he saw the shells over Tortoise's eyes and said, "Now he is on the watch. I shall wait until Tortoise shuts his eyes and goes to sleep." Hare kept waiting and waiting for Tortoise to shut his eyes. Tortoise slept until daylight, and while Hare sat holding the stomach of the goat in his hand, Hare went to sleep.

At daylight, the owners of the goat were looking for it. They came to the house of the guests. They took one look, for

Hare was sitting with the stomach of the goat in his hand. They asked, "What is this?" What have you guests done?"

Tortoise spoke up and said, "Yes, that is right. Your son-in-law is the thief. On that other occasion too, he was the thief. He did the stealing. It was he who slipped the stomach of the goat over the head of Hornbill."

Then they took Hare away and killed him.

hunter, lion and tortoise

One day a hunter followed a herd of roan antelopes.

In the middle of a wood he came onto the spoor of a lion. Studying the spoor, he found that the lion seemed to be following the same herd of roan antelopes which he himself was following. The hunter thought that by this time the lion would have overtaken the herd and made his kill. So the hunter decided to follow on and get the remains of the antelope, which the lion would not have eaten at his first meal from his kill.

While the hunter followed the lion's spoor, he happened to look up and saw the lion up in the crotch of a tree. He moved closer to see if the lion was dead. But when he had come close, the lion heard him and looked around at him. Frightened to see the lion move, the hunter jumped and started to flee.

The lion called to the hunter, saying, "O fellow hunter, do not run away, but come and save me."

The hunter came back, leaned his gun against a tree, and climbed into the tree where the lion was stuck. When the hunter got above the crotch in which the lion was stuck, he lifted the lion out. When the two of them came to the ground, the lion said to the hunter, "O hunter, which way are you going?"

The hunter pointed and said, "I am going in that direction."

The lion said, "I am going that way too."

After they had gone along together some distance, the lion spoke to the hunter, saying, "Brother, I am famished. Give me one of your sandals." The hunter took off one of his sandals and gave it to the lion. The lion ate it.

When they had gone farther, the lion said, "Brother, I am

beside myself with hunger at this very moment. It pains me severely. Give me your other sandal." The hunter gave the lion his other sandal.

When they had gone on still farther, the lion said, "I am not satisfied. Give me the skin cover to your cartridge case." The hunter gave the lion this skin cover, and the lion ate it.

They went on once more. Soon the lion spoke to the hunter again and said, "Give me the cartridge case itself." The hunter gave the lion the cartridge case, and the lion ate that also.

Not long after this the lion said, "Give me the skin cover from your gun." The hunter obliged, and gave the lion the cover from his gun. The lion ate this also. After the lion had eaten the cover from the gun, they went on.

As the hunter walked, he was swinging his arm. The lion asked him, "Is all that yours?

The hunter replied, "All of what?"

The lion pointed to the hunter's arm and said, "It is just hanging there doing nothing. Give it to me."

In reply to this the hunter said, "No."

This reply caused a disagreement. While the two were disputing the matter, a tortoise came along and said, "Brothers, what are you disputing about?"

The hunter told the tortoise the whole story of what had happened on the way. When the tortoise had heard this he said, "Lion, let us go to the place where the hunter found you."

So they went back, and when they came to the place, the tortoise said, "Lion, where was the antelope that you were stalking?"

The lion said, "Here."

The tortoise said to him, "Jump again as you did when you tried to catch the animal."

The lion jumped again, and as before, he stuck fast in the crotch of the tree. The tortoise spoke to the hunter and said to him, "Hunter, just go away."

Then they left, and the lion stayed on in the tree.

the perseverance of tortoise

In the days of our ancestors, there was a king who wished to find a man with perseverance.

The king planted a tall pole into the ground, upright. On the top of the pole he fastened a feather of an okangungu. Then the king summoned all of his people by having his crier call out: "All people, come here to the capital village." When the people had assembled, the king made another announcement: "He who climbs to the top of this pole and brings down the feather of okangungu may marry my daughter, Chiyonga Changeve, the younger sister of Kawape."

Those who attempted to climb the pole, as they climbed, were to sing this song:

> The feather of Kangungu,
> I shall climb and fetch it.
> The feather of Kangungu,
> I shall climb and fetch it.
> This year I shall marry
> Chiyonga Changeve,
> The sister of Kawape.

There was among the king's people a withered old crone. When she heard of this contest, she came to the assembly so that she could distract the climbers by performing comic songs and dances.

When the first contestant had climbed half way up the pole, the old crone began to dance and to sing comic songs. When the climber, as far from the top of the pole as he was from the ground, heard the sound of her songs, he stopped climbing, looked down, lost his balance, fell to the ground, and died.

The same fate befell all the others who tried to climb the pole. These deaths were thinning out the population of the country.

Finally Tortoise came near the pole and said, "Let me climb also."

Those standing near ridiculed Tortoise, saying, "Real men have failed to climb this pole. How can you hope to climb it?" So they picked him up and threw him aside. Still he persisted and came back to the pole. When the people saw Tortoise's perseverance, they finally said to each other, "Oh, let him try to climb the pole."

After he had the permission of the people, Tortoise began climbing the pole, singing the song which the others had sung:

> The feather of Kangungu
> I shall climb and fetch it.
> The feather of Kangungu
> I shall climb and fetch it.
> This year I shall marry
> Chiyonga Changeve,
> The sister of Kawape.

Tortoise climbed to the top of the pole and took the feather.

When Tortoise returned to the ground with the feather, all the onlookers marveled at Tortoise's perseverance, for when the old crone had gone through her dances and songs Tortoise had kept on climbing, not looking down.

When Tortoise came to the king, the king praised him, saying, "You are a real man." Then Tortoise took Chiyonga Changeve for his wife and took her away to his village.

Sometime later it happened that Chiyonga Changeve cooked a dish of bean butter,[8] When she brought this dish to Tortoise, he said to her, "I am not eating bean butter this morning." After hearing this, the woman took the beans away and placed them upon a high shelf. Then she went to the fields.

About midday, long after his wife had gone to the fields, Tortoise began to have pangs of hunger. This made him remem-

---

[8] A paste similar to apple butter is made from beans, after they have been hulled and then individually skinned.

ber the bean butter which he had refused to eat in the morning. He knew that this bean butter was on a high shelf.

Tortoise stacked up stools, one on top of another, so that he could climb on them and reach the bean butter. But as Tortoise was climbing on them, the stools slipped and fell. Tortoise himself fell into a pot of gruel, which his wife had made and put under the shelf before she went away to the fields. Tortoise drowned in the gruel.

Those who have succeeded in great things must beware of small things, lest they go the way of Tortoise.

tortoise at the king's coronation hunt

One day Lion invited all the animals to gather together and join in the king's coronation hunt.[9] All the animals came.

The animals went out into the bush and built there a hunting camp. In the morning, when it was light, they went out to the hunting grounds and all made kills. They returned to camp to skin and dress the animals they had taken.

Early the next morning they went out to hunt again, after cutting up the meat of the first day's kill, and leaving Duyker to cook the meat for them to eat upon their return.

While they were out hunting, Konjombolo[10] came into camp, saw Duyker cooking meat, and said to him, "Give me some of the meat."

Duyker said to him, "The meat is not mine."

Then Konjombolo seized Duyker and killed him. When he killed Duyker, he took the meat, ate all of it, and went away.

When the other animals returned from the hunt, they found Duyker lying dead, and all the meat gone. They were puzzled and said, "This is strange! What could have happened to Duyker? Tomorrow Reedbuck will be left to guard the meat which is cooking."

Early the next morning the animals left to go hunting, leaving Reedbuck to stay in the camp and cook the meat.

[9] When a new king is to be installed, all men of the kingdom participate in a drive hunt to secure a supply of meat for the coronation feasts.

[10] A small animal similar to an otter, whose name in Umbundu means "little sneak."

Sometime later, Konjombolo came and found Reedbuck in the camp. Konjombolo said to him, "Master Reedbuck, give me some of the meat."

Reedbuck replied, "I will not give away any of the meat, for it does not belong to me."

When Konjombolo had heard this, he jumped up onto Reedbuck's neck and cut the veins in his throat, causing him to die. Then Konjombolo ate all the meat that had been cooked.

When the hunters returned and found Reedbuck lying dead and the meat all gone, they were troubled. They said, "We must leave a larger animal to care for the camp. Tomorrow Roan Antelope will stay behind to cook and guard the meat."

In the early morning the animals went hunting again, leaving Roan Antelope to care for the meat. Again Konjombolo came. He said, "Master Roan Antelope, give me some meat."

Roan Antelope said, "I will not give you any of it."

Then Konjombolo leaped onto the neck of Roan Antelope and cut the veins in his neck, and Roan Antelope died. Konjombolo ate all the meat and went away.

When those who had been away hunting returned, they found Roan Antelope dead. They became frightened. They said, "Tomorrow when we go hunting, we shall leave Zebra to look after the meat."

When they went away to the bush in the morning, Zebra stayed in camp to do the cooking. When Konjombolo came he found Zebra in charge of the camp. Konjombolo said, "Master Zebra, give me some of the meat."

Zebra said, "I will not give you any meat."

Konjombolo leaped upon Zebra and cut the veins in his neck, and Zebra died. Then Konjombolo ate all the meat and went away.

When those who had been hunting returned to the camp, they found Zebra lying dead. They were troubled. Then they said, "Gnu is fierce and has sharp horns; so tomorrow he will stay in camp and cook the meat."

In the morning all the others went away to hunt, leaving Gnu to keep the camp and cook the meat. Konjombolo came and found Gnu in the camp, and he said to him, "Master Gnu, give me some of the meat."

Gnu said, "The meat is not your meat."

Konjombolo leaped upon Gnu's neck and cut the veins in his neck, and Gnu died.

When those who had been away in the bush came back to camp, they were perplexed and troubled. After they had talked the matter over, they said, "Tomorrow, while we are away, let us leave Buffalo to look after the meat."

In the morning, when they all went away to hunt, Buffalo stayed in the camp to cook the meat. When Konjombolo came, he found Buffalo in charge and said, "Master Buffalo, give me some of the meat."

Buffalo said gruffly, "I will not. I will not give any of my meat to you, you insignificant little animal."

When Konjombolo had heard this insulting reply, he leaped upon Buffalo's back and then up upon his neck, where he cut the veins in Buffalo's neck, and Buffalo died.

When those who had been away hunting returned, they found Buffalo dead and were confounded. They said, "All the young animals and even stout Buffalo have perished. Tomorrow Hippopotamus will stay to guard the camp and cook the meat."

At daylight in the morning they went away to hunt, leaving Hippopotamus to keep the camp. He had been busy at this for a short time, when Konjombolo came. Finding Hippopotamus in charge of the meat he said, "Master Hippopotamus, give me some of the meat."

Hippopotamus said to him, "Stop making that noise. Perhaps you would like to have me cut you in two."

Konjombolo jumped up onto Hippopotamus' back and then onto his neck, where he cut the veins, and Hippopotamus died. Before going away, Konjombolo ate all the meat.

When those who had been away hunting came back, they found Hippopotamus dead, and being very much troubled, they said, "Elephant will have to guard the meat tomorrow."

The next morning, at daybreak, the others all went away to hunt. They left Elephant to guard the camp. Later in the day, Konjombolo came and found Elephant cooking the meat. Konjombolo said to Elephant, "Master Elephant, please give me some of the meat."

Elephant said to him, "Do not make a noise. Do you want me to step on you?"

Konjombolo leaped upon Elephant's back, then cut the

veins in his neck, and Elephant died. Konjombolo ate all the meat, and then went away.

When those who had been hunting returned, they were astonished to find Elephant dead, so they said, "Who can this be who is killing us off this way? We must find who it is and then catch him, whoever he is."

Then Tortoise spoke up and said to them, "Tomorrow I shall stay and catch him."

All the animals opposed Tortoise. They said in ridicule, "Are you better able to guard the meat than those many strong ones who already have died? You can't catch the killer! Make no mistake, this killer is ghostly and terrible."

Being insulted in this way made Tortoise angry, and he urged the others to let him guard the meat until finally they agreed. When morning came, they said to each other, "Let us leave Tortoise behind and pretend to go hunting, but no one shall go far from the camp. Do not return to your villages, from fear."

Tortoise remained behind in the camp after the others had left. He cut up the meat, put it into the pot, put the pot on the fireplace to cook, and then piled ashes on his back, so that he appeared to be an ordinary heap of ashes near the pot.

When Konjombolo came, he was pleased, for he thought that he had only to eat the meat. On other days he had been forced to kill the one guarding the pot, before he could eat the meat, but today there was no guard. As Konjombolo neared the fireplace, thinking that he would first take the pot off the fire, he stepped into what appeared to be a heap of ashes. In doing this, Konjombolo put his toe inside the shell of Tortoise. Tortoise shut his shell down on the toe, and then he began to shout to the hunters: "Come here! Come here! I have him."

Being near, the others answered and came running. When they reached the camp and saw what had happened, they said, "It is finished." They released Konjombolo from the shell of Tortoise. Then they said, "We shall kill him tomorrow." Then they tied Konjombolo up with rawhide thongs and put him aside.

Early the next morning they sent the young men out with the prisoner, telling them to take him to the woods, and there scorch his hair off, as they would scorch a hog. The youngsters took him and started into the woods with him. When they had

gone some distance, they heard one of the older men shouting
to them, "Do not cheat us of the liver of Konjombolo!"

The youths called back and said, "We cannot hear you."

The elder shouted again and said, "Do not cheat us out of
the liver of Konjombolo!"

Then Konjombolo spoke to the youths and said to them,
"Can't you understand what your elder shouts? The elder said,
'Do not beat him, but take him to the river and let him go.'"

The youths called back to the elders: "We did not understand you. We could not hear the words."

The elder called again: "Do not cheat us out of the liver
of Konjombolo!"

Again Konjombolo said to them, "Your elder said, 'Do not
beat him, but take him to the river and let him go.'"

Then the young men took Konjombolo to the river and
freed him.

tortoise dies

One day during the dry season a man wished to have corn
to eat, so he went out to look at his brook garden. He found
that someone had been into his brook garden[11] and stolen some
corn. This irritated the owner, and he made a big noise about it.

It happened that Tortoise was concealed in grass in the
garden. Tortoise had seen the person who stole the corn. When
Tortoise saw how deeply the owner of the garden was disturbed
by the loss of the corn, Tortoise took pity on the man. So Tortoise came out from the grass and named the person who had
stolen the corn, saying that he had seen him steal it.

The owner of the garden was very pleased to know who had

[11] To steal from a brook garden, or dry season garden, is a very serious offence,
since there is usually a scarcity of food during the period when such a garden yields
its fruit. Apprehending the thief is a matter of private enterprise, with the thief
usually tied if caught. The brook garden itself is planted in early July, near a stream
or spring, which will be moist even in the dry season of mid-winter. Field corn
is not available until April, but brook garden corn bears mature ears of corn in late
December, during the wet season. In addition to corn, the brook garden is planted
with beans and squash, whose leaves supply greens during the rainy season in October.
Unless too many leaves have been eaten, there will be green beans to eat in the
December wet season.

stolen his corn. But as he thought the matter over, it seemed to him that where the thief had entered the brook garden, there also Tortoise had entered the garden. And so he picked up Tortoise, who had named the corn thief, carried Tortoise home, and put him in a pot.

The owner went out after the man who had stolen the corn from his garden, tied him up, and kept him tied until he paid for the corn.

When the owner returned home, he took the pot containing Tortoise, put it on the fire, and said, "Out of this I will get turtle soup as a bonus." [12] As the pot went onto the fire Tortoise said, "Tortoise, you are going to die for knowing too much."

---

[12] The soup is a bonus or extra benefit to the owner of the stolen corn, since, having discovered the identity of the thief, the owner will recover at least the value of the corn from the thief, by demanding a fine from him.

finale

18. the final tragedies of life

a widow's five children

There was a widow who had borne five children and all five
had died. The names of the children had been: Millet-grower,
Red-whiteant-hill, Threshing-floor-by-the-path, From-broken-
bridge, and Little-ash-heap. The name of the mother was
Mother-of-ox.

Mother-of-ox grieved much. She thought, "The real source
of my grief is this, that here on earth I am unfortunate. I have
borne five children, yet when I go to work in the field I go
alone. Wherever I am, I am alone. When I think on this, the
sorrow of it is more than I can endure."

One day she prepared her basket to go and work in the
field. When she reached the field, she found there her children
who had died, at work in the field. They had come to work in
the field with the mother, because of her complaints. The mother
was very pleased to find her children working in the field, both
pleased to see them and pleased to see how well they worked.
Then she bent over with her hoe and they all worked together
until the sun had passed the mid-point. By this time the children
had become tired, so they quit work.

Then the children said to their mother, "Today we are all
going to the village along with you."

The mother was very glad to hear this and said to them,
"Today I shall go to the village with my children."

They all started for the village, and as they went along
they came to a field of millet. When they reached this field,
Millet-grower turned aside and left them. The other children
kept on with their mother.

When they came to a white anthill made of red earth, Red-whiteant-hill stopped there. The other three children walked on with their mother.

Next they came to a threshing floor by the side of the path. When they reached it, Threshing-floor-by-the-path stopped there. The other two children went on with their mother.

Then they came to a small stream with the bridge over it broken. From-broken-bridge went no farther.

The last of the children went on with the mother toward the village. In the village they came to an ash heap. When they reached the ash heap, Little-ash-heap went into it. As the mother then went into her house, she thought of how none of her children had come into the house with her, and she wept.

The next morning she took her basket, put her hoe into it along with a gourd of beer, and went to the fields. She found all the children working in the fields again. She heard their whistle, which went, "Tia-a-a-a." The mother was highly pleased and said, "Soon my field will be finished, for all my children are working in it." When the sun had passed the middle of the sky, they all quit work, for the children were tired.

Again the children said, "Mother, we are going to the village with you again."

"My children," said the mother, "that is the right idea. Let us go to the village. Then my heart can sit on chairs." [1]

They started walking toward the village and soon came to a millet field alongside the path. When they reached the stubble of the millet, Millet-grower went into the stubble of millet and stayed there.

The others went along farther with the mother, but when they came to a white anthill built of red earth, Red-whiteant-hill stayed there.

When they reached a threshing floor by the path, Threshing-floor-by-the-path stayed there.

The two other children continued with their mother until they reached the stream with the broken bridge, and here From-broken-bridge stayed.

---

[1] Among the Ovimbundu women must sit on the ground during their monthly periods, but they sit on chairs at other times. Hence, for a woman to "sit on chairs" is for her to feel well, be at ease.

The mother went on with the remaining child. As they entered the village they came to an ash heap, and there Little-ash-heap left her mother and went into the ash heap.

Mother-of-ox thought of her children and wept bitterly. She went into the house alone. She died there of heartbreak, and went to be with her children.[2]

a grandmother

There were two daughters who were married and bearing children. But their mother, an old woman, knew how to eat[3] children and was killing the children by witchcraft.

When the two daughters came to the conclusion that their mother was using witchcraft to kill their children, they said, "What shall we do with our mother?" After thinking about this, they agreed on a plan and said, "The best thing for us to do is to take her far out into the wilderness and leave her there to die. Then we shall not have her with us any longer and our children will survive. If we do not do this, all our children will perish." [4]

The two women then went to their mother and said to her, "Mother, we do not wish to have you live with us any longer. Today we shall take you out into the wilderness and leave you there. We do this to keep our children well."

The two women took their mother far out into the woods, as they had said they would do. When they were far enough out into the woods, they built a hut for their mother, left her there, and came away.

[2] This and the next story portray the greatest and deepest tragedy of Ovimbundu life: the loss of children. The people need children in their work, in their community life, and to continue their lineage, and they love children very much. The most important lineages pass through women, and no tragedy could be greater than that of Mother-of-ox, who loses all five of her children.

[3] In Umbundu, the verb for "eat" can also mean "collect a debt," "assess a fine," or "possess." Witches are said to "eat" their victims, when they kill the victims by witchcraft and use the victims' souls for their own profit or power. The victims are not literally eaten; their flesh is not consumed.

[4] Like most Ovimbundu, these sisters feel only love for their mother, not enmity. The tragedy of the story and of Ovimbundu life is that the belief in witchcraft creates a conflict between loves, here love for the mother and love for the children. The grandmother herself might have believed that she was unconsciously responsible. For love of the children, the grandmother went willingly.

That evening, after the daughters had left their mother, a lion could be heard coming in the direction of the hut. As the lion came on it coughed: "Chee-ee nju, chee-ee nju!"

When the old woman heard this approaching her, she sang:

> Where is the lion roaring?
> In the far desert of Kandumbu,
> Roaring, roaring.
> Alone! I am here alone.
> May it take me from the earth forever.
> Alone! Oh Death I wait thee.

The lion came on coughing, coughing. The woman kept on replying to him with her song. The lion did not quit coughing when he heard the song. The woman did not quit singing her song until the lion came and ate her.

appendix   proverbs from the umbundu

While you are putting the bounds on your field, fate is putting its bounds on you.

The blind chicken scratches for the others to eat.

While Dog is away, Rooster inspects the bones.

No bird backs into a hole.

Hot water has never set a house on fire.

Two fields: two kinds of soil.

Your neighbor's affairs say, "Look at us." They do not say, "Talk about us."

Children sing the song which they hear from their father and mother.

The squirrel did not talk back to the elephant, he just went into his hole.

Something went splash, it warned those who were bathing.[1]

Do not break your bow—go sleep on it.

She did not catch the fish, and her bracelet went with the water.

That which killed the duyker came from his own head.[2]

Go-fast killed an animal, Go-slow killed two.

A full-grown reed will not hurt you, its tender sprout will stab you.

A young tortoise and his grandfather look alike.

Age has intelligence—trees have buds clear to the top.

The fear of a ghost is not like the fear of a lion.

First consider, drink later.

Drink first, then think about it.

Always they say, "Dog, go catch it." They never say, "Dog, go eat it."

He has thrown his skin to the other bank. He will cross the river.[3]

---

[1] The crocodile makes a splashing noise when entering the water.

[2] Hunters use a duyker horn to produce a call which lures duykers.

[3] Said when a man has committed himself to some project. In the old times, men wore rawhide skin hanging from a string. When a man wished to cross a stream, in order not to dampen the rawhide, he would put a stone into it and throw it across the stream he was about to swim.

That which happened under the water will be known.

He who keeps on asking and asking will not get lost.

If you have drawn the bow shoot, to hesitate will make a cow attack you.

If you have a secret, tell it in a plain, for trees have ears.

Although I go about with head lowered, like a chameleon, yet I am not the ox with which the children play.

Even if you are dying, do not put out the fire, for those left behind will wish to warm themselves.

The eye can look and look at an elephant, while the stomach continues to have meat hunger.

No aroma—no taste.

No pain—no gain.

Although you do not fear the copse—fear the leopard in it.

What you do not know—knows you.

Humbi-humbi for me, sail on and let us go. Nighthawk's worry is for you, just sitting on the ground.[4]

He who throws a stone will forget it. He whom it hits will not forget it.

What the arm cannot do, wisdom can.

He who does not dodge when he sees a strap is liable to die of snake bite.

Go get the water and do not talk back. Now that you are married this is your task.

When you hear a good talker, do not agree in haste, for that hiding in corners has not yet come out.

Fruits do not shake off of themselves. There is a person under the tree.

The hare with a single couch came to a bad end.

Hare has come; guesses are out.[5]

Little ant bite me, so that with reason I may swat you.

Hummingbird does not pass by a flower. Busybody cannot leave his neighbor alone.

Path to the field is short, road to glory is long.

Where many pass, there is a path.

With your own folks is with your own folks. If I am cold, there I find warmth, if I am hungry, there I find food.

He who escaped from the back of the crocodile does not return.

[4] Used when trouble is brewing. The humbi-humbi is a heron. When migrating, these birds circle round and round high in the air with no perceptible movement of wings. One of the stories in this collection describes escape from trouble by flight on a humbi-humbi feather. Many of these proverbs condense the meaning of a story, and many of the stories are told as explanations of proverbs.

[5] This is said when an expert arrives upon the scene of some difficulty. The hare is considered to personify ingenuity.

He who talks behind your back fears you, he who speaks to your face insults you.

The one who has slept with the leopard has seen the spots.

Those who ate the honey hid the gourd.

One head does not contain all the wisdom.

Go-it-alone killed the child of the goat.

There is chaff in my eye, a crocodile has me by the leg, the goat is in the garden, there is a porcupine cooking in the pot, meal is drying on the pounding rock, the king has summoned me to court, and I have to go to my mother-in-law's funeral: I am busy.

glossary

Haka (hah-kah). Among the Ovimbundu, this is a common and much used interjection. Like some of our expletives, it is an emotional release. Umbundu, a language using tone discrimination, thus has at least ten differing forms and meanings of this word. Added differentiation is secured by lengthening either or both syllables of the word, thus: "Ha-a-a-a-ka." "Haka" may indicate exasperation, disapproval, anger, surprise, astonishment, consternation or fear. Again, the term may imply that some statement is questionable, and can be equivalent to, "Do you think that I can believe that?" "Haka" may express admiration and approval, or may be used to offer sympathy for some mishap or misfortune.

Mba. (mbah). This is a term of respect used when addressing an important personage. *Mba* is used in prayer, when the worshiper is addressing a deified ancestor and means, "Oh my father." *Mba-mba, mba-mba, mba-mba* is an enthusiastic way of saying, "Thanks, thanks, thanks." The use of this term is accompanied by clapping of the hands.

Mbui (mbwee). Mbui is onomatopoeic for the sound of water being lightly disturbed, as in the dipping up of drinking water. It occurs in the proverb: *"Cha linga mbui. Chi lungisa ava va yua"*: "That which made a faint splash warns those who bathe." "Mbui" is said to be the faint noise made when a crocodile submerges.

Njembo (njey-mboh). Njembo is the abode of the dead, a mythical place corresponding to the equally mythical *Hades, Sheol,* etc., of classical times. It appears that Njembo was neither a place of confinement nor of punishment.

Suku (soo-koo). The Ovimbundu are, in religion, ancestor worshipers, and apparently they have more than one god. There is no sure evidence that there is one supreme god, nor the personal name of any god. The word *suku* appears to be another form of *kuku,* which means "great-grandfather." In naming a human ancestor, *suku* is not used in place of *kuku.* There are indications that a deified ancestor to whom prayers are made is looked upon as an advocate before a higher power.